D0264371

For The Love
of
My Mother

A MEMOIR

For The Love

of

My Mother

A MEMOIR

J. P. Rodgers

MacRuairi Art

Published by MacRuairi Art
Main Street, Williamstown
Co. Galway, Republic of Ireland.
Website: www. macruairiart.com

Copyright © John Rodgers 2005

John Rodgers asserts the moral right to be identified
as the author of this work.

It is an account of events based on my own recollection. The names of
people and places therein have been changed to protect the innocent.
Any similarity to people past or present is purely coincidental.

A catalogue record for this book is available from the Irish Library

ISBN 0-95502390-4

The author and publishers wish to state that every effort has been
made to ascertain the rights of each song. The publishers wish to be
informed of any unintended infringements on any still existing rights.
The author acknowledges permission granted to him under the
'freedom of information act' in relation to family records.

All rights reserved. No part of this publication may be reproduced,
stored in a retrieval system, or transmitted, in any form or by any
means, electronic, mechanical, photocopying, recording or otherwise,
without the prior permission of the publishers.

Cover origination by Chris Keane.
Artwork and illustration by James Newell.
Typeset by Gough Typesetting Services.
Printed in Ireland by Colourbooks Ltd, Dublin.

Acknowledgements

So many people have been instrumental in helping me achieve my dream. It's not something one achieves overnight, so there's always the risk I might leave someone out. My memory's not what it used to be. So here goes. I would like to thank, my good friend Christine Keane, who was always there to answer the difficult questions; Aine McCarty, who read the early drafts and advised me to keep at it; John Conneely, the 2005 Bard of Ireland; Therese Carrick, my editor; Mattie, my ever helpful tutor; James Newell, illustrator, who worked for me 10 years ago and proved to be as loyal as ever; Gilbert Gough, typesetter; Stephen, at Colourbooks Ltd; Óisin, who rescued all of my material when the computer crashed on Christmas day, well done son, you'll go a long way. To Róisin, Steve, Síle, and my good wife Julie, a special thanks to all of you. To Maureen, who always gave me her wholehearted support: and to Claudia Jennings, who typed up the early drafts, many thanks. A sincere thanks to Idi Ni Laoghaire (O'Brien Press), who took the time to show me where I was going wrong.

To Tom Griffin, Irish World newspaper London, who gave me a new lease of life when I so badly needed it, many thanks.

To Tom Kenny (Kenny's bookshop); Galway City Library; Tuam Credit Union, who, when the hard shillings were not to be found, always came up trumps, many thanks to all of you.

Introduction

My life could best be described as a total disaster. I've wanted so many things, tried so many projects, some good some bad; that either petered out or were left unfinished, which ever way you look at it: it was not good. In essence what I'm trying to say is, I was probably the most successful failure ever to come out of Ireland. All my life I've wanted to write a good book. And although I've the makings of a book, gathering dust somewhere in the house it is not of the most pressing subject. True, there are plays, poems, short stories – bits I might add – but all without direction. But now as I approach the autumn of my life I am going to make one gigantic effort to write a good book and lay the ghost of my past: for undoubtedly a ghost hangs over my life; not a real one you understand, but its there nonetheless: and so I've chosen this day. But where do I begin? Do I begin with an account of a solitary day in my youth or do I begin with the story of my mother, whose life interwoven with mine, which is what really haunts me? Until I do that, all other attempts at writing I feel are meaningless.

5 a.m.

27th April 1997

J.P. Rodgers

Chapter One

It was Friday morning, the third day of March 1930 that you could say the whole rotten episode began. It was the kind of morning when you wished you'd stayed on in bed, instead of having to face into the biting cold wind that swept down the littered streets of old Dublin; towards the Metropolitan Courthouse, situated in the north of the city.

But despite the severity of the wind and cold, several snotty-nosed little chisellers hung around the old Smithfield Market, next to the Courthouse, ready to steal what little they could, in an effort to stem the growing tide of starvation. And for every fleet-footed and successful little chiseller roaming the streets there were at least half a dozen more tiny infants crying pitifully and begging for alms while huddled in the litter strewn doorways.

Every now and again the weakest little chiseller of them all was asked to pay a heavy price by having to appear before the Court of Justice in the nearby Metropolitan Courthouse. And it so happened that morning, that inside the grim-looking Victorian Building, stood the Chief Justice of the Court, Mr Justice Cussens, who was extremely grateful for the indoor warmth as he prepared to put on his wig and gown before exiting his private chambers, to preside over the day's Court sitting.

The minute he opened the door to enter the Courtroom, the Court Clerk gave the order to the assembled crowd, "Will the Court please rise?" The packed courtroom, made up of Solicitors, Garda Síochána and those awaiting trial immediately stood to attention as the Judge made a dignified entrance before stepping up to his bench, where he gave the nod to commence proceedings. When the Clerk was satisfied that Mr. Justice Cussens was ready, he gave the order to the assembled crowd to be seated and called for the first case to be heard.

"Your Honour The Court calls on Rose Clancy Complainant versus Bridgit Nora Rodgers Defendant."

For what seemed like an eternity a great hush descended on the assembled crowd, while at the same time discrete nods and whispers passed between Rose Clancy and Garda Michael Corcoran, a young officer who was summonsing on Rose Clancy's behalf. Garda Corcoran then promptly stood up before making his way hesitantly to the witness stand where he took hold of the small black Bible and swore to tell truth, the whole truth and nothing but the ….

Accepting the Judge's offer to be seated, the young officer glanced nervously at his notes before reading out the charge.

"Your Honour, as a result of a complaint received from Rose Clancy, on the 21st of February 1930 at approximately 2.30 p.m., I proceeded to the market end of Chancery Street, in the said district of Dublin, where I observed a small female child in a very distressed and dishevelled state. She was crying pitifully while begging for alms by holding up an empty vessel and pleading to those who passed by. On further investigation, I ascertained that the child was a Catholic, having been christened Bridgit Norah Rodgers and whose date of birth was given as the 13th day of September 1927 and her address as number 44 North Great Clarence Street, in the said district of Dublin, but who lately appears to reside at Bluebell, Inchicore, in the County of Dublin. Further to my inquiries, I found that number 44 North Great Clarence Street no longer exists, having recently become a derelict site. At present the defendant Bridgit Norah Rodgers appears to be in grave moral danger, being without any family support and whose legal guardians are at this time unknown. That, Your Honour, is a truthful account and concludes my statement."

Chief Justice Cussens, cleared his throat, before remarking, "What a state of affairs…. when people feel free to discard their off spring like unwanted litter onto the streets of Dublin."

Turning to Garda Corcoran he added, "Thank you Officer, you may step down."

Garda Michael Corcoran rose quickly to his feet and breathed a deep sigh of relief as he tugged at the lapels of his neat officer's uniform, and returned briskly to take up his position at the rear of the courtroom as Complainant Rose Clancy was called to the stand.

Dressed in a three quarter length navy overcoat, with a matching broad rimmed hat, Rose Clancy was a local spinster, aged about forty five; with a desire to rid the street where she lived of its unwanted homeless children. She had something of a haughty appearance about her; a sort of cock of the walk look and a thin mouth that never ever seemed to smile. She also had an unflattering gait that made people smile to themselves as they observed her taking the witness stand.

Once the preliminary proceeding were out of the way, Rose Clancy spoke of her discovery of the child and of her desire to rid Smithfield market once and for all of its street children.

While all of this speech-making was going on, Judge Cussens removed his reading glasses and cast a cold beady eye over the Complainant before enquiring,

"Miss Clancy – if I may call you that – you're not married I take it?"

"No Your Honour… I'm not."

"Refresh my memory if you would, I think … we've met before?"

"Yes, Your Honour, as a member of the R.S.P.C.C. I made a previous request to the Court, to have a child committed to care. He was a ten year old boy who stole two freshly baked soda cakes from my …."

"Oh yes, yes! How could I forget!" interrupted the judge as an aside, before asking, "What can you tell me about, Bridgit Norah Rodgers?"

"Your Honour, Bridgit Norah Rodgers, from what I've learned is an illegitimate child. No one seems to know who her real parents are and the register shows her birth mother as a Colleen Rodgers whose cousin Mary Harte of Blue Bell, Inchicore, is supposed to be looking after her…."

"Sorry to interrupt but, 'No one seems to know who her real parents are', unquote, then you go on to tell me her birth mother is Colleen Rodgers: there's a contradiction in terms, surely?"

"Yes…Your Honour. Colleen Rodgers is the mother but I …."

" And where is the Mother?"

"She is supposed to be living in London, I believe she ran away."

"And what about this famous cousin? Why can't she take care of the child and not have her traipsing the streets like something out of…out of a Dickensian novel?"

"Your Honour, Mary Harte has six children of her own. She works as a fruit seller in Smithfield Market because her husband is laid up with tuberculosis."

"Thank heavens *she* didn't go to London as well or else we'd all be in trouble. What state of health is this child in at present or does anybody know if she's been seen by a doctor?"

"Your Honour, the child has been examined by my own doctor and is in good health, although she is somewhat under-nourished."

" How old is this child and where is she now?"

"She is two and a half years of age and if it pleases Your Honour, the child is here in the Courtroom," said Miss Clancy turning to point to where a small frail looking child was trying playfully to kick a ball at the feet of Garda Corcoran, who was keeping an eye on her.

"At present she is under the temporary care of the Children's Hospital in Harcourt St, but as they are unable to accept responsibility for her further welfare; a suitable place will have to be found for her."

Once again, the judge removed his horn-rimmed glasses and peered down into the body of the courtroom where he observed Bridgit Norah Rodgers pick up a small red ball while dancing around with glee.

"Ahem! An elfin child if ever I was one," he remarked to no one in particular, before turning his attention to the Complainant seated in the witness box.

"Miss Clancy do you wish to say anything further?"

"Your Honour, if it pleases the court I request that an order be made to have all of the street children in my area sent to State intuitions where I have no doubt they will receive due care and attention, as well as some sort of religious and educational training."

On hearing these words, Judge Cussen's plump jovial feature turned to that of a grimacing expression, as he remarked, "I don't know if it necessarily pleases this Court, but it is quite clear that an order of some description will have to be made in relation to this child. But before you step down, Miss Clancy, may I also add that however well meaning your intentions were, I would ask that you yourself give serious consideration to establishing some sort of a localised refuge, where these 'Street Children' as you call them can be taken care of, instead of having them continuously brought before this court. That will be all, Miss Clancy", he added, as he immediately pushed the file relating to the matter to one side before entering into a private whispered conversation with the Clerk of the Court.

Miss Clancy, meanwhile, cocked her nose in the air as she plodded her way down from the rostrum, before making her way ungainly to the back of the courtroom where she stood awaiting the verdict.

Holding her head high she smiled ever so dryly, as the Chief Justice picked up his gavel before bringing the weight of it down three times on the bench,

"I shall reserve Judgment in the case of Bridgit Rodgers versus Rose Clancy until three o'clock this afternoon."

On hearing this, Rose Clancy again had a private word with Garda Michael Corcoran before disappearing out the door of the courtroom leaving the child Bridgit Rodgers in the care of Garda Corcoran. The Garda was only too happy to take the child's pleading hand and escort her down a side street to a café where they both had tea and biscuits.

At precisely three o'clock, a mere handful of people sat lounging around the courtroom as the Judge returned to give his final verdict.

"In the case of Miss Rose Clancy Complainant, versus Bridgit Nora Rodgers Defendant, the Court finds that Bridgit Rodgers, a child under the age of fourteen years, having been born – as far as can be ascertained – on the 13th day of September 1927 and who lately resided at Blue Bell, Inchicore, in the County of Dublin and who on the 21st day of February 1930 was found at Chancery Street in the said district, *begging for alms.*

And whereas the Council of the said County has been given an opportunity of being heard. And whereas this Court is satisfied that it is expedient to deal with the said child by sending said child to a certified Industrial School.

And whereas the Religious persuasion of the said child, appears to be a Roman Catholic

It is hereby ordered that the said child shall this day be sent to the Industrial School at Clifden, County Galway.

It being a School conducted in accordance with the doctrines of the Roman Catholic Church. The Managers this day state that they are willing to receive the said child, there to be detained from and after this day the 5th of March 1930 until, but not including the 13th day of September 1943.

And it is further ordered…"

"Ah Jezzus Your Honour! Are yous bleedin' mad or wha'… " came a loud interrupting voice from the body of the Court as Mary Harte, a heavy set middle aged woman, suddenly ran forward from where she had been loitering in the doorway and tried to rescue the child standing next to Garda Corcoran … "her mother will go bananas if she finds out her little chisller…."

"Order! Order!" came a loud reprimand from the bench as Justice Cussens began to clobber the woodwork.

"I will not allow this disturbance in my Court!" he added, as a bit of a melee broke out when the Gardaí tried to stop Mary Harte from gaining access to the child who was now crying pitifully and clinging to Garda Corcoran.

"Ah order me bleedin' arse! What do yous lot know about childer: yous never even saw a bleedin' fanny in your life…."

"Order! Order! Remove the assailant from this Courtroom immediately…."

By now two or three hefty Garda Officers were carrying a screaming Mary Harte out through the door, and for a second, a strange silence seemed to engulf the entire Courthouse, before a loud pitiful cry could be heard coming from Bridget Nora Rodgers, as she clung to the trouser leg of Garda Michael Corcoran, while the flustered Judge raised his gavel before bringing it down heavily to reaffirm,

"Judgment as stated, for the Defendant."

The die was finally cast.

Chapter Two

For some time, the young street urchin struggled to come to terms with her new surroundings in St. Joseph's Industrial School. The School was a fortress like institution, perched on top of a small hill that overlooked the picturesque town of Clifden, situated on Ireland's most Western seaboard and that looked out on to the broad Atlantic Ocean.

Occasionally, on warm summer Sundays, Bridget Nora Rodgers – who was now affectionately referred to as, 'Bridie Rodgers' by the nuns – and a group of her friends were escorted for short walks out along the famous Sky Road in Clifden. These rare outings were to become a feature of her summer days in St. Joseph's, where the broad expanse of sea and sky seemed to stretch for miles and miles; but it wasn't all plain sailing. For no sooner had Bridie made new friends in St. Joseph's, than they suddenly disappeared again having been fostered out to new homes. Boys in particular were soon whisked away to help out on family farms, while the girls were often fostered out to ageing couples to fill the gap left after their own family had migrated to England and America. When Bridie's friends disappeared she would sit pining for hours and hours until the Reverend Mother tried convincing her yet again that all was not lost.

"But Bridie, some day you too will have a new Mammy and Daddy."

"And will I have Brothers and Sisters?"

"Perhaps. You might even have lots of Brothers and Sisters," replied the Reverend Mother, knowing full well that Bridie could never leave St. Joseph's because of the Court order: and wondering to herself what kind of family she had, that could leave such a gorgeous looking child with a mop of jet-black hair, begging for alms on the streets of Dublin.

Weeks and months later Bridie would again ask the Reverend Mother, "But why can't I have a Mammy and Daddy now, what are we waiting for?"

"Bridie dear, you have got to be patient and wait for the right Mammy and Daddy to come along, and besides amn't I your Mammy here? What's going to happen when you go and I'm left all on my own and I'll have no one to sit on my lap and sing *Away in a Manger.* Will you sing it again?"

Bridie shook her head shyly, she wouldn't.

"Ah go on, please!"

"If I sing and play the mouth organ, will you get me a new Mammy and Daddy?"

"I promise, I'll do my very best."

"And you'll get me Brothers and Sisters, and Cousins and Aunties and everything?"

"It will be awfully hard but I'll try."

Bridie sang:

Away in a manger, no crib for a bed,
 The little lord Jesus lay down his sweet head
The stars in the bright sky looked down where he lay,
The little lord Jesus asleep on the hay.
The cattle are lowing the baby awakes, but the little lord Jesus no crying he makes.
I love thee lord Jesus, look down from the sky,
And stand by my bedside until morning is nigh.

This bargaining chip was something Bridie Rodgers used during her long stay in St. Joseph's. And although there were many rows between herself and the Sisters, as she grew older and bolder, the time seemed to fly by, until one day she was unexpectedly called into Mother Superior's office.

She wondered what she'd done wrong now and whether or not she was going to be punished yet again for some minor indiscretion, like burning the bread or putting too much salt in the butter. She had already made up her mind last time that she would not do another tap of work, in retaliation if she were ever punished again. Instead she was relieved now and mildly surprised when the new Reverend Mother, said,

"Bridie I'm sure you'll be pleased to learn that for your Sixteenth birthday I've found you a new job, as a Housekeeper for a wonderful farming family who live in a big mansion known as 'Conly House.' It's situated in the village of Cill Conly about halfway between Tuam and Galway."

For weeks some of the nuns had being dropping hints about her being free to leave the Industrial School on her sixteenth Birthday. She was so amazed at first that she did not believe them, and yet when she asked them straight out, if she'd be free on her Birthday to leave St. Joseph's for ever they all pleaded ignorance.

Bridie was gob smacked on hearing the Reverend Mother add,

"…You'll be working for a very wealthy family, the O'Malley's; Gerald and Beatrice. They're a middle-aged couple, with two boys, aged eight and ten, and a girl of twelve. Your job will be to take care of the children, to cook, wash and sew for them. You may of course be asked to do a little house cleaning for them from time to time. In return, you'll receive free accommodation, clothing and footwear and have every Sunday off. They are very nice people and I have no doubt you'll be treated as one of their own. You're leaving tomorrow morning, at ten o'clock, if that's all right with you?"

"What's common-dation?" asked Bridie, in obvious delight.

"The word is, accommodation, child – meaning to accommodate someone, to give them a free bed. I thought that by now you'd have learned that much at least. It means you get free meals and a bedroom to yourself in return for the work that you do."

"And do I get paid as well?" asked Bridie, delighted by the sound of things. She recalled all too clearly the nuns teaching them, that few things in this world were as powerful as money, where people bought and sold and exchanged goods at will, and all arising from the money in your pocket, which you earned by the sweat of your brow, either as a kitchen maid, a farm labourer, a village shopkeeper or a city bank manager.

"Bridie the first thing you've got to learn, is that a girl such as you with no professional training or decent family background is in no position to expect anything other than free accommodation. You may be entitled to a small wage at some future date, but not just yet. Your present qualifications are limited to a little basic cooking and general housekeeping duties such as washing and ironing. You're probably more suited as a priest's housekeeper but this is all we can offer you now. So if you'd care to go gather up your personal belongings and stack them on your bed, I'll see if I can get you a nice suit case and then I'll check that you've got everything you need. I will, of course be keeping an eye on your progress and I shall be available should you need to write to me for help or advice," said Sister rising from her chair and escorting Bridie down the corridor.

"You're to address your new employers as Mr and Mrs and say, Thank you Sir, or Thank you Mam," the Reverend Mother continued.

"You only ever speak when spoken to and always ask for something by saying 'please' or 'may I'. You've been through all this in school already and now its time to put your good learning into practise. And I wish you the best of luck, Bridie," added the Reverend Mother, as she turned right at the end of the corridor that led directly to the convent situated opposite the tall entrance gates.

For a long time Bridie sat in her room, in shock and disbelief. Imagine I'm leaving St. Joseph's, she said aloud to herself, before running excitedly across the school grounds to the bakery, where she knew her friend Alice was cleaning out the ovens.

"I'm leaving! I'm leaving!" she beamed, as she began jumping up and down; but when she saw Alice's reaction she wished she were old enough to join her. But Alice still had another year to go to her sixteenth birthday, unless of course some rural family badly in need of some help came to her rescue. After a hurried chat, Bridie went straight back to her dormitory and began to pack up her bits and pieces. I can't wait to tell the rest of my friends, she sighed, as she sat down again and realised that this was the greatest thing to ever happen to her. Her new life was merely a few hours away. She would be free to go for long walks on her own. Free to eat at a nice big table with a family, instead of eating and nibbling whenever she could while trying to mind a large group of young children.

She'd live in a big fancy mansion and have her own bedroom. Not alone that, but she'd have a real mother and father, she figured: well almost. But most important, she'd be able to have a boyfriend. A subject totally frowned on in St. Joseph's. But Bridie knew she had picked up a lot of useful information from some of the unruly young girls who were brought in from Galway city where every young girl it seemed had at least one boyfriend. She didn't care if he were a farmer's son, a shoemaker, a tinker or a thatcher, as long as she had some nice boy as a friend. Perhaps she might even find a husband and then have lots and lots of children. She danced on the bed again and sang with glee, I'm free! I'm free! as she bounced up and down,

I'm free to go wherever I roam,
I've found myself a Home.

Where oft at night, as the fires burn bright,

I'll read myself...

Sister Rita appeared at the door, "Why are you jumping on the bed like that with your mucky boots. Bridie, your behaviour is ghastly! You're behaving like a tramp, and an idiot. Now pull yourself together."

"Sorry Sister, it's just... that I'm so happy. Thank you and the Reverend Mother so much for finding me a job, I promise I'll do everything you and Sister Bernadine told me."

"Yes. Yes. Well you'd better start pulling yourself together," said Sister, with a stern gaze.

"Oh, and I almost forgot, one last thing", she began in a barely audible whisper, "You're to take good care of your chastity. We can't have you coming back in here again just because you've been stupid or careless. You must not under any circumstances, harbour any impure thoughts or desires because unfortunately the world is full of evil men whose only interest is to possess your body for their own wanton pleasure and destruction. You must never allow yourself to be alone with any man, be it in a house, a field or a country lane. Should you ever find yourself in that position, you must pray for God's guidance and seek help by going to the nearest house. Purity of body is God's greatest gift to you so guard it as if your very life depended on it. Now, where are your clean petticoats and I'll help you to pack," added Sister Rita thoughtfully.

"I've it all done," said Bridie cheerfully.

And what in God's name does she mean, 'a house, a field, or country lane.' Jesus, that one's daft. Won't I be working in a house, and what would I be doing in a country lane, thought Bridie, as she watched Sister make her way down the corridor and she herself went to see some of the other girls who were working in the kitchen preparing tea for the little ones.

She made up her mind there and then she'd spend the rest of the evening discussing this latest problem with her friend Alice when she finished work. Surely she'd be able to throw some light on this 'wanton pleasure and destruction business.'

Surely.

At ten thirty the next morning, Bridie found herself seated in the back seat of a Ford motor car as she waved goodbye to all her friends and staff who were themselves standing on the gravelled entrance to

St. Joseph's waving her their good-byes. She had witnessed this scene so many times down through the years from the sanctuary of her bedroom window, that she had almost given up all hope that she too would one day be driven like a lady to a new place in the country. Then one tiny tear unfrocked her emotions as she looked round and waved one last time to Alice, who stood waving with a white handkerchief. Bridie recalled for a moment their days of daisy chains in the big field and the famous lost coin. Oh yes, and the burnt cakes and Sister Bernadine constantly lecturing her, the oul' bitch! Perhaps she meant well, thought Bridie. Pity it wasn't the old Mother Superior, Sister Concepta, who was standing there, though. I would just love to have hugged her. She would have understood me more but what matters now, I've a brand new home to go to; I'll be living in 'Conly House.'

Chapter Three

The scorching summer sun shone brightly and a cool breeze swept soothingly through Bridie's hair as the gleaming motor car wound its way through the Connemara mountains like the birds of prey that were soaring and gliding their way through its picturesque valleys.

The driver said they'd stop in Galway and have a nice cup of tea near the beach and be at their destination in three hours. Bridie wondered what was in the letter that she had been given to pass on to the O'Malley's, perhaps a reference. They'd probably need a reference on her ability to cook – Oh my God, she thought, more burned cakes and soggy soda bread and botched needlework No, don't be silly, rich people won't need any socks darned, she sighed to herself, besides I'll have Sundays to recover and perhaps I can go to the beach, wouldn't that be wonderful. Then I could learn how to swim.

It was almost one thirty. And Bridie's stomach did a lightening roll as the car suddenly turned left and up a long winding gravelled path to a big white house surrounded by lots of beautiful trees, flowers and shrubs. On either side of the driveway were immaculately kept lawns, with large bronze statuettes and a water fountain; not to mention acres and acres of green pasture.

Bridie stepped down from the car as the driver took her small brown suitcase and began to escort her to the door as Mr and Mrs O'Malley appeared with outstretched arms.

"You're very welcome Bridie. I'm Gerald, and this is my wife Beatrice and of course, you've already met Tom, our chauffeur. How are you?" asked Mr O'Malley.

" I'm fine," said Bridie, as she unwittingly did a little curtsy and shook hands first with Gerald and then with Beatrice, who appeared to cast a critical eye over her or was she imagining it.

Mrs O'Malley thought her new housekeeper was very frail and thin for such a demanding job. Though she had to admit to herself that she was a very attractive girl with waves of black curly hair. In a way she felt disappointed. She expected her new housekeeper to be more mature and dowdier looking.

"I won't be needing you 'till seven this evening and thanks," said Mrs O'Malley, turning to address Tom.

"Let me help with your luggage," said Gerald as he politely took the suitcase from Bridie as she was about to pick it up and they all traipsed into the house.

"Bridie! Gerald will take care of your luggage, just let me show you down stairs and then I'll take you through the rest of the house. You won't be starting work until tomorrow morning. I'm sure you must be exhausted after that long journey and those horrible winding roads," said Beatrice.

"No, I'm fine," smiled Bridie. "The scenery was magnificent and Tom showed me the 'Lazy Wall' in Salthill. It was unbelievable, watching all those people lying there sunning themselves. He said that's why it was called the "Lazy Wall.""

"Did he now! Hymm! Oh, that's our Tom."

Bridie was amazed at the size of the house for just five people. There was the conservatory, the reading room, the sitting room, the dining room, the kitchen, the scullery and the games room; as well as the laundry and two lavatories. Upstairs was the master bedroom, the children's bedrooms – Sinead, being the eldest had her own room. The maid's room was where Bridie would sleep and there were four other rooms and a bathroom and lavatory besides.

Soon the children came in from the fields where they were riding ponies and arranging jumps. They were introduced to their new housekeeper. Bridie was immediately struck by the likeness of the daughter Sinead. She thought it was like looking at Beatrice when she was twelve years old. She had such bright blue twinkling eyes and such light-coloured wispy hair, so fine you'd almost need x-ray eyes to see the few strands hanging over her face. The boys, Daniel and Darragh, she couldn't figure out because of their mischievous grins.

After tea and sandwiches Bridie was invited to dine with the family for the evening meal before being handed a work schedule for the rest of the week.

Tomorrow, Tuesday, she'd be expected to be up at seven o'clock in the morning to light the fire in the drawing room – because Gerald liked to read for an hour while enjoying a cup of tea. She'd have to cook breakfast for the workmen and when they had finished, she'd cook breakfast for the whole family before washing up and preparing her own meal. Then it was time to sort Monday's wash and put the dry clothes into the various wardrobes. She'd have to change and dress all the beds, sweep and dust the rooms before preparing dinner for whoever was in the house.

Afternoons were to be taken up with more cleaning and polishing, before getting the dinner ready for the children on their return from school. Then it was their homework before accompanying them for fun and games. Wednesday and Thursday was more of the same with a little baking and sewing. Friday was fish day all round with no meat of any description, which was something Bridie was well used to. The O'Malley's, it seemed to Bridie, had fish of a Friday, in one form or another, for breakfast, dinner and tea. To Bridie, Saturday seemed the worst day of the week. Stairs, landings and corridors had to be cleaned and polished in preparation for Sunday's expected visitors. Bridie was given strict instructions, by Mrs O'Malley, to consume her own meals in her own time in the kitchen.

She was surprised and a bit disappointed to hear this cold remark and recalled a little yarn the Reverend Mother had once told her. Her next door neighbour, she said, had a loyal servant, who on being invited only to the afters of her master's wedding, bravely replied, 'A bone-picker or plate licker I'll never be to those who think they are better than me.' Bridie wished that at that moment she could have come up with some similar answer or quick-witted reply for Mrs O'Malley, but she couldn't.

That evening, Bridie dined in splendid and sumptuous surroundings, as the dining room was brightly lit and the oval mahogany table laid out in the famous blue of Mason's Iron stone china delph and King's cutlery which Bridie recognised.

Candles and bottles of red wine adorned the settings as Mrs O'Malley served up prawn cocktail followed by roast beef and sherry trifle. During the meal Beatrice and Gerald questioned Bridie extensively about life in St. Joseph's. Bridie had nothing but the highest of praise for her former custodians, as she felt that the O'Malley's were merely digging for malicious gossip that might well find its way back to Sister Bernadine. And while they divulged very little of themselves, it became clear that Gerald was indeed a gentleman farmer with a penchant for rearing horses.

Bridie couldn't wait to snuggle down in her own bedroom, with it's new feathered bed, and hand-embroidered quilt. But when she did and the lights were out she found she couldn't get to sleep. The day's events kept going through her mind over and over again, and then suddenly she was gripped by an awful fear. First, there was the strange silence and stillness of the night that was so different to St. Joseph's. There was never any noise in St. Joseph's, but this new-found silence was terrifying, and it was made much worse by minute creaking noises that made her want to sit up and scream. She couldn't make up her mind if it was her room door being slowly opened or someone tip toeing on the floorboards at the foot of her bed. Several times she held her breath; she was afraid even to breathe, because she couldn't see anything.

Yet on and on it went; the awful silence for long periods followed by faint creaking noises. What if someone was trying to kill her or attack her in bed, she thought. Were the O'Malley children spying on her? Worse still, had Mr O'Malley sneaked into her bedroom? Sister had warned her that, 'the world was full of evil men whose only interest was to possess your body for their own pleasure and destruction'. But what pleasure would they get out of killing me and taking my body? What, she wondered, if Mr O'Malley had come sneaking in to the room to take her body away. What would he do with it? At that moment she heard the creaking noise again and sat bolt upright in the bed, screaming,

"Who's there?" But nobody answered as she peered into the darkness and expected to feel hands clutching at her body. She thought the room was starting to spin, as she tried to figure out where things were. Where was the room door, the dressing table, or the washstand? She closed her eyes and lay back in bed covering her head with the blankets. She was practically gasping for breath. She thought 'that's it, the house is haunted'. She had heard so many ghost stories in St. Joseph's, she was convinced this must be one of those haunted houses she had heard about. If she ever again saw daylight she'd run away and go back to St. Joseph's. She could hear footsteps approaching her room now and started shaking violently in the bed. She threw down the blankets from over her head and was about to scream to high heaven when the bedroom door opened and Mr O'Malley appeared, dressed in his night attire and holding aloft a lantern in his hand. "Bridie, are you all right? I thought I heard someone calling."

She was so relieved; seeing Gerald standing there with the night-light; she was completely lost for words. And when she did not reply, he again asked, "Are you all right dear?"

"Yes, yes, I think I must have been dreaming," croaked Bridie.

"Oh. You're all right then. We're just down the hall if you need anything," he replied, quietly closing the door behind him and Bridie once again heard his footsteps retreat down the corridor. Slowly she submerged her tortured body beneath the blankets, closed her eyes and started to say her night prayers once more.

Bridie felt as if she had just nodded off to sleep when Mrs O'Malley shook her in the bed and said, "Bridie, what's the meaning of this, it's nearly eight o'clock, and the workmen are below in the kitchen waiting for their breakfast. If this is an example of your behaviour after the way you were treated last night then I wouldn't give much for your chances of staying on here."

"I'm sorry, Mrs O'Malley, I'm sorry. I must have overslept," said Bridie as she sprang from the bed and proceeded to dress quickly, as Mrs O'Malley left the room, slamming the door behind her.

Bridie was in the kitchen preparing the late morning breakfast, as the three workmen sat around the large kitchen table, well aware of Bridie's dilemma. They were having great fun amongst themselves. With the young slightly balding farmhand, saying "…and did you ever notice when there's work to be done you could stay in bed all day; but when it's your day off, you're up at cock crow, because you can't sleep."

"I don't know about you," replied his dark haired co-worker. "But if I had a good-looking girl beside me in the bed of a morning, the devil-a-up I'd ask to get."

"If you had a good-looking girl in the bed and you didn't rise every morning, it wouldn't be long until she'd come running to me, because I'd be up! And up! And up!" replied Baldy obscenely, as Bridie began to drop the hardboiled eggs into their eggcups.

"Ah, you dirty bugger. Shut up. That's all you ever think of, Sex! Sex! Sex. I think there's a bit of the farm animal about you."

"Take no notice of him, girl, 'tisn't a brain he has in his head, it's a cesspit," said Darkie, winking and smiling at Bridie as she started to cut some more bread.

Bridie, said nothing in response to their coaxing, as she had other things on her mind and was well aware that Mrs O'Malley was hovering around somewhere in the background.

A few hours later she was beginning to feel the pressure in relation to the number of jobs she had to do; which wasn't at all helped by her having to continuously ask Mrs O'Malley where was this or where was that, because she didn't know where anything was or the household ritual, despite being shown around the house the previous day. Much earlier she had decided to do without her breakfast, but found she was still struggling to cope after dinner, when she knew she should now be on schedule with her chores. She decided on the spur of the moment to skip some of her duties and to concentrate on the more pressing ones like getting ready for the children's return from school. Later, she gave them their tea, helped them with their study before they showed her round the farm. The children were nice and courteous to her, showing her all the horses, sheep and cattle, and telling her that Dad liked reading the sporting chronicle, because sometimes his name would appear along with the name of his prized horses.

On her return, Mr O'Malley asked her how her day had been.

"Fine, thank you."

"Sorry about this morning, herself thinks it's a crime to sleep in of a morning, but sure we all make mistakes some time or other. So don't take any notice of her Bridie; her bark's worse than her bite."

As if waiting for an opportunity to intervene, Mrs O'Malley suddenly appeared and said to her husband,

"Oh, there you are!" Then, folding her arms across her chest, added, "I hope Gerald you had a word with Bridie about this morning. You know Bridie, it's not acceptable."

"Yes, yes, we've just been through that, and Bridie has apologised," said Gerald, as he abruptly turned to go out the door now that his wife had come in. She in turn, followed him out and Bridie carried on with her tasks.

Bridie thought she'd love to stick a pin in Mrs O'Malley just to shut her up. After all, what was I supposed to do, she sighed to herself as she finished the last of the day's chores. I feel wrecked after all that and I not getting a wink of sleep last night. And what am I to do tonight, if it's the same thing? I just dread the thought of that room. What if I don't get to sleep? I'll be out of a job tomorrow, if I sleep in again. That reminds me, I must check the rota and see what I'm cooking for the workmen and the children. At least the workmen were nice and polite. What were their names again, the nice one that winked at me while I poured the tea? He wasn't too bad looking. I wonder how old he is? Twenty? Twenty-two? Yeah. That would be a nice age. But how would I know what was the right age for a fellow or a girl to be together.

Bridie's thoughts were blown to smithereens by the explosive charges in the Grandfather clock that stood in the hallway. She decided she'd done enough for one day. She had deliberately stayed hanging about in the kitchen, just leaving enough to do, should Mrs O'Malley appear again. Now, she'd rinse out a few dishcloths, spread the tea towels to dry and go to bed. Hopefully tonight she'd get some sleep, and dream about Blackie, the nice one because that's what she'd call him till she found out his real name. What way did he say it? *'If I'd a good lookin' girl beside me in the bed of a morning the devil-a-up I'd get'*. Umm. I wonder what that would be like. It would be lovely and cosy and safe, like when I jumped into Alice's bed that night during the thunder and lightening. And next day I had to listen to a lecture from Sister Bernadine; 'Bridie, what you did at your age was very wrong. It's a bad habit to get into, as it can only lead to sin'.

Strange that neither Alice nor I could ever figure out what she meant by that remark. Anyway she can't stop me now. Imagine, I can do what I want, go where I want. Perhaps I'll go somewhere on Sunday? I could go to Tuam or Galway I suppose. I'd Love to go to Tuam. But how will I get there? What if I can't ever leave here and there's nobody to bring me anywhere? Surely they wouldn't leave me here all day on my own, would they?

It was getting late, but the O'Malley's hadn't gone to bed yet; she could still hear the steady drone of their voices downstairs. She lay in bed, reliving the horrors of the night before, expecting them to return at any minute. She tried to think about Blackie, but it was the presence of Mrs O'Malley standing over her bed that morning that kept intervening. She couldn't concentrate on anything else. She found herself listening in the dark for the creaking noises she'd heard before. All was quiet. In fact it was much too quiet, apart from the occasional voice coming from downstairs. And when she thought about the stillness of the night, the earlier feeling of terror that had haunted her the night before started to creep back again. She survived it last night, she told herself, only because she wasn't tired; whereas now she was exhausted after the day's exertions.

What, she wondered, was she going to do to get some sleep? She could get up and go downstairs now and tell them about the noise. Then she heard the chairs downstairs being moved about and people were saying 'goodnight, see you tomorrow'. They must have had visitors. The O'Malley's were coming up stairs. It's too late to say anything now, thought Bridie. Besides Mrs O'Malley might get angry with her and send her back to St. Joseph's. Would she go back to Clifden or should she run away to Galway or maybe Dublin? It was hard to know what to do. If she went back to St. Joseph's, she might be kept there forever, or made to join the nuns and sent to some convent where she would have to look after children for the rest of her life.

Oh, my God, there's that queer noise back again, and the faint night-light that was under the door, had gone out. God, it's so creepy in this house, she sighed. She hugged her shoulders and pulled the blankets up around her neck for added security and protection because she could still feel the goose pimples on her arms and shoulders. She turned over and tried to get comfortable. Maybe I suffer from a fear of strange houses. That's silly. If only there was some light I could get comfortable and go to sleep. Could that creaking noise be a mouse or worse a rat? Her body gave an uncontrollably nervous twitch at the thought of seeing a rat emerging from a hole in the floorboards, like she once saw in St. Joseph's. As bad as that experience was, she'd still settle for the peace and tranquillity of St. Joseph's right now, with her friends sleeping all around her.

Here, in this big house she was all alone out in the middle of nowhere. She forced herself to try and face reality. The O'Malley's lived here, so it must be all right. God, maybe that's it, she thought. How could this place, this house, even this room; be like St. Joseph's? Here, I have my own room, my own bed, while in St. Joseph's there was always a beautiful comforting sort of noise I never realised existed. Someone was always coughing, snoring, or talking in their sleep. Someone would scream aloud because they were having an awful nightmare of being beaten by their drunken father, but always you could hear the soothing voice of the night nurse as she said, 'It's all right pet, it's only a dream' as she tucked them in again and said 'Go back to sleep now. And if the screaming woke me I'd lift my head to see who it was then I'd turn over and go back to sleep again and I wouldn't be a bit afraid.

Besides several night-lights hung on the dormitory walls, so you could go to the lavatory at any time if you wanted. Here, there are no lights and no friends, and it's such a small room compared to the size of the one in St. Joseph's. Listen, there's nothing; not a sound, except when the creaking starts. Maybe it's from the floorboards in the next room. That's silly, there's no one sleeping in the next room. Whatever it was, she wasn't hearing it now, and the thought that she was beginning to deal with her fears gave her confidence. She realised for the first time that this was how it would always be, she'd have to get used to it. And with these comforting thoughts she turned over and whispered, Dear God, thank you for coming to my rescue, as sleep carried her away on a tidal wave of happiness.

It was Sunday. The O'Malley's, were preparing for Mass and had arranged to give her a lift to Church. She sat waiting in the living room. On her return she would be treated to dinner with the family. Gerald had already told her there were some nice sights, if she wanted to get out and about for a walk. The children would show her around. But deep down she was expecting something more on her day off. She thought how nice it would be to get away from the house. She was only here six days she told herself, nevertheless she would almost certainly be here for another six days before she could go anywhere again. Here, she was supposed to be free, only she had nowhere to go. She thought how lovely it would be to go to the cinema. She had seen two pictures while in Clifden and would love to see another one. But how would she go? Maybe there are no pictures in Tuam. And, if she did go to the cinema, whom could she go with? She didn't have any friends here to go anywhere. Then she remembered the workmen saying something about a dance tonight at the cross. God, if only I could think who it was that said it. Oh, yes, 'twas Peter. What did he say? They're organising a bit of a Ceilí at the cross. What Cross? And who's they? What if I could get an atlas and learn the geography of the area. That's stupid, she thought. It would probably only show: *Gallimh agus Tuaim agus Maum*. Seems they don't speak much Irish here either, except what the children learn going to school and in Clifden everyone speaks Irish; even the nuns use it. But the only language they were really interested in was religion, and the wages of sin. No mention about my wages and all the work I did for them. Oh, what did I do with the five shillings the Reverend Mother gave me? I'll run upstairs and bring it with me to Mass, just in case we go somewhere.

They went to ten o'clock Mass in the small village Church in Cill Conly. The children wanted to go to the Cathedral in Tuam, but Gerald said no. Bridie was more disappointed than ever, because the children had lead her to believe that going to Mass in the Cathedral was a regular event. Instead she had to smile and pretend to be happy when introduced to the various Aunts and Uncles of the O'Malley clan, while all around everyone appeared to stop and gawk and whisper as she moved around the circle.

"A fine slip of a girl," the men said.

"Ahem. But does she know how to boil an egg?" asked Auntie Biddy, cocking her snoot in the air.

After Sunday dinner, the children began showing Bridie the ancient castle in the grounds of an enclosed orchard; where children came in the autumn to rob and plunder all the apples. The O'Malley children were strictly forbidden by their parents, from entering the orchard grounds because some of the high broached walls of the castle hung precariously, and were a danger to anyone in the vicinity.

"...Anyway, the apples aren't nice. They're huge green things only good for tarts, not like the beautiful ones we have in Granny's garden. Bridie, do you have apple trees in your garden?" asked Sinead, as they stood looking over a low stonewall at the ruins of the castle.

"Yes of course, lots."

"And are there castles near your house?" asked Daniel.

"Not as near as yours, but quite near."

"Can we go there someday?" asked Daniel, his eyes dancing as the three of them now surrounded Bridie.

"But...But...Where do you live?" asked Darragh coming closer.

"Oh. It's a long, long way from here," said Bridie. "Clifden. Have you ever heard of Clifden, it's in Connemara?"

"Is that in Dublin?" asked Darragh, hopefully.

"You shut your gob, I was talking to her first," sneered Daniel at his brother angrily.

"No. It's on the coast. It's a beautiful seaside town," said Bridie quickly, hoping they'd realise that not everyone gets to live near the sea.

"Ah no. You mean you live by the sea?" said Sinead, excitedly.

"Yes," answered Bridie triumphantly, just when she was beginning to think she wouldn't have anything good to say about herself.

"Oh, I want to go there, I've only ever been to Salthill. Can we go and stay in your house?" asked Sinead, hopefully

"Well...I don't think that's possible," said Bridie after an agonising delay.

"But why?" asked Darragh. "Do your mother and father not like us?"

"Shut your streece, her mother and father have never even seen us," interrupted Daniel as he playfully pushed his younger brother out of the way.

"I won't. I won't," shouted the little fellow defiantly as his older brother laughed and the two of them started to wrestle on the ground, before running across the field.

Sinead was delighted. She now had Bridie all to herself. She prayed the boys would carry on playing on their own, because she liked the new housekeeper who was so much younger than the last one. Sinead was shocked when she realised she herself was only four years younger than Bridie. Out here in the country she thought Bridie was lovely while at home she seemed awfully quiet.

"Do you have many brothers and sisters?" asked Sinead, as they both walked towards the river that divided the farm.

Bridie, caught unexpectedly, didn't have time to think and answered rather hastily, "No, I have no brothers or sisters."

"Uck! I'd hate that! You mean you never had a brother or a sister? Who minded you then? Whom did you play with?"

Bridie, now felt she had made a fool of herself by telling the truth. Worse still, she felt a strange kind of anguish on hearing, Sinead, use the work 'Uck!, just because she was on her own. Perhaps she should have lied. But what, Bridie wondered, would Sinead say if she knew she had no mother or father either. She would have to invent something quick or Sinead might grow to dislike her and no longer be her friend.

"I had a younger brother once, but he died when he was three," said Bridie.

"Died? What happened to him?"

"I don't know. He just died...I think it was the measles or something. Is that the river?" said Bridie, changing tact and realising that she was entering dangerous territory, telling lies.

"Oh, how awful." "Darragh and Daniel," shouted Sinead, as the two boys came into view over the rise, pretending to be galloping horses. "Bridie had a brother that died of measles, and you've not had measles or mumps yet."

In an instance the galloping horses came to an abrupt halt, and reverted to curious boys again.

"What's measles?" asked Darragh.

"What's mumps?" asked his brother.

"Measles. You're covered in spots, your eyes, your ears, your nose, your mouth, your chin, right down to you know what. Besides, Mum has already told you." laughed Sinead, "And anybody who even touches you or goes anywhere near you gets it straight away. And mumps...are great big things; lumps that cover your face," added Sinead triumphantly.

"Why do only boys die?" asked Darragh, worryingly.

"Not many boys die..." intervened Bridie quickly, lest she be accused of frightening the children. "Only some one who is very ill; too weak, or not able to take their medicine," she added.

"Gosh. I don't think I've had, measles or mumps yet," said Sinead, thinking that she herself might still be at risk, and that if one of them got it then the whole family would be wiped out. But it didn't kill Bridie, so it might not kill her, if the boys got it.

"But why didn't your mother and father get another boy when your little brother died?" queried Sinead.

"I don't know," answered Bridie, "Maybe they were afraid he would die too."

"Oh, that would be awful. Anyway, I'd rather have a sister. Sisters are more fun," said Sinead suddenly grabbing Bridie by the hand, because she knew it would annoy her brothers, who hated girls.

"Heh! And I'd rather have a brother. Heh!" snorted Daniel, sneering right into his sister's face. "Because girls are sissies and cry babies."

"Come on, I'll race you to the river: then we'll see who's a cry baby," said Sinead knowing full well that she could out-sprint Daniel, anytime. But once wasn't enough. She had to do it three times to convince Daniel that she beat him fair and square, even if she did grab him by the sleeve when it looked like he might beat her the first time.

Later when they all returned home, Bridie decided it might be a good time to write to Alice and Sister Bernadine in St. Joseph's and went quietly up to her room.

Meanwhile the children on being asked how they had enjoyed their afternoon told their mother how Bridie lived in a house by the sea, and how she had invited them there next summer. That they too had loads of apple trees and lived near a castle, and that Bridie had a brother who got the measles and died; and that her father and mother had decided not to get any more boys in case they died too.

"Mum, does that mean we'll die if we get the mumps or measles?"

"Of course not dear, don't be silly," said Mrs O'Malley. "Did Bridie say anything else?"

"She wanted to know about the dance at the Cross, and if you and daddy ever went and how old Danny and Peter were, and where they lived and if they had girlfriends. She said she'd love to go to the pictures; that she used to go in Clifden," said Sinead.

"She said the pictures were like big photographs that moved on a white wall, and that it was real scary at first. But they're not real, but very, very funny. She said there was a very funny man; his name was Charlie. He had a funny walk, with a moustache and a stick," added Daniel excitedly.

"It wasn't that man," interrupted Darragh, "She said he was a fat man, who doesn't talk; none of them talk. Mammy, can we go to the pictures?"

"I don't know. We'll have to ask your father, and we all know he only likes looking at horses. Now, don't you think it's time you got ready for bed, you've school in the morning?" She said, as Gerald came in and proceeded to put his shotgun away in a secure cabinet after an enjoyable day, shooting with his friends.

"Oh, there you are. I need to have a word with you about something important, later."

Her words were almost drowned out by the excitement of the children relaying the day's events. An hour or so later, when all was quiet in the house, she turned to Gerald as he sat reading the newspaper, and remarked,

"I don't think Bridie is the type of person I'd come to expect as good company for our children."

Gerald, somewhat startled, put down the *Racing Chronicle* and looked over the rim of his gilt framed glasses at his wife.

"Whatever makes you say that?"

"Surely you were startled at the lies she told our children this afternoon, 'A big house' my foot! And inviting them there next summer! Surely you don't think that's acceptable behaviour?"

"Perhaps she was only trying to be friendly: after all, she's only sixteen."

"Upon my word, and a dangerous sixteen at that. Did the children tell you she was asking about the workmen? What they did on their days off and when was the next dance in 'Cross'. Besides, she's not very good at housekeeping. She doesn't know how to bake properly, and I have to constantly remind her to clean up after herself, whenever she does the cooking, and you know how tiresome that can be, just keeping an eye on her."

Gerald picked up the newspaper and started to read again, to show his distaste at his wife's pettiness.

"You're not listening. You never do. I knew I should have gone to St. Joseph's myself and vetted the girls personally, instead of letting them send out a half-trained girl without an ounce of parentage."

This line was enough to rile Gerald. He flung down the paper and removed his glasses, because he knew he'd get no peace.

"I thought we'd both agreed, we'd consider giving a job to a nice homeless girl after we'd read about their plight in the newspaper. Did we or did we not agree to that?"

"Of course. But she's totally unacceptable. You saw how she behaved that first morning. I almost had to cancel my appointment with the tea ladies, and now these lies. It's not acceptable Gerald. I will not have my children's prospects tainted by someone whose only ability is to fill them with false hope and lies; not to mention the fear of death from some hideous disease or other. I think we should both accept it's been a horrible mistake and go for a more mature lady in her early thirties."

"I don't accept any such thing," said Gerald in exasperation. "We've had three different housekeepers in the last five years. They could cook, sew, and were very good with the children. But they all left; didn't they? At least Bridie's young. She could become part of the family; she seems eager enough to me, and besides the children like her, especially Sinead…they have a certain understanding of each other."

"That is precisely my point Gerald. She would be a bad influence. This talk of dancing and pictures and farm boys is not good listening for any daughter of mine. What we need is a nice sophisticated girl, a trained Nanny, somebody with a proper pedigree. You've said it yourself, you'll not buy a mare; unless it's a thorough-bred."

"Ah Beatrice, don't talk a load of poppycock. We're talking about people here, and as far as I'm concerned, Bridie's OK. She's attractive, pleasant and the children like her; which is more than could ever be said for Peggy. She wouldn't let them express themselves in any shape or form. Granted, she was good in the kitchen, but she's gone," said Gerald as he stood up to leave the room. "As far as I'm concerned there's nothing wrong with Bridie that a little chat wouldn't put right. Have a word if you must. But for God's sake, leave it at that."

Next morning when the children were gone to school and the workers had vacated the kitchen, Mrs O'Malley sat Bridie down at the kitchen table.

"Bridie dear, I feel obliged to inform you, that Gerald and I have been rather taken aback by your comments to our children yesterday. Have you anything to say?"

Bridie was somewhat gob-smacked at this turn of events. She didn't know what Mrs O'Malley was talking about. But her mind raced like clockwork to the bridge, the castle, the orchard, the measles... surely it wasn't the dreaded talk about the mumps and the measles. She decided quickly it was best to plead total ignorance.

"What do you mean?" said Bridie.

"You, Miss Bridie Rodgers led my children to believe you were a person of distinguished background, whose parents owned property on the seafront. You claimed you had a younger brother who died tragically as a result of contracting measles. When we all know you were a homeless child sent down from Dublin. You also intimated, to Sinead – who God knows, is an impressionable young child – that you fancied one of the farm hands. That, Miss Bridie Rodgers, Gerald and I find most reprehensible."

"Excuse me," said Bridie, her eyes ablaze, "I said no such thing. I'm only here a week and I don't know anyone around here. I've slaved every single day and all I did was have a friendly conversation with the children. I asked Sinead about the other workers and what they did in their spare time. That's hardly claiming to fancy somebody."

"What about the lies?" retorted Mrs O'Malley, "the so called parents of yours that don't even exist; brothers that don't exist, and a big house by the sea: that's obviously a figment of your tiny imagination, and you not even owning the rags on your back."

Bridie could not believe she had been so stupid with the children, but the way Mrs O'Malley portrayed her personal background was like thrusting a knife into her heart, she felt so hurt. She rose from the table shouting,

"Yes. The very rags you gave me. I'm going to tell Sister Bernadine the sort of person you are," and with that she ran crying from the kitchen and upstairs to her room.

Mrs O'Malley could barely conceal her anger, that such a brazen hussy could treat her like that. She meant to give Bridie a good lecture, but somehow Bridie, who hadn't said a word all week, managed to make her feel small by running away from her. Nobody, but nobody does that to me, intoned Mrs O'Malley to herself. If that lady thinks she can ignore me after I, out of the goodness of my heart gave her a bed to lie on, and a station to be proud of, then she has another thing coming.

Bridie, who'd gone to her room, sat on the bed and cried. What's wrong with me? I'm always in trouble, she sighed. I can't do anything right. If it's not the baking, it's the cleaning up after myself. If it's not what I do, it's what I say. Why can't she accept, I've done nothing wrong? Surely it's not a sin, to pretend I have a mother and father; or a brother who died, she sobbed. Besides, I do have a home if I want, you oul' hag. I'm sure Gerald never said those things about me, he always seems so nice to me, when she's not there. But he leaves the room the minute she comes in. I'm sure he hates the sight of her. I'll write and tell Mother Superior; but I already wrote, praising the O'Malley's. How can I write again and say I don't like them.

What will I do now, she cried as she tried to pull herself together and to reason the whole thing out. I'm not going down stairs again. But then maybe she'll throw me out and then I'll have nowhere to go. I've no food. No money; except the five shillings. Maybe I should leave now and go into Tuam where there's a convent: and I could work for wages. I suppose I was wrong to tell the children I had a brother, but I didn't mean it. I never said I fancied any of the farm lads. Saying, 'Blackie' was nice; does that mean I liked him?

Deep down Bridie knew that it did. But then she liked Gerald and the children, and Alice. Language and words and suggestions are stupid she thought. Pure stupid. Everything I say or do is twisted. Even Sister Bernadine didn't believe me when I found the two shillings in the nuns' field, and she tried to say I stole it. Now that hag, Mrs O'Malley, is trying to say I led her children to believe I was a person of distinguished back round.

I am a person of distinguished background. I've been taught by the nuns; in a proper school. I made my First Communion. I learned to cook, sew and play the mouth organ, so I'll not let anyone belittle me like that, thought Bridie. I'll stay right here, till that bitch says she's sorry.

Mrs O'Malley, with her arms folded, stood looking studiously out the rear kitchen window. She could see the workmen in the distant fields harvesting the corn with Gerald's best horses at the helm. But horses were the last things on Mrs O'Malley's mind. Bridie, what was she going to do with her now, she began to wonder. If the workmen weren't to be deprived of dinner, then somebody would have to prepare it, and quick. She, as head of the household was not going to do it while, *'that one'* was upstairs. But how would she get her down without losing face. The way she saw it, she had two choices facing her. Dismiss Bridie instantly and do the cooking herself, which was her preferred option, or apologise straight away and get Bridie down quickly to do the cooking. She considered the latter a horrendous idea. It meant she would have to grovel in order to get Bridie back to work. She turned on her heel quickly and decided she'd do the cooking. She had a bucket of washed spuds on the table, ready to peel, when the thought suddenly struck her, that she would have to do them again tomorrow if Bridie were dismissed. Worse still, she would have to wash and peel, scrub and sew, and bake for the entire week. And if her friends and neighbours ever found out that her home had been reduced to self-catering, simply because she didn't have a housekeeper, then her standing in the community would be considerably reduced. One simply must not allow that to happen: a new housemaid, only here a week and gone. What would the neighbours think? She frowned, as she washed her soiled hands quickly. Gerald of course, would get very cross if he found I'd dismissed *'that lady'* without his agreement, and after what happened with the last maid that would be unthinkable. I know, thought Mrs O'Malley, I'll pretend it was all my fault and get it over with for now: then when I'm good and ready and when *'that one'* least expects it, I'll get my revenge.

She knocked on Bridie's door, "May I come in please?"

Bridie opened the bedroom door and stood looking at Mrs O'Malley.

"Bridie I've been thinking. Perhaps I'm not very good at expressing myself. But what I really want to say is…. I've been a bit hasty. You're only here a week and you've been very good and everything and we're all very fond of you. So let's just forget everything I've said, and go back down stairs."

Bridie did not answer. She stood looking at Mrs O'Malley in disbelief. There must be a reason for this sudden change of heart she was thinking, as her eyes took in Mrs O'Malley's gem encrusted brooch, fancy earrings, and multiple wedding and sovereign rings.

The hag, thought Bridie, all that's missing is the bag. You're far too grand Missus to be washing spuds, cutting cabbage or scrubbing kitchen floors. But do I have a choice? No. But true as God is my Judge Mrs O'Malley, I'll bide my time, wait my chance, and then I'm off, as she silently side-stepped Mrs O'Malley and ran down the stairs

Bridie soon realised that labouring under Mrs O'Malley was one major ordeal she had not bargained for. She decided however, not to respond to her continual goading. After much thought she came to the conclusion that she didn't have any choice but to keep her head down and say nothing, for the time being. This restriction on herself was most painful in the company of the children, especially Sinead, whom she loved to talk with. Bridie felt she could no longer wear her heart on her sleeve, because there was no knowing how her words might be construed by Mrs O'Malley; should the children ever engage in a harmless bout of tittle-tattle.

Instead, Bridie turned her main thoughts of occupation to the workmen, Peter, Thomas and Seamus. Of the three, Seamus was now her favourite. And although the oldest by far he had a certain charm that made her enjoy being in his company. Seamus and Peter usually regaled Bridie over breakfast with lurid tales of the local community; where according to Seamus the village was rife with snobbery and where the working class begrudged you the steam of their piss. She just loved their facial expressions and witty remarks that went with their recounting of a tale.

Her favourite memory was Seamus's belief that, 'nothing good ever came out of Cill Conly, because it's the sort of place where if the neighbours have anything at all against you, they'll bide their time; and then give you the full contents of their steaming piss-pots in the face of a morning when you least expect it. And if you're lucky they might even rush out and plead ignorance, by claiming it was a pure accident: while deep within their hearts, they're just delirious with pleasure, at having scored a direct hit. For days and days their household will simply revel in the sordidness of it all. So don't say girl, you haven't been warned, don't say.'

She was warned too by Gerald that the local village was not the place to be seen at a Sunday Crossroads dance. There everyone would know she was a stranger in their midst. And 'twas only fair she should know the place was full of lecherous looking men well past their prime, so that if she were ever to consider going to a dance, then the place to go was 'Cross' or 'Toureen' across the border in Co. Mayo.

But Bridie never got to go anywhere except when the children were brought to the Cathedral in Tuam, which was very rare. Her only means of social contact was preparing tea for the weekly visitors and listening to the daily episodes of the farm workers, as they pulled up a noisy chair to attack breakfast each morning.

It was Thursday and Bridie was on her knees, cleaning the stairs and dreaming of a possible romantic interlude with Seamus, who had said he was going to the Dance at 'Cross' on Sunday night. It was only four miles away. Perhaps she should consider walking there herself she thought. It's high time I got to see a bit of the world. Shag it: I'll think I'll go on my own, one way or another.

Suddenly, she was aware of a disturbance behind her, but she was too late to avoid the handle of the sweeping brush as Mrs O'Malley laid it across her back.

"What's the meaning of this?" (wallop!) she began. "You've ruined my best blouse with your blasted iron. (wallop) Don't you know you can't iron a silk blouse if the iron's too hot," she shouted.

Bridie ran for protection to the top of the stairs.

"I didn't know! Mrs O'Malley, I didn't know!" she pleaded, but Mrs O'Malley continued to lash out at a retreating Bridie.

"You're nothing but a wastrel; thrown out of the Industrial School by a shower of nuns. I should have known better than to hire the likes of you."

Bridie turned, her eyes ablaze. She pointed, gesturing to Mrs O'Malley

"If you hit me once more…"

Wallop! "How dare you point a finger at me," hissed Mrs O'Malley, as she hit Bridie a short sharp crack across the hand.

"Go to your room at once," ordered Mrs O'Malley as she closed in on Bridie. Bridie saw this as a very dangerous move, and knew she might get a severe beating in the confines of her room. So, acting purely on instinct, she shot forward and bolted past Mrs O'Malley, almost knocking her back down the stairs.

Bridie stood for a fleeting moment in the relative safety of the hall, looked up and shouted, "I won't. I won't. You can get some other body to do your dirty work."

Mrs O'Malley, recovering her composure, started to come quickly down the stairs as she screamed at Bridie, "Come back here at once! Come back here; now!"

But Bridie had shot out the rear door and was running for dear life down the long gravelled drive. She kept running until she was out of sight of the house and then she climbed over a wall and into a field in case anybody saw her. Struggling to get her breath, she sat down on a rock and started to cry. This in turn led to fits of convulsions and fear of the unknown. A fear that her hand might be broken for it was now slightly swollen. Besides, her back ached and stung whenever she moved.

She stayed there, sitting on the huge boulder for a long time; till a cold chill took hold of her and she knew she'd have to seek shelter. Lightly dressed, she soon realised she had no clothes no food or no money. She made up her mind she was not going back to that house again. But somehow she had to get her clothes and money. She had nothing else to wear and was powerless without them. A light rain was starting to fall. She knew she'd have to do something quickly. Using her vague knowledge of the area, from the walks with the children, she decided to go by circuitous route back to the farmyard; where she'd hide and shelter until she could go into the house and get her belongings.

Better still, she might ask Peter or Seamus to get them for her. Otherwise, she would have to stay hiding until tomorrow morning because the children would be around in the evening, and Mrs O'Malley was not due to go visiting anywhere until tomorrow. Terrified of the animals in the field, she scurried along by the ditch, climbed over a barbed wire fence; crossed a little stream and was now only one field away from the Granary where she planned to hide in the hay, for the time being. Inching her way slowly along by the nearest fence, she made a short run across the farmyard and into the large shed that housed the Granary.

She was now more frightened than ever, being so close to the house and possibly so close to being discovered by the O'Malley's. If that happened she knew her chances of freedom were slim. They were, in a way, responsible for her care and they might not let her go.

For what seemed like a long time, Bridie stood hiding behind the half opened door, peeping across the yard in case anyone came out of the house. After a time she thought she heard someone coming, and tiptoed up stairs and hid in the rear of the building. She'd gone into its farthest corner when she heard one of the workers whistling his way casually into the building. If she tiptoed out to the top of the stairs and peered down she might see what was happening downstairs. But from the whistling she thought it was Peter and not Seamus whom she'd prefer to see. After a while, the whistling stopped and she thought who ever it was had gone out of the building. She was thinking of venturing out when suddenly an uncontrollable urge to sneeze came over her. She put up her hands quickly to smother the sneeze but only succeeded in muffling the sound. This was followed immediately by another and another. Then she knew someone had heard her, and was coming to investigate because she could hear them tiptoeing up the stairs, which reduced the amount of light coming into the Granary.

"Who's there?" said a voice and Bridie recognised it instantly as Peter's and gave a sigh of relief because she felt sure he would not betray her to the O'Malley's. Again the voice asked as it moved tentatively closer to where Bridie hid.

"Who's there? Is somebody there?"

Bridie thought she'd better answer, lest somebody else hear him talking. She whispered loudly, "It's me! Bridie!"

Peter came within feet of her before he saw her form in the hay. He turned and stood sideways so that he might be better able to see who it was, for sure.

"Bridie! he exclaimed loudly, "What are you doing here!"

Bridie could not answer. The words just lodged in her throat and would not come out. She wanted to burst into tears, to tell someone how Mrs O'Malley had beat her like a dog, and that she had a pain in her heart far worse than anything she'd ever known.

Again, Peter asked, "Are you all right?" as he moved closer. "Did Mrs O'Malley say something to you?"

Bridie nodded her head and started to cry, as Peter stood beside her. He could see she was very distressed and placed an arm around her shoulders to reassure her. For a few minutes she sobbed uncontrollably, burying her head in his chest as she babbled on, telling him what had happened. After some time she recovered her composure and Peter forced himself to remove his arm and stand aside, because he could not trust the wayward feeling creeping into his body. Instead, when he stood apart and looked at her dishevelled face, her pleading eyes and tender red lips, he was over come with an insatiable desire to seize her face between his hands and kiss her passionately.

Bridie too knew she felt a strange sort of comfort while she rested her head against his chest. She had distinctly heard the heavy boom of his heartbeat and felt the strength of his comforting arm around her shoulder. She straightened herself up to brush the hay from her hair and petticoat, and as she did so, Peter saw the shapely outline of her body. It was too much; he could not control himself any longer. He suddenly seized her pale cheeks and turned her face up to the light, to admire her porcelain beauty for a lingering moment, before planting his course stubbled chin onto her moist red lips.

For a split second, Bridie was in a daze and did not know what was happening. Then a surge of excitement swept through her body as she realised she was being kissed for the very first time and it was everything the Galway city girls out in St. Joseph's told her it would be. Peter's strong arms were wrapping themselves about her shoulders as his eager lips sent shockwaves through her system. Without realising it, she placed her hands on his shoulders to tell him stop, but somewhere along the line conflicting signals emerged to tell her wait a second: followed immediately by an urgent message.

Stop! But she was powerless, as her intellect screamed again, Stop! Stop! But she couldn't, because Peter was now nuzzling her neck, nibbling her ear, while all the time pressing her closely to his firm body. She felt a warm shiver of excitement that sent flesh-quakes down her spine. "Stop, Please!" she whispered nervously. "Stop it Peter, Please!" she cried, as she tried half heartedly to push him away.

Peter hesitated for a second but when he began to kiss her again, and his strong arms again moved to explore her body she lost total control. Her mind was lost. She could feel the strong muscles of his thighs and body as he squashed her body ever closer to his. His hands were everywhere, as a strange tingling sensation took control of her, and she savoured his hungry searching lips once more. She thought his body reeked of a strange odour that wafted into her nostrils and put her head spinning. Then a gust of shame swept over her, because he was now exploring the naked flesh of her body as she begged him to stop. "Peter! Peter!" she pleaded. And when she realised his strong hands were tearing at the flimsy material of her undergarments, she again cried aloud, "Stop! Stop! But it was useless because in an instant his powerful arms had raised her, clean off the ground, and as he again kissed her passionately on the lips, she was forced to cling desperately on to his shoulders, as he forcibly spread her legs and wrapped them around his waist.

This single act was like nothing she had ever imagined. It sent a bolt of excitement through her entire body; and an urgent request to her brain. What was he doing: was he trying to kill her by smothering her to death? Why was he now panting and breathing so hard? His legs and lower body were trembling uncontrollably. She was about to force her mouth away somehow and scream, "Stop it Peter! Stop it!" Instead it was a scream of mercy she unleashed followed by a faint cry, when the hot pole of his excitement plunged straight into her lower body, and she cried out "Ah! Aaah! Peter! Peter! Stop!" She felt at that moment as if some sort of mortal wound had been inflicted. Like a knife thrust deep into her flesh that sent hot waves all over her being. Suddenly she was gripped by the most awful fear that the man she knew and trusted was now going to kill her. She too was gasping for air because her whole body felt as if it had been set on fire by some unforeseen force and when a faint voice called out,

"Peter! Is that you?" She thought she'd surely die. For a moment, she felt his taut body turn to stone, before he let her aching limbs slowly dissolve away from his grasp. Again, the voice asked,

"Peter! Is that you?" as Sinead came inquisitively into view.

Peter turned his back quickly to hide his shame, as a cold sweat suddenly enveloped his body, he barked urgently,

"Stay! Stay! Stay where you are Sinead, I'll be out in a second."

"Is that you Bridie?" asked Sinead, tentatively after a pause, feeling that her friend Bridie was in some sort of a dilemma, so she stood her ground at the top of the stairs trying to peer into the darkness.

"For Christ's sake, go down stairs Sinead. I'll be out in a second," roared Peter distressingly.

Sinead turned and ran down stairs and into the house as Bridie tried rearranging her clothes as best she could and Peter turned abruptly and disappeared almost as unexpectedly as he had appeared. What was she going to do now that Sinead had seen her there in the hay, she wondered. She felt physically sick at the thought that she had been discovered with Peter. Bad enough that Mrs O'Malley would soon know, but she felt positively guilt-ridden and dirty after what had happened. She was terrified to even move because of what had happened and when she did, she thought she felt something oozing down the inside of her leg. She plucked up the courage to step into the light and examine herself. She was shocked to discover she was bleeding. She almost fainted at the thought that she was due again after only two weeks, when clearly it was only meant to happen to her every four weeks.

Menstruation, from what the nuns had told her, was part of growing up. They told her that her body would undergo major changes: from that of a young girl into that of a mature woman. But why was it happening to her again so soon? She felt weak and dizzy and rested her body against the giant stack of hay.

Her head was now spinning and she could not think clearly. She told herself she must have committed some awful sin, by allowing a man to kiss her like that. But surely it was all Peter's fault. But why did I allow him to do it? He must have cast a spell over my body. Sister Rita had said, 'The world is full of evil men whose only interest is to possess your body for their own wanton pleasure and destruction; does that mean her body was possessed, by some evil spirit? It must be, she thought, because deep down, her body felt torn apart, battered, bruised and broken. She hated the O'Malley's, she hated the children, she hated Peter, but most of all she hated herself because she was a coward who let other people abuse her, mentally and physically. She just wanted to lie down and die, and never again to wake up. Oh God, maybe, just maybe, it was all a bad dream and that this day never happened.

But when Gerald suddenly appeared at the top of the stairs and made his way over to her she thought she'd surely die of shame and embarrassment, because she knew it was only the beginning.

Later, as she lay half asleep in bed and was still struggling to erase the day's horrible events from her head, she heard a lot of shouting and noise downstairs. Then a gentle knock came to her door. It was Gerald. He came in and stood beside her bed and asked,

"Are you feeling any better?"

Bridie nodded. She was. In fact she felt much better since she'd had a hot bath and a change of clothes. She just wanted to rest now and get her thoughts together, and see where she was going to go from here. Gerald had brought her into the house where Mrs O'Malley had suddenly become very concerned for her welfare. She insisted she rest herself for the remainder of the evening, and told her she could have tomorrow off. Tomorrow off? That was a major treat to look forward to. She made up her mind as soon as she heard about her day off, that she was going to walk into Tuam and decide her future.

"Do you mind if we talk?" asked Gerald, a worried frown on his face. Bridie shook her head.

"Would you like to tell me what happened? And start from the beginning," he urged after a momentary pause.

Bridie didn't feel much like talking, but wondered did Gerald know what Mrs O'Malley had done. She thought it best to say nothing at all. But then the prospect of being able to put the record straight and tell Gerald about his awful wife was too good to ignore.

She lay, looking out blankly at Gerald, as he spoke.

"I understand that, maybe, it's not easy and that perhaps you'd like to talk to someone else. Would you like me to get a doctor?"

But Bridie did not feel bad enough to need a doctor; although her back and arm were still sore – not to mention the rest of her body. She pulled the bedclothes about her shoulders and lay staring up at Gerald for a few moments. She didn't know for sure if he was a nice man, or just Mrs O'Malley's husband pretending to be nice. What if she told him everything and he didn't believe her. Then there would be two people who hated her. It didn't matter whether she stayed or not, she still wanted people to like her. Surely that was not too much to expect. Nevertheless, there was that niggling fear that everything was going against her. The nuns, Mrs O'Malley, Peter: and now Gerald; he might be no better, she thought. Even the children, particularly Sinead, they would now hate her, she felt. How could she ever again meet her face to face without recalling how Sinead had caught her in that distressed state in the Granary.

Gerald was studying her. He could almost read her mind as he said softly, "You've a lot on your mind. Sometimes it's good to talk, it soothes the spirit, calms the fears."

After a long pause he continued, "You got up today and made the breakfasts and the children went to school and I went to Spring Field. What happened then? Where did it go wrong?" he urged.

"It's your wife Gerald. She's horrible and I don't like saying it," cried Bridie as her eyes welled up and she started to sob.

"She's the cruellest person I ever met, who treats me like a beggar. I wouldn't do to an animal what she's done to me," said Bridie as she sobbed uncontrollably, letting her tears flow.

"She treats me as if I'm a piece of dirt in off the street. She calls me names and today she beat me with the brush. I had to run away because I knew I'd stick a knife in her if she didn't stop. I don't want to hurt anyone, but she's always at me. Look what she did to my arm," said Bridie pulling up her sleeve and showing him the red swollen welt across her arm.

"And she hit me across the back...just because I made a mess of a blouse I'd never ironed before," she sniffed, as she dried her eyes with the sleeve of her pyjamas.

A shocked and distressed Gerald looked at her flushed expression and was himself, struggling to control his own emotions. He knew this girl was telling the truth, that if nothing else, Bridie was a person of substance. He rose from the chair and turned to face the bedroom window so that she could not see his tortured face. He had to accept that his wife was now pushing things close to the edge, that perhaps it was time to face reality. She had already been the cause of several staff members leaving 'Conly House', and now she was resorting to violence; the latest bout having led to an assault by one of the farm hands. He turned around before leaning against the wall to face Bridie again. Then he asked her "What happened then? After you ran away?"

Bridie told him how she ran down the road to get away from the house, but then decided to return for her belongings and to hide in the Granary until she could get her clothes. Bridie turned her face away from the prying eyes of Gerald as he waited for her to finish.

"Then what happened?" asked Gerald, a resigned look spread across his already pained expression.

But Bridie could not tell anyone how she had shamed herself before the world; by being caught red-handed in the most vile unladylike position, by Sinead, his own flesh and blood: a child that she herself was meant to be minding. She closed her eyes because it was all so revolting. Gerald came and sat on the edge of the bed and placed his hand gently on her tiny closed fists, but Bridie pulled her hand away quickly and said, "Please don't."

It was as if his hand had stung her. She didn't ever want to feel another man close to her again. It sent a chill down her spine because of what had already happened when she thought she could trust someone.

Gerald rose from the bed. "I understand," he whispered, "You don't have to tell me everything. It's just that I need to know where I stand. I have to look after the staff and make sure everyone is treated equally and with respect. At the same time I need to know if someone is stepping out of line."

After a pause, he asked the question that really galled him, because of what Sinead had said, 'Dad….I caught Peter and Bridie kissing in the hay.'

"Did Peter take advantage of you today or is something going on between ye?"

Bridie did not answer but slowly gathered the blankets about her before turning over to look away. Gerald knew it was time to go. As he quietly left the room, he already knew the answer, but he had other things on his mind.

He walked wearily down the stairs, his legs heavy as lead, and went into the reading room. He would have to think. What if Bridie had been assaulted, and he felt sure that she had; then what? He decided very quickly that in his opinion, Peter was guilty of assault; his wife was guilty of wounding and he himself was guilty of neglect: and of allowing his house to become a place of ill-repute: where a hired staff member had to run away, only to return and be sexually assaulted by another member of the household. Gerald buried his head in his hands and prayed the migraine would go away because he just couldn't think straight. He was ruined, destroyed, or as close to it as makes no matters, he told himself. If this got out, if word spread, then he was finished entirely because no self-respecting man or woman would ever want to work here again. He would be shunned in the local community. Horses and show jumping were his one passion, and now it would be seriously curtailed because of more pressing matters.

For a long time he paced up and down the room before deciding what to do. His only hope of salvation was to be strong and resolute, to do the right thing. The time for decisive actions had long since passed. If he didn't act now, there was no knowing what might happen next. And by doing something positive now; at least whatever transpired in relation to village gossip, it could be always said, that he did what he could.

Bridie was sent immediately on the pretext of a holiday for a few days to stay with Gerald's sister in Tuam, while Gerald rearranged a new working schedule for Conly House. But not before he had a long and heated discussion with Peter, who denied any improper behaviour towards Bridie. He described what transpired in the Granary as mere horseplay. But Gerald was adamant. Peter would have to go, and go he did, to be replaced by a young chap from a neighbouring village. From then on however, Conly House was no longer the place to be. Gone were the hearty breakfasts before commencing work in the morning. Gone were the days of boiled bacon and cabbage for the workers and worst of all gone was the freedom to ever set foot in the house again, or to mix with any of the household staff. Instead the farm hands sat on milking stools in the stables, come hail rain or shine, with their sandwiches and bottles of cold tea: while Mrs O'Malley was said to have gone to America for an extended holiday.

Bridie was persuaded to return after a few days when the driver collected her and she was asked by Gerald to put forward her ideas in relation to the reorganized running of the house.

"Bridie, as you can see, the situation is anything but ideal at present, but I appreciate you returning after what has happened. However, we must all do what we can, especially for the children. I would like you to continue working as normal. My sister, Mary, will be only too glad to come over and relieve you on your days off. And besides, the children will be delighted to see a little more of their auntie. So hopefully we'll all get back to normal as soon as possible. I cannot, however, guarantee that you will be able to remain with us. I can't say for definite how long my wife will be away. But in order to give you a start in life and in readiness for any plans you might like to make, I am putting you on an income of two and sixpence a week plus your keep. How does that sound to you?"

"Fine," said Bridie, as a warm glow of satisfaction spread across her pale face, at the prospect of earning her first pay.

Bridie now had more time to herself, and felt she might be able to enjoy a little bit of freedom about the house; to go places, to make new friends: to go to Tuam or Galway, or even Dublin. The nuns had told her in school she was from Dublin. Even Mrs O'Malley had upcasted the fact to her. Perhaps she should go there and see for herself. Who knows I might even find my mother and father; not that they'll be much good to me now, she thought, But still, 'twould be nice to know where I came from. If I started to save a few shillings I could soon get the train. But first I want to be able to buy my own clothes and get my hair done.

Her plans were working out fine. She had no more workmen to feed and the children were at school most of the day. So, every room in the house was now spotlessly clean and a smell of bees wax wafted from the antique furniture after she did her rounds each morning.

One day, Bridie heard a heavy knock at the front door. Gerald was away at Ballinalsoe horse fair, and she wasn't expecting anyone. She opened the door, and there stood Peter, half-smiling,

"Oh, how ya? I just thought I'd come to see how you were….."

"I'm fine," said Bridie, surprised to see him and wondering what he wanted, because he wasn't supposed to ever set foot inside the door again.

She stood looking at him for a moment then he asked,

"Can I come in?"

"Gerald is not here, do you want to see him?"

"No, no," he answered quickly, "Someone told me he was gone to the fair and I thought I'd stop by to see how you were, you know," but thinking to himself maybe he could renew the friendship; that's if she hadn't taken things too badly last time.

Bridie was very aware of his body language and half-closed the door lest he should try to barge his way in. She suddenly had a fear of the man, as all the thoughts came flooding back: the arm around her shoulders, the sudden kiss, the excitement in his body and the way his hands wandered all over her body.

Without realising it she had almost trapped herself between the door and the jamb in an effort to keep him out.

"No, no. I never want to see that man again. This was something between you and me. He should never have interfered. I like you, and I want to be friends, we were always friends, weren't we?" he said, hoping she'd open the door and let him in before anyone saw him.

If she was in the house on her own, he might just be able to get at her again, and now that he saw her in the flesh, he knew that he had been right in his thinking all along, that she was indeed a beauty: and he would give anything to get her in that position again. He might never ever get another chance, as Mrs O'Malley would surely get rid of her the minute she came home and God knows where Bridie would end up. Girls like her could end up anywhere: right next door to one or maybe a hundred miles away. But usually it was far, far away, where a man might never lay eyes on the likes of her again. He thought, she might be a bit cross with him, because he knew he'd been a bit hasty the last time, but then again she seemed to enjoy the experience, he thought

Bridie was looking at his shifting restless eyes and sensed that he was capable of doing the same thing to her all over again. She was now positively petrified. She had trusted him before and thought he'd be sympathetic to her problem. But when she thought of the way he had treated her and spread her legs, she felt herself getting weak at the knees. It was frightening the way he seemed to have some sort of strange effect on her. Now she thought of Gerald. He had warned her; nobody was to be let into the house in his absence. Only the children and Auntie Mary who was not due till this evening. Gerald was a kind and decent man she thought: she would do what she was told, and he had said, nobody, but nobody, must ever be allowed in while she was on her own, especially any of the workmen. She summoned up the courage to say,

"I must go now. The children will be coming home from school and I must get their dinner," surprising herself at how quickly she came up with an excuse.

"Arrah, they're not due home for ages yet," he laughed trying to seem relaxed and cheerful about the whole thing.

The idea was to get inside the door. He'd ask for a drink of water. That should do the trick, then he could walk in ever so casually, talking by the way, and then...

"Oh, they're getting off early, and Auntie Mary's coming over and stopping for a few days to help clean the house," said Bridie lying, and beginning to feel her confidence coming back.

"Home early?" said Peter, alarmed that his plans might be about to fail. "Why would they come home early?"

"I don't know," answered Bridie, thinking, she had put her foot in it. "Oh, the teachers sent word yesterday to say they'd be letting them out early. I must go now, or Gerald will be cross with me if the jobs are not done. I'll tell him you called."

"Oh no! Jesus no! Don't say I was here," said Peter, alarmed at the thought that she could be so stupid. "I only came to see how you were. I thought we'd have a little chat."

He was disappointed that his timing had been so bad and that there was the ever-present danger that he might be caught in the act again by one of the children. He had only just managed to convince Gerald the last time that nothing unseemly had happened between himself and Bridie; that he merely had his arm about her, reassuring her after her beating at the hands of Mrs O'Malley: convincing himself in the process that the reason for his dismissal was because he dared to side with Bridie.

At that moment the rumbling of a horse cart on the gravelled drive could be heard as one of the workmen turned in the gateway from the main road on his way back from town. Peter turned to look and a sense of urgency crept into his voice as he ran to grab the bicycle leaning against the wall "Don't tell anyone I was here. I'll see you again Bridie. Good Luck," he said, as he jumped on his bike and disappeared down the bridle path that ran from the back of the house.

"Oh, thank God for that," sighed Bridie to herself as she returned to the kitchen. If he comes round again, what am I going to do? I'll have to tell Gerald he called and that I wouldn't let him in; he'll be pleased about that.

But Gerald was not at all pleased to hear that Peter had the gumption to call around in his absence, proving he was right to dismiss him and even more correct in his beliefs that he should warn Bridie never to let anyone into the house.

Bridie continued to live in fear that Peter would return, by fair means or foul, and when Mrs O'Malley returned home unexpectedly, she felt as if one evil person was being replaced by another. But the Mrs O'Malley she had known, was now a much-changed person. She appeared more at ease with herself and those around her. Nevertheless, she spent days and days in her room as Gerald, instructed Bridie, to carry on as normal; that Beatrice was on medication and that he himself would take care of her.

Gradually and by degrees and after a few months, the lady of the house returned to something like her old self and then one day she approached Bridie with a rather strange request.

"Bridie, we're going into Tuam tomorrow, Gerald and I think you too should come along for the drive. We're going to the Doctor's. You haven't had a check-up since you've been here, have you?"

Bridie, somewhat surprised, replied,

"Alright."

"It was Gerald's idea dear. He thinks we should all have regular check-ups, as TB is now so rampant in the country."

Bridie decided that if it kept her *ladyship* quiet, then she was only too happy to go along; besides it would be a rare treat to be going somewhere after all the months of monotonous housework. All she did since she came to work in Conly House was to go to a show jumping event in Athenry with Gerald and the children. She'd go to Mass every Sunday and then write to the Reverend Mother, when she came home.

When they arrived in Bishop Street, Gerald, Beatrice, and Bridie all traipsed into the waiting room and after a lengthy wait Bridie was called in to the surgery and given a thorough examination. Bridie didn't particularly like having doctors examine her as she felt it was all such an invasion of her privacy particularly as she wasn't ill or anything. She couldn't understand why it was always men who had to examine girls but then maybe there were no lady doctors, she thought. Sometimes she thought they could be off handish enough, especially that time when the nuns thought she might have had appendicitis. But thankfully this doctor was much nicer and though he didn't say an awful lot, she didn't feel too bad about it; now that it was all over.

Afterwards, Gerald insisted on taking them to a nearby hotel where he treated them to tea and some lovely sponge cake. Then after going on a quick shopping spree they all returned home, and Bridie thought the news might not be good, concerning Mrs O'Malley, as both herself and Gerald were extremely quiet on the way home; but nothing was said. She herself was in good health, and that was all that mattered, thought Bridie, as they approached the quiet seclusion of Conly House, after the excitement of Tuam.

That evening Gerald, asked Bridie, to make a pot of tea and to join him in the study. When she had done this and sat down to face him, she got the distinct feeling that something awful was about to unfold. There was something about the way Gerald watched her pour out the tea that convinced her she was being sent back to St. Joseph's. He had told her before, he could not guarantee that she would be able to remain with them, so it looked as if once again, Mrs O'Malley was calling the shots; even though she no longer interfered with Bridie, except to call for her medication.

"Bridie, I'm afraid I have some disturbing news," he said, as he sat forward, elbows resting on his knees, and rubbing his hands together as if trying to soothe away some pain or other.

Bridie, meanwhile, thought this is it. I knew I was right, but little does he know, I'm not going back to St. Joseph's; no, never. I'll say nothing, just go along with whatever he suggests. I have some clothes and money and can run away for the first time in my life.

"I think I know what it is," said Bridie, a resigned look on her face that caught Gerald by surprise.

"You know?" he queried, with a raised brow, as a visible wave of relief swept over him that transformed the corners of his mouth into the faint outline of a smile.

"Yeah," she added confidently. "I have to leave. You're sending me back to St. Joseph's. You said before, I might not be able to stay, remember?"

Gerald's features collapsed into a heavy scowl and his heart gave a painful lurch that he'd been so taken in by Bridie's innocence, that he was after all, going to be the conveyer of bad news. Get it over with quickly, he told himself and stop beating about the bush.

"Bridie, you're pregnant. You're expecting a baby. The doctor says you're seven months gone; which means you're due in eight weeks."

Pregnant? Pregnant? But how could…? The words sent a shiver down her spine. Seven months! Eight weeks! She felt faint. The doctor…? So that's why he quizzed her as he placed his hands gently on her abdomen. But how could I be…?

Gerald was saying something but she didn't hear because it was all coming back. She was still cleaning the stairs; Mrs O'Malley, was shouting and hitting her, and she was running down the drive, climbing stone walls, and then making a horrid decision that would lead her to the Granary. She could clearly hear her garments being torn and then Peter lifting her like a rag doll and her cry for help. Stop it, Peter. Stop. She could still feel the pain, and now the shame. She closed her eyes for a split second to shut out the world, because she didn't want to recall that day again. Yet here it was now being thrust at her, forcing her to accept that an event had taken place whether she liked it or not, because she was pregnant. Pregnant, she thought; only mothers get pregnant; how could she be pregnant? She wasn't married. She had never been to a dance in her life, not even a house dance. A Baby? She stared at Gerald. He was looking at her and saying, "I'm so sorry it turned out like this."

But she wasn't listening, only studying his lips as he spoke. She had allowed a man to kiss her, and now she was pregnant. It was Peter's and now she was going to have his baby.

She was still in shock and bewilderment when a smiling Mrs O'Malley came in and said, "Congratulations Bridie. I understand you're going to be a mother."

Gerald sprang to his feet, "Beatrice! Come. Bridie needs time to herself. We'll go into the other room," helping to escort his wife out again, and turning to wink at Bridie, whose expression did not change as she watched them both leave the room.

After a few minutes Gerald put his head around the door and said, "I'll leave you for a minute, I'll be in again to talk it over so just try and relax." Bridie did not answer. But nodded agreement.

The more she thought about it, the worse it got. How could she have a baby, in a house with the likes of Mrs O'Malley sneaking about in her slippers? She might harm the child. She couldn't very well run away now, because she'd only be settled, somewhere and then the baby would be born, and nobody, not even a priest, would want a housekeeper if she had a child. It looked as if she'd have to stay with the O'Malley's, for the rest of her life. The mere thought of it was enough to make her sick: unless of course…she got married, but she didn't have a boyfriend: unless Peter? Did he have a girl, she wondered. Nobody could tell her anything when she made discrete inquiries although there was a suggestion that he was married. But Bridie didn't believe it. He didn't behave like a married man the way that Gerald had. And if he wasn't then he might marry her, she thought. But suppose he was cruel to her and beat her like some of the fathers, whose children had to be put into St. Joseph's. She would not under any circumstances marry someone who'd do that to her.

While working in Conly House, Peter had seemed so nice, always ready to make her laugh but then in the Granary he seemed to change. One second he had his arm soothingly around her shoulder, the next he was forcing his lips on hers. She closed her eyes again to squeeze out the memory. She heard a gentle rap on the door. It was Gerald, he was coming back into the room; he had two glasses on a tray. He gave one to Bridie, saying,

"I don't approve of young ladies drinking, but under the circumstances a little sherry won't do you any harm. In fact it will help you relax while I outline a few things to you."

"I don't think I should," said Bridie, "I don't drink."

"Nonsense," interjected Gerald, "It's just a little tipple, which we all need at a time like this: and please don't say anything to herself. A Brandy!" sighed Gerald, "Now that's what you call a proper drink," holding up his glass to Bridie. "Cheers."

"Cheers."

Bridie pretended to be shocked at the taste of the sherry, but she had sneaked a little sip of it once before when she was on her own in the house and had made up her mind that she didn't like it. But she'd better drink it now whether she liked it or not, she thought, as Gerald eased himself into a chair the other side of the coffee table, and said,

"You were very close to the truth Bridie, when you said you'd be leaving. I have to be straight with you and tell you, you can't stay on here indefinitely, because of the children. It would be unthinkable for you to have your baby here and even if, I allowed it, I don't think Mrs O'Malley would."

Bridie, coughed, and nearly spewed her drink, when she heard she was expected to leave at a time like this. So she'd be going back to St. Joseph's after all.

"Are you all right?" asked Gerald, as she continued to cough and splutter.

"Yes, I'm fine," she answered hoarsely as she accepted a handkerchief from Gerald.

"Of course we'll make proper arrangements for you to go somewhere safe, where you can have your baby in comfort; where you won't have to worry about anything. You'll be well looked after, I promise you that."

"Am I going back to St. Joseph's?"

"Only if you want to. I'll arrange for our local parish priest to call around to discuss a few things with you."

"The Priest?" said Bridie in surprise.

"Yes. I think he's in a better position than I am to advise you on your best options. I don't know him personally, but I know he's helped one or two others in similar situations. Of course you don't have to go yet, not for a couple of weeks anyway," said Gerald, trying to reassure her.

"But he'll send me to St. Joseph's, and I don't want to go back there again," said Bridie, a look of distress spreading across her pale complexion at the thought of living again among the nuns, and looking after screaming pitiful looking children.

And now that she was old enough she would probably have to help feed and care for every single one in the school. The thought of having to cook, wash, dress, and feed scores of children – not to mention her own – where she'd never have a minutes peace or privacy was too frightening. With no freedom or prospect of ever meeting anyone to marry or have a family of her own. These thoughts were reverberating round her head as Gerald said,

"There are several places around the country where they give care and assistance to unmarried mothers. As far as I know, you should be free to choose. As a matter of fact, there's a place right here in Tuam, but I don't want to cut across anything the priest might say. So why don't we leave it and see what he says. In the meantime, I best go back to work; you can stay on here and rest a while."

"Yes," said Bridie, "I'll be out in a minute," starting to feel buoyed by the drop of sherry; happy that she could now think for a moment in private.

The phrase, 'a family of my own', seemed to be taking root in her thoughts. Suddenly she realised the words had a meaning beyond her wildest dreams. She almost jumped out of her chair with joy. I'll have a family of my very own she whispered aloud. I've never had a family and now I'm going to have one. I've never had a father, a mother, a brother, a sister, a niece or an uncle. I've not even had a first cousin; a second cousin; and not even a thirty-second cousin; but now I'm about to have a son or daughter. She raised her eyes to heaven and whispered, Thank you God for sending me someone. I'll have my very own family; I don't care whether it's a boy or girl. I'm going to be a mother. Imagine. I'm going to be a mother, she said aloud, smiling to herself as she stood up to go back out to the kitchen.

* * * * *

"This way Father," said Gerald as he showed the priest into the Reading room. "She'll be with you in a moment."

His reverence could hardly wait to see the new housekeeper, he wasn't sure if he knew her or not. No doubt, he surmised, she's another one of them ready to lie by the ditch with every other...

"This is Father Michael, our parish priest," said Gerald, escorting Bridie into the room. "Bridie Rodgers, our housekeeper," he said, introducing her to the priest. "I'll leave ye two to have a chat. Beatrice will join us later and we'll have a cup of tea."

Bridie's first inkling on seeing Fr. Michael was to recall the parishioner's reaction to his sermon as they came out from church a few Sundays ago.

"That would be lovely," said Fr. Michael as he sat down opposite Bridie, and Gerald left the room closing the door behind him.

Although she was extremely pale, Fr. Michael thought, Bridie had some noble qualities about her. Her raven black hair greatly enhanced her wide eyes and high cheekbones: which gave the merest hint that she might be of Spanish origin.

"And how are you Bridie? I think I've seen you in Church,"said Fr. Michael," as he opened the conversation and Bridie sat down opposite him.

"Fine," said Bridie as she settled down, her mind made up that she'd listen carefully, and say as little as possible because she didn't really trust priests. Why? She couldn't say, but she thought the fact that she'd seen so many of them visiting St. Joseph's Industrial School might have had something to do with it. From what she could see, they were always planning to put someone in or take someone out.

"So, Gerald's been telling me what a wonderful job you do here; that you're able to cook, and look after the children."

Bridie smiled shyly, waiting for his pastoral advice. She thought he looked much older and not near as young as he appeared on the Church altar on Sundays, where he ranted on about the evils of drink, and on the odd occasion thumped the pulpit with his clenched fist as he hammered home the point. *'It's the work of Satan himself, his very own brew, drawn from the tainted waters of the river Liffey.'* His words made history in the parish where people loved to spread the Gospel, particularly if it was of a controversial nature.

"How long have you been here now?" he asked her.

At that moment Bridie was recalling the parishioners reaction to his famous words. *'Ah aren't them Dublin people cute hoors all the same, makin' us believe we're drinking Arthur's finest: Instead we're drinking oul' Liffey dew. Sure Satan himself must be a Dublin man if what the Priest says is true. Ah ha, I'd swear if the priest himself got it for nothing, he'd drink it out of an oul' Well, who the hell can tell?'* But she had to banish the memory from her head, quickly, and answer Father Michael.

"I'm...I'm here eight months, Father."

"And before that you were in St. Joseph's?" said his Reverence, thinking, it won't be too long 'till you're back there again.

"Yes."

"Would you like to go back?" asked Father Michael, with a smile.

"No Father, I don't ever want to go back there."

A little touch of arrogance, thought Fr. Michael, but he said nothing for a moment, as he sat looking at her as if in deep thought. Then he said,

"Of course, you realise a girl in your predicament has precious few options. You do realise that, don't you?" he said, lowering his head and glaring, as if to emphasise the point.

Bridie said nothing, but continued to stare back, eyeball to eyeball. Finally he gave way and said, "Would you care to tell me how you got into trouble in the first place Bridie?" as he sat back, stretching his long legs across the floor, waiting for the story to unfold.

Bridie looked at him and wondered how much of the story he already knew. Gerald must have told him something about it, and she certainly did not feel like telling such a sordid story to a black stranger; so she made up her mind to be curt in her reply.

"Got into what trouble?" she asked, pretending to be surprised.

Dumb, as well as stupid, were the first words to enter the priest's head, as he gave her a look that said, don't mess with me lady for I have the power to make life most uncomfortable for you.

"Pregnant? How did you come to be pregnant, Child?" he growled.

Bridie could tell from the look he gave her that he was not at all impressed, and she started to revel in his discomfort. After all, it was really none of his business, so she decided to make life a little more difficult for him and await his reaction.

"Do you want the full story or part of it?" she asked brazenly.

"Why the full story, of course," he replied, as he drew in his spider's legs and sat up with interest, so he might better absorb the gory details.

But Bridie knew she had pushed out the boat too far and that she could get into very deep water indeed if she told the whole story. She had no desire to tell him anything. And if she did, it would be about the way she was treated by Mrs O'Malley. But she also knew she could never betray Gerald; and tell the priest about his awful wife. Gerald was too good to Bridie. She would not like to bring pain and suffering on his family by telling the Priest everything. Besides, how was she supposed to tell him about Peter? There was no way was she going to tell him anything about that.

"There isn't that much to tell," she said, and watched Fr. Michael's eyes roll back in his head.

"I was caught off-guard by one of the workmen," she added quickly.

His Reverence waited for her to continue and when it wasn't forthcoming, he asked, "Which of them?" in an exasperated tone, showing his distaste at her shilly-shallying.

"Peter. Peter Murtagh," she replied with glee, knowing full well that Gerald would probably have told him this already.

"Peter Murtagh" he repeated. Peter? Peter? "I don't know any Peter... except... Where is he from?"

"I don't know. He worked here," said Bridie surprised that he didn't already know that. She thought priests knew everything; and everyone's business, especially within the Parish.

"Is it the Peter Murtagh, that works here for Gerald?" he asked, "Yes," replied Bridie.

Fr. Michael sat bolt upright, a look of horror on his face, his piercing blue eyes casting a look of disbelief at Gerald's housekeeper.

"Bridie! How you could say such a thing? I'm absolutely appalled that you should tarnish the good name of one of my parishioners." Bridie, completely taken by surprise, sat in momentary shock, as her blood started to rise, listening in awe as he went on, "I know Peter Murtagh; he happens to be a very respectable man: a married man as a matter of fact, who takes great care to provide for his family...."

"Well, he can take great care of mine so," said Bridie sarcastically.

"I will not listen to lies from a servant girl like you" replied the Reverend Father thumping the arm of the chair. "It's a damn lie, and you know it. The truth of the matter is Bridie, you do not know who's the father. But you choose the most convenient candidate, which in this case happens to be Peter Murtagh...."

Bridie, devastated by the attack, jumped to her feet and shouted,

"It's not a lie! It's not a lie! Ask Gerald, he'll soon tell you," she said, running for the door.

But His Reverence, belying his age, sprung like a panther to try cutting her off at the door, pleading,

"Bridie, please! Leave Gerald out of it. This is strictly between the two of us. I'm here to advise you. Besides, you don't even realise what you're saying?" he added, holding her firmly by the arm.

Bridie, suddenly terrified of the man and the way he tried to control her, managed to get the door slightly ajar and screamed,

"Geraaallddd!"

Gerald, on hearing the commotion came running down from the top of the stairs, as the children appeared from the kitchen, followed by Mrs O'Malley.

Bridie, her head sticking out of the room was about to shout, he's calling me a liar. But the words lodged in her craw when the children and Mrs O'Malley came running out of the kitchen, before standing abruptly to gawk at her.

Gerald, sensing something serious was amiss, ordered the rest of the family into the kitchen; before returning quickly to enquire what was the matter.

Fr. Michael who was already beginning to perspire under an uncomfortably tight collar turned as red as an over-ripe strawberry as he tried to explain himself.

"I'm sorry about this Gerald, it's..."

"He called me a liar. He doesn't believe...", intervened Bridie.

"Wait. Wait," said Gerald authoritatively; showing the palms of his hands in mock surrender. "Let's discuss this in a reasonable manner. I hate to see people squaring up to each other in a pugnacious fashion." Closing the door behind him; hands on hips, he asked, "What's the problem?"

His Reverence spoke up quickly, "Bridie, here seems to be making some sort of an outlandish claim that one of my most respected parishioners is the father of her child."

"Is she now?" asked Gerald, in obvious annoyance, "And who might that be?"

"Tell him what you're after saying," said Fr. Michael, indicating with a nod of his head to Bridie to tell Gerald what she had just said.

"I told him it was Peter Murtagh; and you know it as well, But he doesn't believe me.... he thinks I'm not capable of telling the truth" added Bridie.

"Shush. Shush, let's not have a slagging match here. As far as I'm concerned, what's done is done. We're here to plan a way out of a very unfortunate situation, not to decide who is right or wrong," said Gerald with a great deal of self control.

"Gerald, I couldn't agree more, which is why we can't have a decent man's name dragged through the mire. Peter's an honourable man, even you know that," said the Priest looking directly at Gerald.

"I knows a lot of things; too much for my own bloody good, if you'll pardon the expression Father," responded Gerald, peeved, that what was meant to be a charitable call, was instead turning into an act of recrimination and if there was one thing he detested it was politicians or the clergy refusing to face facts or to administer fair play. "Now let's get one or two things straight. I asked you here, Father, to help arrange suitable accommodation for this young lady, so that she might have her child in comfort...."

"Certainly, certainly. I'll be only too glad," interrupted his Reverence.

"One moment, I'm not finished Father and when I am, you'll have your say," said a visibly shaken Gerald, with a raised palm and a furrowed brow. "When I asked you here Father, I confided only that a young lady was in trouble. I did not mention who the child's father was; other than to say that I suspected it might be one of my men. I had no desire to bandy anybody's name about. And while we're on the subject Father, there are many things in life that we just have to accept as fact whether we like them or not: some of which are not very palatable. And as you correctly pointed out, Peter Murtagh is a very popular man: who appears to be a regular churchgoer and everything. But he's the father of Bridie's expectant child; not only that, but he's also reputed to be the father of two other children in the parish. Surely, you're aware of that or have you chosen to turn a deaf ear."

When Bridie heard Gerald beginning to speak in such forthright terms, she could hardly conceal her glee, but quietly stood her ground in the centre of the room, her hands fidgeting with the pleats in her skirt. And when she heard, Gerald say 'two other children', she could not resist taking a sideways glance at his Reverence. He stood solemnly, hands joined at the waist, his head held high in an air of defiance as she watched him take out his handkerchief and mop his brow before contesting Gerald's words.

Father Michael thought he had known the O'Malley family well, but was never really privy to their thinking and was shocked that they too should suspect Peter Murtagh of such a distasteful act, and Peter's wife already expecting their fifth child.

"Bridie, there must be some mistake, some misunderstanding", the Priest began, "After all, when a girl is young and free it's only natural that they develop a keen interest in the opposite sex, be it out walking, visiting or at a dance. And where large numbers of people congregate like that at a crossroads dance, who's to say for certain; who's the father of an expectant child."

"Gerald, you're well aware, the number of times I've preached from the altar about having to break up young couples, that I found in compromising positions by the side of the road."

At this point, His Reverence paused for a deep breath. He'd been caught so unawares he didn't really know what he was supposed to say. He was more used to people latching on to his every word, and looking up to him with the greatest of respect. After all, he thought, I'm supposed to be in charge of the Parish I'm the one who decides who's right and who's wrong. So it looks like once again I'll have to emphasise the seriousness of the situation.

"Like I've said, I've had to wallop them home from the side of the road with the crook of my blackthorn stick, and I got very little thanks for it…."

Gerald had heard enough. He was getting sick listening to his rabble-rousing approach to a subject that required a degree of compassion. He intervened sharply, "Listen Father. I'm sorry I brought you here. I think it's better for you to go home, because there's nothing more to be said. Thanks for calling. Oh, and by the way, in relation to Bridie, we'll make our own arrangements," he said, turning to open the door and show Fr. Michael out.

"But it's no problem! No problem! I can arrange whatever you want! I'd be only too glad to help…." replied Fr. Michael, coming forward reluctantly.

"Thanks," said Gerald.

"Thanks," added Bridie, unable to resist a parting gesture and giving Father a wan smile at the door.

"But…But why wasn't it reported to the Guards?" he asked, trying to claw back lost ground, "It's such a heinous crime."

"It was reported, directly to me. And we have witnesses," replied Gerald, with obvious glee as he stood at the door and politely waved Fr. Michael out.

Two weeks after the Priest's failed mission to assist Bridie, Gerald arranged for her to be taken into the care of St. Mary's Home for unmarried mothers in Tuam; run by the Bon Secour order of nuns, led by Sister Hortense, a noted humanitarian and defender of the poor.

Bridie, however, did not warm to the idea that her prospective guardians might be akin to what she had known in St. Joseph's, out in Clifden This bad feeling was fuelled in no small way, by the fact that she now felt aggrieved at having to leave 'Conly House' under such a dark cloud. Ever since that memorable walk through the farm on her arrival, things had never been the same again. When Mrs O'Malley accused her of telling lies to the children, Bridie immediately felt at odds with everyone except Gerald. Now it was even more painful trying to avoid eye contact with Sinead, and to hide the growing bulk of her pregnancy.

So it was with a sense of relief that she woke on her last morning in the big house. It had been agreed that she should leave quietly while the children were still in school; and on their return, they would be informed that Bridie had to go to Dublin to look after an elderly relative. When Gerald entered the sitting room to check on Bridie's readiness, he was touched to find her kneeling on a rug, ticking off a number of horses on the racing page.

"Bridie," he said, "I want you to know you've been a great help to us here. Personally, I was very happy with your work; but regrettably, fate – call it what you like – wasn't very kind to you. Who knows? Maybe it's for the best," he said smiling lamely, as he took out his wallet.

Bridie felt embarrassed to be caught idling on her last morning and stood up quickly to respond. "Thanks. I enjoyed working here too," she lied. She didn't know what else to say. Then Gerald, going forward, took Bridie by the hand and said something very strange,

"Here's a little something for yourself, for a rainy day," shoving a crisp one pound note into her hand. "Now I want you to remember this Bridie, always take a little gamble in life...."

He had her tiny hand clasped in his as he looked into her eyes.

"I can tell you now that you'll never be rich; but then again, you'll never ever be poor, because someday perhaps years from now when you least expect it and need it most, you are going to win."

Then looking up at the clock he said,

"Now, have you got your things? I think it's time to go."

"Thank you," said Bridie, as they both made their way out of the room.

Getting into the car, beside Tom, she turned round and waved to Mr and Mrs O'Malley, as the car slowly pulled away down the long gravelled drive. They were on their way to the home for unmarried mothers, Tuam.

Chapter Four

A strange eerie feeling seemed to transcend the decaying walls as she waited patiently to meet the new Matron of St. Mary's, Sister Hortense. What it was about the place that gave her such a feeling she did not know; and the appearance of bowed elderly nuns carrying dilapidated old iron bed-ends and sunken coarse-haired Victorian couches, along its musty-looking corridors, did nothing to allay her fears. On the one hand it was as if the church was now going to dictate the shape and pattern of her life to come, just when she thought she had left it all behind in St. Joseph's; and on the other, it was as if she could feel the presence of a thousand ancient ghosts roaming about the place. Bridie, shivered nervously, and tried to drive the demon thoughts from her head, but they would not go. Suddenly she looked around in terror as she distinctly felt something touch the back of her long black hair, but there was no one there.

"Jesus!" she cried aloud, as she jumped up and looked about the wide hall leading to the long narrow corridor, "What's wrong with me? Am I going insane?" There was no one there. She sat down and placed her hands about her shoulders for support. She now felt something was happening to her and she prayed that the Matron would come quickly. Instead, she felt a strange power enter her body through the soles of her feet, like a warm tidal wave that did not stop until it had moved up her entire body, as if she had slowly submerged herself into a steaming hot bath. She was now positively petrified and stood up to flee from the building, but before she could make up her mind which way to run, a miraculous sound cast a hypnotic hold over her. It was the most tranquil sound she thought she'd ever heard. It was a beautiful church Choir, and came from somewhere within the building. It was so sweet and melodious in its rendition that Bridie closed her eyes for a brief moment, raised her eyes to heaven to thank God, and luxuriate in its spiritual healing; so that by the time the hymn was finished she felt a small miracle had taken place because she was no longer afraid. It was her favourite hymn while she stayed in St. Joseph's, and it was such a coincidence that it should come to her aid at this time.

Be not afraid, I go before you always
Come follow me and I will give you rest

As Bridie gazed out the window and thought about the words she heard someone say,

"You must be Bridie."

She wheeled around and saw a serene smiling Sister extend a welcoming hand. "How are you dear? Sorry to have kept you waiting. I'm Sister Hortense, your matron."

"I'm fine," said Bridie, accepting Sister's welcoming hand.

"Shall we go into my office?"

"I don't mind," answered a relieved Bridie, as she followed Matron down the long corridor and into a small ill-furnished room, badly in need or repair.

"Here, take a seat," said Sister Hortense referring her to a small spoon-backed chair, "and I'll get you a cup of tea."

Sister went to the door and called on a maid going down the corridor,

"Annie, would you ever tell Mary Wade to bring me a fresh pot of tea, please?"

Turning around she opened a big red book that lay on her desk and ran her forefinger down the middle pages before stopping to digest some relevant details. "I see you've spent most of your life in St. Joseph's," before raising her eyes to look at Bridie and ask, "Was there any particular reason for that?"

"No, I don't think there was."

"And then you went to work in 'Conly House?" said Sister, closing the book, and pulling up a chair behind her desk to face Bridie. "Strange that no family ever came to foster you out," she said, looking intensely at Bridie.

Bridie, who couldn't think of anything to say, stared back at Sister Hortense. She hoped she wasn't going to hold it against her, just because she wasn't one of the lucky few.

"Perhaps it was your own choice; did you like living in St. Joseph's?" asked Sister, thoughtfully.

"No. I would have left... but nobody ever seemed to want to take me out," replied Bridie, feeling sorry for herself, then realising that maybe she was after saying the wrong thing. That it sounded awful, 'nobody wanted her'. "It just never happened," she added quickly, hoping Sister didn't notice the inference.

"And you get on well with people?"

"Yes, I think I do," she said, delighted she had an opportunity to redeem herself.

"Oh, you do, you do" responded the Matron, as if quelling any lingering doubts she might have had. "Mr. O'Malley spoke very highly of you; said you were good with the children."

Bridie permitted herself the bones of a smile, as acknowledgment that she was good for something. At least somebody wanted her.

"The poor man, I think his wife has her problems?"

"I think…she… has," said Bridie hesitantly.

"Never mind," said Sister Hortense, as if to reassure her everything was OK. "You'll be fine here with us. Now when is your baby due?"

"I'm not sure, I think it's about five weeks."

"Wonderful, you won't feel, you'll soon have it all over you. Dr. Waldron is our resident doctor and he does his rounds every day, just in case anyone has a problem. So you need have no worries about the birth. Now, have you thought of a name?"

"I haven't made up my mind," said Bridie, surprised at the Matron's caring attitude.

"Of course not. There's plenty of time for that yet. Besides, we have a small booklet here, with loads of names to choose from. I'll get one of the girls to give it to you."

"Thank you," said Bridie, delighted that there was a human face about the place, despite her earlier apprehension.

"Tell me, do you have any relatives at all?" an air of deep concern creeping into her voice.

"No," responded Bridie, somewhat alarmed. "I may have, but I don't know of any."

"That's no problem; I just wanted to know if you had a relative who might like to adopt your baby. But then, if you did have relatives, you probably wouldn't have spent all those years in St. Joseph's. On the other hand, you might be better off without them, because people don't always get on with each other."

This question sent alarm bells ringing in Bridie's head. Why would a relative adopt my child when I can rear it myself?

Sister Hortense, reading Bridie's mind instantly, tried to put her latest inmate at ease by saying,

"If you had somebody to care for the child, then you'd stand a far better chance of getting a job, and a far better chance of meeting up with a nice young man. Not many men are willing to take on a mother and child, you know."

"Can't I keep the child myself? I don't want anybody else to rear it," said Bridie, a hint of desperation cloaking her voice.

"Of course you can. But first we've got to pray for a safe delivery," intoned Sister, after she'd detected Bridie's highly-strung attitude. "Time enough to plan for the future when the baby arrives. It's you we must worry about now. I'll arrange for Dr. Waldron to see you first thing tomorrow, morning. He's very good with expectant mothers you know, and he'll know almost to the hour when the baby is due."

She stood up to take the tea from Mary Wade, who hesitated with a tray at the door. "Thank you Mary. This is Bridie Rodgers; you'll probably be working together from time to time in the kitchen. When Bridie has finished her tea you might arrange to show her around, please, and I'll get Annie Kelly to give you a hand with the dinners."

The girls nodded agreement before Mary left the room, and Sister took up the conversation again.

"As you are probably aware from your time in St. Joseph's, we have a fairly strict routine here, Bridie. It's designed specifically to be of benefit to the mothers and their children. You're expected to rise at 7 a.m., each morning and attend to your own child before going out for an early morning walk around the grounds. You must attend Mass in the chapel each day and then help to feed and bath the children. For the first three months your priorities lie with your own child at all times, though you're expected to leave them in the nursery during the day, only returning to feed them when ever necessary. All other times you're expected to help in the running of the Home, in return for free care and attention. How does that sound?"

"Fine, I like working with children, so I'll look forward to it," said Bridie proudly, delighted to see Sister's warm expression at having someone with experience to help with the children.

"Good. So shall we leave it at that for now?"

"Yes Sister."

Sister Hortense, told Bridie to wait there for Mary Wade to show her around, while she went scurrying off down the hall.

During the late afternoon when Bridie started to help out, she felt much more apprehensive, for there was a great deal of lamenting from grieving mothers in the corridors. She watched in horror as two nuns forcefully removed a mother to another section of the building.

Soon it was time for tea, and then they all knelt in the rest room to say the rosary.

A walk in the garden, for those who could, was considered a must before everyone went to bed. Bridie found herself halfway down the dormitory listening to a middle-aged woman with a wild look in her eyes. Bridie wondered if the woman was all right, or if there was something the matter with her. While at the same time, she could see a group of young girls huddled together in a corner. They appeared to be trying to console a young girl who was crying. The middle-aged woman next to Bridie's bed seemed to be studying her as she undressed for bed. She was mortified that a complete stranger was looking at her and tried to ignore her by facing the wall.

"How yah?"

Bridie half turned to look at her and the woman said,

"Is this your first day?"

"Yes."

"I'm Margaret, but everyone here calls me Madge. Are you with me a grá?"

"Yes," said Bridie, somewhat relieved and getting into a sunken old iron bed that felt as if it might collapse at any moment.

"You'd need to push that bed closer to the wall or it will fall asunder, a grá." And in a flash she was out of her bed and gave Bridie's bed such a drive, Bridie thought the bed would go straight through the wall.

"Them beds have seen more births and deaths than Methuselah. Is that better now?"

"Yes," said Bridie, wriggling as if to test it.

The woman tumbled into her own bed and addressed everyone in the dormitory in a loud voice, "Remember now girls, this is the workhouse, you'll have no airs or graces around here. No amount of grand talk will change that. We are what we are, a grá: workhouse women."

Bridie watched everyone's head in the room turn and give a little smile as Madge turned to Bridie,

"This is the workhouse, didn't they tell you that when you came in?"

Bridie looked, but said nothing, trying to decide if it was even safe to be in the same dormitory, never mind in the next bed talking to this woman.

"This is the worst place in Ireland that a woman can be. It's worse than jail. You can be in jail, a grá, for stealing a neighbour's hen, or a new bicycle, and be out after six months. But here it's for life; because we're mentally deranged. The workhouse," she sighed, looking at Bridie.

"Surely to God you know that?" But Bridie did not answer: instead she pretended to be looking round the dormitory.

"Oh, I. This is as low as you can get. What did you say your name was?"

Bridie looked again at the woman and smiled to herself at the thought that she could hardly go any lower. Her bed was almost touching the floor as she replied,

"Bridie. Bridie Rodgers."

"You mean Bridget. Always use your proper name. It's more respectable a grá: not that you'll be needing it in here because like I said we're all mentally deranged. That's why we're here. We're fallen women and fallen women are put away for life."

This line struck a disturbing cord in Bridie, and she asked hesitantly,

"What's fallen women?"

"Fallen women? What's wrong with you a grá?" asked Madge, as she sat up straight in the bed and looked at Bridie, as if talking to an oul' eejit.

"Are you stupid or something?" she said aloud, so that anyone who had ears could hear. The girl across the room from Madge shouted,

"Madge, leave her alone, she's only a young girl, give her a chance," and turning to Bridie, she added. "Take no notice of that lady, that's just the old name for this place…and don't pay any heed to her," she added with a wave of her hand.

"'Tis the truth," retorted Madge angrily. "Honesty is the best policy. I tell no lies."

But Bridie was beginning to feel she'd heard enough; that there was, undoubtedly, some truth in what Madge was saying. We're all in here *'Because we're mentally deranged'*. Bridie, had made up her mind that Madge was disturbed to some degree; but what about herself? Was she mentally deranged too, if she was sent to a place like this? No, she decided. She was here because she was going to have a baby. Peter Murtagh's baby. So that must be what a fallen woman is.

"A woman with a baby," said Bridie quickly to Madge, lest she catch her embarrassingly with another query.

"That's right Mrs. A fallen woman is a person of cheap morals, who lays down her body in any oul' haggard to be used and abused until she becomes pregnant. Then she's thrown into the workhouse to keep her off the streets for the rest of her life."

"So there you have it Mrs," said Madge heaving her ample bosom beneath the bedclothes and looking up at the cracked, fungus-strewn ceiling. "We're two of a kind, a grá" she continued, turning her head to Bridie, "Although speaking for myself, mind, I gave me body away with a heart and a half, because me oul' fella wouldn't agree with me seeing poor old, John Joe. So I climbs out the winda… is it Biddy or Bridie or Bridgit I calls you?"

"Bridie."

"Begging your pardon Bridie, …so I climbs out the winda in the dead-o-night to stay at my true loves. Instead we ended up sleeping rough in the hay, because his mother, God be good to her, had a face like a sow and wouldn't let us get married. In the end poor John Joe went to England; promising me the sun, moon, and stars and I've not seen sight or light of him since, a grá. And I'll be whipped entirely if they don't let me outa here soon to see my adopted daughter…"

"Is that you Madge Courtney, spreading them fairy tales again?" intervened Sister Hortense as she came silently down the aisle.

"Girls, what are ye doing out of yeer beds?" she added as she clapped her hands and set about turning down the oil lamps hanging on the walls.

"They're no fairy tales Sister, and well you know it," replied Madge as she snuggled down amid a sea of creaking, squeaking bedsprings. "I know the history of this place since the time 'twas built. Sure me great, great grandfather built this Poorhouse. A master carpenter he was, as was his father before him, and his father before him, going back, back, back, back…right back to St. Joseph…"

"Madge, that's enough of that now!" snapped a stern looking Sister Hortense, as she held aloft her oil lamp at the foot of Madge's bed, to show her displeasure.

Madge raised her head slightly, showing her two mad eyes over the blanket, "Beggin' your pardon Sister, I was just tellin' Bridget or Bridie, here, I don't know where we'd all be if it wasn't for the Sisters of Bon Secour," turning her head, "Isn't that right Bridget?"

"That's enough of your shenanigans. Now go to sleep," said Sister, as she turned briskly to leave the dormitory.

But Bridie had closed her eyes when Sister first came in and was pretending to be fast asleep. Inwardly she was laughing like she'd never laughed before, and in her sleep, was already looking forward to the next day, as the distant sound of Tuam's town hall clock rang out the last hours of her first day.

* * * * *

She'd only been there five weeks and was already filled with dread and apprehension about her future. There were so many thoughts going through her head. Mary Wade was aware of this as the both changed and dressed the beds in the women's dormitory, well away from the tears and heartache that filled the day room on an almost daily basis.

"When's your baby due?" asked Mary, as they both stretched the clean white sheets across the bed and began tucking them in neatly at the corners.

"The doctor says it could be any time now, and I think he's right. I feel as though it's getting very near. But I could be wrong."

"If the doctor says it's near, then you can be sure he's right. He's spot on every time. What do you think you'll do with it?"

"I don't know. Some of the girls said I should put it up for adoption; others reckon it's better to have them boarded out in the West of Ireland when they're five or six. But to be truthful to you, Mary, and I hope you won't say anything, I don't want to part with my baby at all. I want to keep it myself. I'm so looking forward to having my own child."

"Well speaking from experience, I decided to put my Patrick up for adoption, so that he'd have a good home, and I wouldn't have to part with him then when I was too fond of him. I had me mind made up long before he was born. I could see what it was doing to the mothers here, who had to part with them after a year," said Mary, as they both stood facing each other.

"And where is he now?" asked Bridie, thinking it must have happened years ago because Mary Wade was getting on in years by the looks of her.

"He was in Sligo for a while. A lovely middle-aged couple that couldn't have any children came and adopted him. He was three months old at the time. I found it very hard at first, but I'm over it now, thank God, and I've a job here as long as I like. I don't want to leave here because I've nobody belonging to me, and I couldn't face the world on my own; besides I like it here."

When Bridie heard her say 'I like it here', she knew it was the exact opposite of what she felt herself.

Ever since she'd that horrid feeling on arrival in St. Mary's she'd been unable to shake off the belief, that there was something intrinsically evil about the place, that made the hair stand on the back of her head at the most inopportune times.

Mary, meanwhile felt as though she was talking to the wall because Bridie wasn't paying the least bit of attention to her. She had that far away look in her eyes. It was something that annoyed her more than any other because she felt she was insincere She knew she'd enjoy her own company much better if she could get rid of Bridie: ask her to go for a walk or tell her to rest for a while or something.

"Where was I?" asked Bridie embarrassingly as she realised she'd lost the run of the conversation.

"We were talking about your baby," said Mary, annoyed that her own child didn't merit a decent discussion: as she bent down quickly in anger to gather up the soiled sheets. "Why don't you take a little rest now or go out for a breath of fresh air, Bridie, and I'll finish up around here," she added as she crossed over to the other side of the room.

"Oh, I couldn't do that and leave you on your own…."

"No, no, it's all right; sure we're nearly finished. Off with you, while you have the chance," said Mary, praying silently that she'd go and leave her in peace.

"Oh, all right, maybe I'll go for a walk, seems to be nice outside now. But are you sure?"

"I'm sure, I'm sure," said Mary, hurriedly as she beat a few pillows into shape and then watched Bridie disappear down the long corridor.

Mary sat on the bed nearest the corridor so she could hear anyone coming, and took out the butt of a Woodbine cigarette. She had only two left and was afraid Bridie would have taken one if she stuck around and then she wouldn't have any left for the night.

Bridie went for a short walk around by the perimeter wall, and around to where some of the inmates were seated on a low stonewall sunning themselves; amongst them was Madge Courtney. At times, Bridie felt in her own tin pot way, that there was a lot more to Madge than meets the eye. Madge had already informed Bridie that her daughter Sarah was adopted a few short months ago, when she was five years old, and believed that she was being reared somewhere in Co. Galway. But the nuns would not disclose her whereabouts to mad Madge; other than to say the child was doing well, because they were legally bound to withhold such vital information.

"How ya! It's a new pair of boots you'll be getting Bridget, not a new baby if you don't put an end to the walking," said Madge, as Bridie drew near them, smiling broadly.

"I wouldn't mind a new pair, but then I like wearing these because they're very comfortable."

"Push over there girls, and show a bit of respect for the one that reared ye," said Madge, as the girls tightened up along the wall, tittering and giggling as one of them was almost pushed off as Bridie sat down at one end. Bridie thought some of the girls looked very young, certainly no more than fourteen or fifteen.

"Doesn't *that* ivy over there look lovely," said Bridie, to no one in particular.

"Well it's said, that the ghosts of six Irish soldiers haunt this place, since they were executed by that very wall. You can see where the ivy never grew and never will again. And 'tis well I know it Bridie, because I have seen their ghosts, march to the sound of beaten drums at daybreak."

"Ghosts! Ghosts! Will you shut up Madge! You're always trying to frighten us," said one of the two young girls who got up and ran inside.

The blood too drained from Bridie's cheeks and she felt a slight tremor in her body when Madge spoke these very words. She didn't want to hear them, because deep down she had the feeling they were true, so she said to Madge,

"Why does everyone seem to talk about ghosts in this place?"

But Madge turned quickly and said, "Because it's the truth a grá. Have I ever told you a lie?" she asked turning to Bridie, who was looking into her piercing blue eyes but said nothing in case the woman grew violent, because she still couldn't make up her mind whither

Madge was the full shilling or not.

"Have I? Have I ever told you a lie?" she asked more forcefully.

"No. No. You've never told me a lie," said Bridie meekly, wishing she would just tone down her monotonous voice, because it was beginning to get on her nerves.

"No, a grá, I have not, because we're two of a kind. Fallen women. We're supposed to be mentally deranged. Oh, I. It's all arranged," she sighed. "All arranged to hide the truth. And when I think of all the poor children, that must have died here during the famine" she added shaking her head and folding her arms across her ample bosom as if going into a trance. "Imagine being put into the workhouse: the poor house just to die. Oh they were dark, dark days. Orra-worra-worra-worra: when I think of all the stories me Grandfather told me. Died all along the road so they did. Only for the weak to arrive and find this place was a hundred times worse than their own homes. The Workhouses were riddled with the cholera and the pox. They couldn't wait to bury the dead so they couldn't," turning her head slightly to look at Bridie.

Bridie didn't mind listening to Madge, when she wasn't so wound up, but now she was beginning to wish Madge would shut up: because somehow she just wasn't in the mood. While she was walking the grounds Bridie though she was getting cramps but she wasn't very sure. Now she thought they were slowly getting worse or was she imagining it. But the famine was a subject she was very interested in because she'd been told all about it herself while in St. Joseph's. So she sat quietly listening to Madge as she rambled on.

"…That evening, as the lad threw the bodies into the coffins he came to a man who moaned 'Wait! Wait! I'm not dead yet.'

'You're a damn liar,' said the grave-digger, 'the doctor knows best.'

What did he do a grá, only fired the creature into the wooden box, singing: *Rattle his body over the stones, he is a pauper nobody owns*!"

Bridie was already on her feet, a tortured expression on her face, as she bent over holding her tummy.

"In the honour of God, Madge. Stop. Stop…Oh! The pain! Hold me hand. Quick. Quick. Oh God."

Twelve hours later the nurse delivered a seven-pound baby boy to Bridie who cried out in agony and then with joy on being handed the tiny infant.

"Thank you Sister. I never thought I'd be a mammy. Isn't he lovely?" she whispered emotionally, as tears of joy filled her eyes at the thought that she had produced such a beautiful child, after all the distress.

"What are you going to call him?" asked the Sister, showing her how to put the child to her breast.

"I think I'll call him Patrick or John. I can't make up my mind, yet."

"Why not call him John Paschal – after the feast of the Passover? Besides, the name Paschal is French, and as the Bon Secour Sisters originated in France, it would be a nice name."

Bridie took her sound advice and had him christened John Paschal, almost two weeks after the birth.

They stayed together for three months in the Nursery, where Bridie helped with the feeding and bathing of all the other children.

Just before she was due to be moved into the main building where the older infants and mothers were segregated, Sister Hortense summoned her to the office.

"Bridie, I think it's about time we discussed your baby's future, and of course your own. What are you going to do with the child?"

This was a conversation Bridie dreaded, because she didn't know what she was supposed to do, in order to do the right thing. She knew that if she gave the baby up for adoption she might never see him again. She wasn't sure what she was going to do or how she was going to manage.

"I want to keep the baby myself," she blurted out almost before she realised she'd opened her mouth.

"Yes. Well, in an ideal world that would be wonderful, but in this situation, it's one that I don't think will work; quite simply because you haven't got a home to go to. Secondly you have no means of support, and last but much more importantly, you're destroying any chance of future happiness you might find, by being free to find a husband and get married. You must have thought of those things," said Sister Hortense, with a very concerned look on her brow.

Of course Bridie had thought of those things, indeed she thought of lots of things, but she could find no answers. If she kept the baby and could get away from St. Mary's, where would she go? How could she find a job and look after the baby? She would be at the mercy of the world, and what would happen if someone attacked her or the baby? She was thinking of staying in the home for a while and looking after the baby herself, and maybe after a while she could leave to go somewhere else: but now Sister Hortense was looking at her and asking, "Well Bridie, what are you going to do?"

"I'll stay on here working ... and keep my baby," answered Bridie hesitantly.

"I know, but that won't work either. There are already one hundred and twenty girls here – thirty-five in the maternity wing alone. We can only keep on four or five full time staff and they have to be trained, and even if we could keep you on Bridie, you would not be allowed to keep your child. This is a full-time job – twelve hours a day, and keeping a child as well wouldn't work. Now there are a few people I know, who would love to adopt a little boy, and I think you should consider it...."

"I won't give him away," said Bridie determination creeping into her voice.

"Fine," said the Sister, not in the least surprised at her attitude. In a way, she secretly admired mothers like that because she felt it was an indication of superior motherhood. Some mothers would go to any lengths to protect their offspring; and it was the parting of these mothers and their children that caused her most unhappiness. But, what could she do when they didn't have a place to go.

"Your mind's made up then? You're sure about that?"

"I am," said Bridie, a relieved tone in her voice.

When she had gone back to the nursery, Sister Hortense came up with an idea of her own and decided it was worthwhile writing a letter. Who knows there was still a chance for the mother, the boy and the adoptive parents, she thought.

A week later, Bridie was summoned to the Sister's office again and was surprised to see Mr. O'Malley waiting to greet her – handing her a big box of chocolates and kissing her on the cheek, he asked,

"How's the baby?"

Sister Hortense excused herself for a few minutes and left the office. When the pleasantries were over, Gerald added, "Bridie, how would you like to come back to work with us again?"

Bridie, taken completely by surprise, didn't know what to say; she just looked at Mr O'Malley, her mouth half open, and replied,

"I...I don't know."

"Well, you're quite welcome, we'd be pleased to have you back.

We have an elderly lady who comes and helps every day, but the children miss you a lot and we must find someone who's willing to live in again."

"But what about the baby? They might not like me bringing John Paschal home," said Bridie thinking that maybe they'd get jealous of her or that Mrs. O'Malley might not have much regard for her now, after all that happened.

Mr O'Malley's gaze fell as he said solemnly, "Yes, we were hoping you might put the baby up for adoption, as rearing a baby as well, would not work …as things are at present."

Bridie wasn't sure what he meant, but she knew by his expression and behaviour that John Paschal would not be welcome in 'Conly House.' And if she couldn't bring the baby then she certainly wouldn't go herself. She was almost ready to cry at the thought that Mr O'Malley could even think such a thing. For some unknown reason she found herself standing up as if about to run away.

"I'm sorry Mr. O'Malley, but I must stay with the baby;" she said turning quickly on her heel and running out the door just as Sister Hortense was about to come in.

Some uncontrollable instinct made Bridie rush down the corridor to the nursery where John Paschal lay gurgling. Picking him up she held him firmly to her breast as the tears rolled down her cheeks. Hugging and nuzzling him, she paced up and down the floor for a long, long time, whispering softly,

"How could anyone ask me to give you up, pet? I'll never ever part with you son as long as I live. I'll never ever part with you," she added as she again kissed the top of his frail bumpy head and he began to cry.

The mothers feeding the infants around the nursery turned and looked on as Annie Kelly came over to Bridie and said, "Are you all right? Is there something wrong?" But Bridie shook her head tearfully. Then Mary Wade came and placing a comforting hand on her shoulder, asked,

"Bridie, Are you all right? Why are you crying?"

But she could not tell them. She didn't think she could ever tell anyone about the awful pain that was festering in her heart. How she herself never ever knew the love of a mother; and did not have a single moment's recollection of ever having been hugged or kissed by a mother or father and now that she had someone to love for the first time in her life, people were planning to take that joy away.

She turned and sat down to feed the crying infant and gave a huge sigh of relief. She felt she'd come so close to losing her child forever. Right now She didn't want to talk to anybody. She just wanted to be left alone with her son and to get on with working in the Home. But she knew that forces were ranging against her and that sooner or later something bad was bound to happen. She could sense it in the Home ever since she first set foot inside its front door. And now she would have to be constantly on her guard.

Chapter Five

In the days and weeks leading up to John Paschal's first birthday, Bridie tried to spend more and more time with him. There were constant rows between herself and the nursing Sisters in the nursery because she continually overstayed her welcome in the Day ward The regulations stated that infants should only be breast-fed when necessary, at most three times a day, and only for a period of half an hour each time. But Bridie loved feeding and caring for John Paschal and often stayed longer by pretending to help the overburdened staff so that she could be near him, to rush over and comb his little bob and watch him smile.

During these precious moments she would continuously comb his hair into a fancy quiff, and noticed he had a beautiful gold like streak running through his hair. On a few occasions she managed to spend most of the day with him, pretending that he wasn't well and that he needed her attention. But the nursing Sisters soon grew wise to her motherly ploys and put a stop to it.

The days were now long and sunny and the birds sang in the early morning dew as inmates went to early Mass and joined in the church choir that rang out loud and clear. It was the only time in an otherwise cold, hard existence when both staff and inmates felt truly at peace with each other. Then it was back to dealing with the screaming infants, the scrubbing and the sewing.

Bridie was working in the kitchen helping Mary Wade and had decided to ask her a few questions if the opportunity arose. And because there was a continuous cycle of expectant mothers coming in one door and being sent to God knows where out the other; rumours were rife. Even if only half the rumours were true, then it was curtains for every mother and child in St. Mary's. 'Twas widely accepted that children were being sold to wealthy childless couples in Ireland, England and America. It was even said, the mother's were being sent to work in places in Dublin, Cork and Galway. It was even said that some of the mother's were put into Mental Institutions because they would not accept the loss of their children. While more were said to work in big houses in the country and that children not adopted at birth were put into foster homes between the ages of three and nine years. And their mothers were never again informed of their whereabouts and had no more contact with them.

But amongst the mothers themselves, it was felt that fostering out their children was by far the best option – from a mother's point of view. Generally speaking, most of the children appeared to be fostered out in County Galway, they said, so there was always an outside chance – slim though it may be – that you might meet up with your child again.

Trying to extract any worthwhile information from a reliable source was Bridie's greatest problem. Those she felt should know something; didn't seem to know anything. And those who might know something were either too afraid to say anything or wouldn't tell out of jealousy, and those who were in a position to tell you everything about how the system worked couldn't be trusted because they were the nun's pets and were the most reviled people within the Home. Every little detail no matter how insignificant usually found its way back to the nuns and in particular to the Mother Superior. Bridie knew that Mary Wade was Sister Hortense's pet so she set about fishing for information, as they were both up to their elbows in flour.

"Do you ever hear from Patrick now or how is he?" asked Bridie, adopting a calm, innocent attitude.

Mary was somewhat surprised and looked sternly at Bridie who kept her eyes firmly fixed on the mixing bowl, feigning complete innocence. Mary did not like to be reminded of her son; especially by someone whom she knew would be gone out of the Home in a matter of weeks, and who really didn't care about how her son was.

"No. Why do you ask?" said Mary in a curt tone of voice.

"Oh, I was just wondering" replied Bridie. "Were you ever told by his foster parents how he was getting on or anything? It might help me make up my mind about my own son?" she said as she raised her eyes and looked pleadingly at Mary.

This line cut no ice with Mary as she replied, "You'll have to do what we all had to do, and that is give up your baby, and pay for your sins."

This reply shell-shocked Bridie, so much, she was on the verge of picking up the mixing bowl and hurtling it to the floor, but suddenly she though better of it and said,

"Well excuse me, but I refuse to pay for a sin I did not commit. I'm here because of what someone did to ME. Why does everyone here just accept that you can't keep your own child? It's my baby and I'm the one who should decide its future…."

"There's no need to loose the run of yourself" said Mary. "Remember you're no better or worse than any of the other girls in here. We're all a bit unfortunate in some way, otherwise we wouldn't be here, would we?"

Bridie instantly realised she'd lost her whole plan of action, and that she had made a complete mess of things, so she decided she'd have to row back a little, because getting on the wrong side of Mary Wade was akin to committing suicide. So she replied, wearily,

"Yeah. You're right."

Then Bridie decided to play her trump card by saying, "You know, I really admire yourself and Sister Hortense. You're so good to all the mothers. I'm sure if ye both had yeer way, ye'd change the rules. I thought, you'd be the ideal person to give me advice, because to be truthful, I don't know what's going on here. But I do know that handing over a child is a big decision and I know that by now you must have a good idea of what's right and wrong."

Mary was scraping away the heavy dough from between her fingers with the blunt knife, as she looked thoughtfully across at Bridie. She began thinking to herself Bridie, you're smarter than I thought. Anyone that'd see you hanging around with mad Madge would take you to be a real amadán.

"Would you like a cup of tea?" she suddenly whispered as she glanced at the other girls working in the huge kitchen.

"Oh, I'd love one," answered Bridie, who felt as if she had scored a direct hit, she now knew that Mary was going to say something, but Mary continued working in a business-like fashion.

"Girls," she said, turning round "You can stick these in the oven now."

She then beckoned Bridie into an alcove where they usually weighed the flour and oaten meal, and where no one could really see what was going on.

As Mary Wade pushed a cup of lukewarm tea towards Bridie, she said,

"You're right, it's probably the biggest decision you'll make in your life, and I envy you this minute."

Bridie said nothing as she looked at Mary who again said, "I really do envy you this minute."

"Why?" asked Bridie

"Because of your courage. If I only thought like that years ago, maybe I'd still have my son. At least I'd know where he was. But no, I was such a fool. I did what the Sisters told me to do but now it's too late to do anything else," she sighed.

Bridie immediately felt guilty for reminding Mary of her past and putting her in a distressed condition, so she added quickly, "No. You mustn't start to think like that. You did the best you could at the time. Could Sister Hortense not help you?" she asked, realizing she was asking this question for her own benefit.

"No. Unfortunately she was away on retreat when I gave up the baby and it didn't bother me too much that time. But ever since it has haunted me: how I gave up my beautiful little boy without a fight. Sister Hortense was very good to me and tried again – only last year – to trace the couple. But they're in America somewhere, but no one knows where they are. So I'm warning you Bridie; don't give up your baby for adoption or you'll never ever see him again. I don't know how the adoption system works, because I've never been outside these four walls except once. But some of the older mothers, who've been in here once or twice, said they knew lots of children in Tuam who were reared here in St. Mary's and then fostered out to complete strangers. Some children are sent over to England and America just to get them out of the way, because their father's name- usually some big shot – would be destroyed if anyone ever found out. So they pay a lot of money to the nuns to keep the whole thing quiet."

"I heard that," said a relieved Bridie, knowing how close she could have come to giving up John Paschal, so she could go and work for the O'Malley's again.

"Could Sister Hortense do anything to help me, do you think?" asked Bridie; half-afraid she might over-step the mark by delving too deeply into their personal relationship.

"I can't say," she replied, as she turned round to rest herself against the small table and fold her arms across her white Calico apron. "I know she's the only one who gets anything done around here. When she first came here from Glenamaddy, you know, this place was a tip and she has transformed it as best she could. But some of the other Sisters! They'd near cut you with a knife, they get such perverse pleasure from watching the mothers suffer."

"How do you mean?" asked Bridie, in surprise.

"Do I have to spell it out for you?" she whispered aside. "If Sister Imelda or any of the other Sisters don't like you, they make you hand over the child yourself for adoption and then watch you go demented."

"Oh, but that's horrible," said a fearful looking Bridie.

"I know, but we live in a horrible place. Oh! Where'd you get that?" she said in delight, as Bridie offered her the butt of a Woodbine cigarette, half afraid she'd refuse it, after she herself specially cadged it off one of the mothers for this very purpose.

Mary Wade seized the fag, lit it and dispelled a blast of smoke towards the rotting fungus stained ceiling, before adding, "By making the mother do that, they will always be able to say, 'Well, you handed over the baby yourself for adoption so don't blame us if your suddenly feeling sorry for yourself.' And of course, they're right, you did hand him over."

"And what happens to the mother? What do you think they'll do with me?" asked a worried looking Bridie.

"Oh, you're for the mad house; you're for the asylum." said Mary, relishing an opportunity to take a rise out of Bridie. "But make sure to bring a length of rope, so you can hang yourself," she added gleefully, much to Bridie's consternation.

"Mary! What are ye doing there? Have ye not finished the bread yet?" asked Sister Imelda, as she came silently in to the kitchen and almost caught them unawares.

Mary dropped the fag instantly and ground it into the floor before nudging it under the table "We're just finished," replied Bridie and herself in unison. "We're just tidying up now," added Mary, lest she be seen to be lacking in her responsibilities.

With that, Sister Imelda went towards the other girls preparing meals on the long tables, and checked the bread in the ovens.

Just as Sister was coming through the door, and Mary had said, 'you're for the mad house,' Bridie thought she felt dizzy and immediately took a few faltering steps out towards the lavatory in the corridor.

She thought she'd never get there. For though she knew Mary's words were spoke in jest, Bridie believed that in certain instances, mocking was catching and a curse was now trying to take control of her. She locked herself in the lavatory and sat down as she broke out in a cold sweat. It happened so suddenly it terrified her. It was, as if she were in some telepathic mode and knew that John Paschal would be removed at any moment. She felt that if she did not do something, she would suffer at the hands of some unseen power that would sweep part or all of her, along its evil path forever. She could feel it clutching at her heart, trying to remove her inner being.

I must be possessed by some evil spirit she thought as she tried to get her breath and struggled to swallow her spittle. At that precise moment she made up her mind that though she and John Paschal might be parted in body, they would never be parted in spirit. And to ensure that, she knew she would have to be on her guard twenty-four hours a day, for the remainder of her stay.

For the next week Bridie spent every possible moment she could with John Paschal, because she knew the hour had come. She and John Paschal were now thirteen months together – mothers and babies were separated at thirteen months.

On Sunday evening Bridie was summoned to Sister Imelda's office. Earlier in the day Mary had informed Bridie that Sister Hortense was in Dublin for a few days; so Bridie did not like it at all when she had to face Sister Imelda in her office.

"Bridie, I have some good news for you," she began. "You're going to Galway tomorrow morning: there's a lovely job waiting for you."

Bridie looked at Sister Imelda for a long time, before she asked.

"Does that mean I'm leaving for good?"

"But of course. You'll be a free woman. Isn't that what you want?" said Sister, with a sarcastic smile.

"What about John Paschal?" asked Bridie feebly, forcing the words from her drying focal chords.

"What about John Paschal?" repeated Sister Imelda.

On hearing this insincere remark, Bridie was fit to jump up and grab Sister Imelda by the hair, but she told herself she must keep absolute control and suffer the pain, and not let Sister Imelda succeed in upsetting her.

"Will he be coming with me?" she asked, knowing full well that he wouldn't.

"Really Bridie, you can't be that stupid. You know very well that you wouldn't survive out there on your own; you'd be back inside here within a year – with another baby," she replied in an exasperated tone, before adding firmly, "No. John Paschal will remain here until he is old enough to be fostered out or until a suitable home can be found for him. So you need have no worries, he will be well looked after."

"Oh, thank you Sister. You know how much he means to me; and I appreciate how much you have done for both of us," said Bridie plucking up the courage to ask for the unmentionable.

"Sister, I'd like to ask a special favour: only because I know you'd like to help me" she lied brazenly as she watched Sister Imelda raise her eyebrows in dismay. "I'd like you to send me John Paschal's new address wherever he is being sent when the time comes."

Sister stood up and stared down at Bridie for what seemed an age. She was amazed at her cheek and her seemingly calm acceptance of her sudden departure to Galway. What a welcome change, she thought to herself. But rules were rules. And she had no desire to break them; now that Sister Hortense was considering retirement and she herself was next in line for promotion. As regards this lady she could never make up her mind whether she liked her or not. She often thought there was something devious about Bridie. And now here she was making demands.

"Bridie, as much as I'd like to help you, you know full well that your request is out of the question. Were I to say yes, then every other mother in Tuam would want the same treatment; so I'm afraid the answer is no. Besides, all contact between mothers and their children is strictly forbidden once fostering or adoption has taken place. Now, if you don't mind, I'd like a little time to read my breviary. I've had a long day in the absence of Sister Hortense."

Bridie stood up and proceeded to escort Sister out of the office. But once she'd heard the word 'No', she was planning to make one more desperate plea.

"Sister, can I stay in the nursery for tonight? Please?" she begged.

Sister looked at Bridie as if she were insane, and said,

"Really! You know Bridie, you're trying God's patience – not to mention mine. Go child, out of my sight this instance" waving her away with the back of her hand, "I don't care where you sleep, it's up to the Night Sister."

Bridie flew through the corridors like some demented woman and pleaded with the nursing Sister, who let her take John Paschal into bed with her.

For ages and ages Bridie sat up in bed cradling John Paschal, hugging and kissing him and trying to control her own ever flowing emotions, knowing that these were going to be their last hours together. She didn't want him to close his clear blue eyes at all, so that she could sit and gaze at him all night long. But eventually he grew tired and cranky and cried for his feed, which she gave him, and then at last he fell asleep. Bridie combed his quiff of golden hair, one last time, before gently laying him beside her on the bed; as the night Sister did the rounds of the nursery with her lamp.

"Time to get some sleep, Bridie," she whispered. "Tomorrow's another day, and don't forget your prayers."

But Bridie could only think of one thing: tomorrow morning when John Paschal would be gone out of her life forever. She didn't know if she would ever see him again. The mere thought that she might not; caused her more pain that night than she could ever have imagined. She went through his few personal belongings. A little suit, and a teddy bear, Sister Hortense had given him and her own hand-knitted, Blue Boy. But none of these things seemed appropriate as a keepsake to bring with her. In the end, tear-laden eyes over-came her and she fell into a restless sleep.

* * * * *

She woke with a start, as Sister Anunciata the ward sister was removing the child, and telling Bridie it was time to get up to get ready for Galway. For a split second, Bridie was in a state of panic as she made a protective grab for John Paschal, as she'd just been in the midst of a most horrible dream. She dreamt that she had cut off the child's ear, because a spirit had told her that if she did that, then the child would return. Nobody would be able to claim they had fostered out John Paschal, because part of him was missing. If Bridie kept the ear then one day he would return to her and the union would be complete.

Bridie was so relieved to see his ear intact, yet so struck by the message in the dream, that she was utterly convinced it had a valid meaning.

Sister was saying, as she picked up the sleepy infant,

"It's time for you to get dressed; your car will be leaving shortly and you have to go down for breakfast yet."

By now Bridie was in the midst of a tug-o-war battle, and trying to wrestle the crying child away from the Night Sister, as she pleaded,

"Please! Please! Give him back to me, just for five minutes," she begged, as nervous mothers in nightgowns, infants at their breasts came together and started crying pitifully in the centre of the room, each looking at a premonition of their own sad days to come.

Then a lone voice cried out, "Ah, Sister!"

This encouraged another voice to add "Go on: give her another chance."

But before any dissent could ferment, the Night Sister had turned on them in an aggressive manner.

"Go back to yeer beds the lot of ye and look after yeer own children; 'twould be more in yeer line."

"Bridie Rodgers, you should not have been allowed to sleep here last night. Look at the trouble you're causing now," she shouted as she tried to back away from the grasping hands of Bridie.

"But there'll be no trouble if I can hold him; just five minutes," pleaded Bridie desperately, as she started to grapple more forcefully with Sister for possession of the child.

Sister Anunciata managed to turn around and get away from Bridie: the child secure in her arms. She went towards the tiny medicine room situated in the corner of the nursery as the grieving mothers started to close in all around. Bridie spotted a pair of gleaming chrome scissors on the small medicine table. Quick as a flash she slipped the scissors into her dressing gown, as Sister Anunciata turned on them with renewed aggression.

"I said, go back to bed all of you this instance, and don't be so nosey! Bridie, will you please go and get dressed and stop making a fool of yourself. If you'll just do that, I might let you hold him for a second."

Bridie went and started to dress quickly.

Sister Imelda came in and looking around said, "Bridie, are you not ready yet? Your porridge is waiting below."

Bridie ignored Sister Imelda, while she finished dressing and brushing her hair; all the time thinking frantically about what she was going to do.

When she'd finished dressing she went towards the Sisters who having finished changing the child, were watching her every move. With outstretched arms, and trembling emotions, Bridie asked, "Can

I hold him now?"

Sister Anunciata looked suspiciously at her, as she herself tried to control the whimpering child in her arms. She answered,

"On condition that you hand him over immediately without creating a scene."

Bridie nodded in agreement, unable to speak as tears began to well up in her eyes. Taking a firm hold of her only son one last time, she walked across the room, towards the bed, as every mother in the nursery clung desperately to their off-spring; helplessly watching Bridie, and John Paschal's last goodbye.

She lay the little boy down on the bed as the tears rolled down her cheeks; and reached for the scissors beneath the pillow. Just as the nursing sisters suspected she might be up to something, she took the scissors and cut off a quiff of the child's hair, which she had so lovingly trained for months on end. Kissing him quickly on the cheek and forehead she sobbed hastily, "Good bye John Paschal, Good bye. Some day please God, we'll meet again."

Sisters Imelda and Anunciata, on seeing the glint of the scissors came running frantically, to grab Bridie who struggled free and ran down the corridor. The young mothers, deprived of a last farewell cried out,

"We'll mind him for you Bridie. We'll take good care of him."

They immediately went as one to honour their commitment. While Bridie, unable to look back, disappeared at the end of the corridor, forced to part now, and perhaps forever, with the only true love she had ever known.

Chapter Six

The early morning sun rose majestically into a deep blue sky, slowly peeling away the early morning dew that hung over the tribal city, like some ancient shroud. And as the last residue of dawn faded it revealed a bright sparkling city awaiting the arrival of yet more visitors to its scenic shore; as a black 1937 Austin motorcar came into view

This was Galway, where city transport buses vied with each other for the right to transport day-trippers to its famed Salthill Strand. The black car however was not holiday-bound, and came to an abrupt halt at the city end of College Road; where it parked alongside a high, stonewall. The three occupants in the back seat looked questioningly at each other but said nothing. They didn't know where they were, and they didn't dare ask.

This must be it, thought Bridie as the two nuns in the front of the car got out, and opened the rear doors to escort the three girls to their new place of work.

'There's a lovely job waiting for you,' was the one thing that had stayed in each of their heads since they'd left Tuam, almost an hour earlier.

And here they were, standing at the bottom end of a steep hill, with a neat row of red-bricked houses directly facing them. Bridie noted the green and white metal nameplate attached to the end house that said, 'Mary Magdalene Terrace'.

The girls looked anxiously around at the high imposing wall that seemed as if it might collapse on top of them at any moment. They shivered nervously despite the warm summer sun; as they each waited patiently to be handed their small brown suitcases.

The 'job' thought Bridie, must be in one of those houses, because there are no shops, no hotels or no hospitals here. Nothing.

Then a sudden notion struck Bridie that she should run away while she still had the chance. Why should she go working for the nuns? Couldn't she find her own job somewhere in Tuam, and be near John

Paschal? But then again, she might not get a job in Tuam or Galway, and she'd have to sleep out, because she had nowhere else to go. Besides she didn't think she had the energy to run away after such a restless night and the struggle she had this morning just to say goodbye to her son. And as she looked sideways at the other two girls accompanying her, she thought, if the new job is good enough for them, then it's probably good enough for me. She followed the two nuns as they walked ten short paces before unlocking a small entrance set in a Massive oak door that stoutly guarded the secret of whatever lay behind the high stonewall. Once inside, the girls looked in awe at the picturesque grounds before them. A huge, impressive two-storey, stone-cut building stood thirty yards away and to its right was a winding path leading via stone steps to a beautiful grotto of the Blessed Virgin. And further to its right again was a small enclosed, ironclad graveyard, housing numerous black-painted iron crosses.

A graveyard! What in the name of God was a graveyard doing here? This was the question running through the girls' minds. This place must be some kind of a church they foolishly thought.

But the Magdalene Home laundry in Galway City was a bit like St. Joseph's Industrial School Clifden. A place steeped in religion with rare religious artefacts adorning every single room, and where religious garments from the four corners of the province were sent to be taken care of, as well as dirty laundry from the regions tourists resorts, hotels and guest houses.

Once inside the main building the girls were ushered into a small office and told to wait. Almost immediately a stoutly built nun with a rugged complexion came into the room and said, "Good Morning girls."

"Good Morning," replied the girls sheepishly.

"All the way from Tuam. Did ye have a nice trip?" she asked, as she sized them up and began rubbing the backs of her large blue hands as if trying to inject some life-blood into them

"Yes Sister", they answered with no great enthusiasm.

"Now, I'd like to get your details if I may. I'm Sister Antonia, the Mother Superior. Any problems you may have, from time to time you come straight to me," she said sternly, before going behind her desk and opening a great ledger; which stood out amid a mountain of receipt books.

Then looking straight at Bridie, she pulled up what looked like a heavy kings chair to support her ample posterior, and said

"Now, young lady, what is your name?"

"Bridie Rodgers."

"Bridie Rodgers," she repeated entering her name in the great book. "How old are you Bridie?"

"Seventeen."

"Seventeen, and your address?"

Bridie looked nervously at the Mother Superior, but said nothing. She didn't know what to say.

"Your address Dear? We'd like to know your address and next of kin, who are you and where you came from, just in case someone comes to take you out; although I doubt very much if anyone cares."

"Dublin", replied Bridie doubtfully. The problem was she didn't know what she was supposed to say. She didn't know if she any longer had an address. She didn't want to say St. Joseph's. She didn't want to mention the O'Malley's, and she didn't know whether she should say Tuam because it seemed she was no longer living there.

"Dublin", repeated the red-faced Sister. Is that it? No house, street or suburb.

"No Sister" replied Bridie.

"You were born somewhere in the slums I expect. Do you have children?" she asked,

"I have a one year old boy; John Paschal."

"And I take it he is still in Tuam?"

"Yes Sister. Will I be able to go and visit him?" asked Bridie, without giving the idea any great thought.

The Mother Superior put the gold embossed fountain pen back in its holder, as her already ripe complexion visibly flushed in anger at Bridie's outrageous suggestion. Then joining her hands as if about to pray she leant back in her monumental chair and said,

"My dear! Let me explain one thing in the clearest possible language; you are now resident in the Magdalene Home Laundry: an asylum if you like; a place of refuge for the unloved, unmarried and unidentified. It is not a three-star hotel where guests can come and go as they please. You are here because nobody wants you, or because of your past sins. Here, we help you to atone for the sins of your past life or else you face eternal damnation in the eyes of God forever and ever. Here you have an opportunity to make your peace with God. You are his servants and from this day on are penitents in the eyes of

God and must do his will. Furthermore, you are in the finest place in the whole of Ireland; safe and secure from the evils of the outside world – which by now you all know only too well."

Then, taking a deep breath she continued, "Bridie Rodgers, the task facing you in particular is a daunting one. But my job as a servant of God is to ensure that you learn from your past, and to lead a better life. As for any children you may already have, I have no doubt that they will be well looked after. It would serve no useful purpose whatsoever to entertain family visits. On the contrary, such visits would only help to sow the seeds of dissent, doubt and disarray."

Then smiling lamely she added, "Now, can we get down to business. Please remember the sooner you all settle into your new posts, the easier it will be for everyone."

Then looking directly at the girl next to Bridie, she asked, "And what is your name?"

"Noreen Donnellan."

"Address?"

"Kilbeg, Winnamstown."

"Where is that?" asked Mother Superior with a furrowed brow.

"Co. Galway……… it's near Castlerea."

"You mean, Williamstown?"

"Yes," answered Noreen, growing uneasy at this line of questioning.

"Yes, what?" growled the Mother Superior.

"Yes, it's Winnamtown."

"It's yes Sister, to you! You are to address me at all times as 'Sister!' Do you understand that?" barked the Mother Superior.

"Yes Sister," replied Noreen nervously.

"And it's pronounced Will-yam-stown As far as I know there's no such place as Winn-am-stown. So get that into your thick skull now!" Then, turning to the book again she said, "And how old are you – all the way from Will-yam-stown ?"

"I'm fourteen."

"Fourteen Sister!" roared the good Mother. We'll stay here all day if we have to; so get it right. Have I made myself clear?"

"Yes Sister." said Miss Donnellan as she shifted uncomfortably from one foot to the other.

"And what, may I ask, brought *you* to Tuam?"

"The Parish… Priest put me in… Sister"

"Why did he put you in?"

"I don't know... Sister, yet."

"Were you beaten by your parents in Williamstown?"

"A biteen, yet. I mean yes."

"A biteen," repeated Mother Superior. "Perhaps you didn't get half enough. Maybe that was the problem. If you addressed your mother and father the way you addressed me, then I think I'd be giving you more than a biteen."

Then turning to the third girl the Superior asked,

"And what is your name please?"

"Josephine Finn, Sister"

"Age?"

"Twenty-one, Sister."

"And your address?"

"Lisnagerra, Dunmore."

"Lis-na-gerra," she replied writing it in the big book. "An bhfuil Gaeilge agat?"

"Níl. I can speak a little Irish, Sister"

"But you have a baby?" said Sister, an air of sarcasm in her voice.

"No, I haven't, Sister," said Josephine, emphasising the word, no.

"And why were you in Tuam then?"

"I was told it was only for a while – that I'd be given a decent job somewhere."

"But why were you sent to Tuam in the first place? It's a Home for expectant mothers, or were you ill-treated too?" queried the Sister as she detected a rebellious tone in Josephine, that made her blood pressure rise.

"No, Sister," replied Miss Finn, who was beginning to dislike the Mother Superior more and more.

Josephine hated all nuns and priests because they seemed to lead such perfect lives. Any lingering hopes Josephine thought she had of ever becoming a Saint in civilian life were dashed the day she met Cathal Swanick. Her whole world was turned upside down when she refused to stop seeing him – just because he was a Protestant. And the more her parents demanded she give him up, the more determined she became in her belief that she would not. So they enlisted the help of the local parish priest who promptly had her forcibly removed from her home and sent to Tuam. She was determined not to divulge any of this to Sister Antonia, who was now looking at her and awaiting an explanation. When nothing further was forthcoming Sister said,

"Am I to take it that you were removed from your home because you were something of a rebel? A nuisance perhaps or company keeping?"

"No, it wasn't," replied Josephine in a manner that reflected her wounded pride. She wasn't going to tell anyone anything; it was no one's business, but her own. She didn't want the nuns or any of the other girls to know what went on in her past life because pretty soon herself and Cathal would run away to England and get married. Cathal would surely come to her aid, she thought, although he had not shown up when her parents kept her at home after they forbade her ever seeing him again. But this was different. He would surely come to her rescue now that the whole parish would know that she had been forcibly removed from her home and put away by the parish priest. Perhaps she would write to him, now that she was in Galway and see what happens. But then Cathal's father might see the letter and urge him to have nothing at all to do with her. No. No. Cathal wouldn't let her down; he'd surely come to her rescue. She had no doubt about that. Sooner or later he would show up and whisk her off to England, so no one in the parish would ever know where she was and she could live happily ever after.

"Disobedience," sighed the flushed Mother Superior, as she leant back in her great Oak throne and studied the three girls standing before her.

"Let me remind you girls, the world is full of disobedience coming in that door; but I can assure you it abounds with meekness before it goes back out again." Then coming out from behind her desk, she scowled at them as she summoned in a loud voice from her office door. "Sister Philomena."

Sister Philomena appeared at the door as if by magic and the Mother Superior said,

"Will you please arrange to have these girls assigned as quickly as possible? Perhaps you can find work for them in the kitchen and let Lilly MacAlastair and Peggy Neary go back on Calender duty."

The word 'Calender' rang an immediate bell with Bridie. She knew it was for smoothing out sheets and blankets in a laundry. So it must be like St. Joseph's and St. Mary's. But the Mother Superior said this was an asylum, a place of refuge for the unmarried, unloved and unidentified. I better stop thinking and say nothing and see what happens, thought Bridie, as the three of them followed Sister Philomena down the corridor towards the rear of the building and into another room.

Handing each of them a white uniform and cap, a small towel, a bar of carbolic soap and two pieces of linen cloth, she whispered softly, "They're for your monthlies. Take great care of them as they are only given out once a year. They will not be replaced should you lose them. And make sure to keep all of your personal possessions in your bedside locker at all times. Also I must warn you that smoking is strictly forbidden. Please remove all of your clothes now and put on your uniforms. You don't have to remove everything, just your outer garments. You can change the rest later this evening after you've had a hot bath."

Then all of their good clothes and personal items were put into their small brown suitcases and taken away. But Bridie did not part with her son's lock of hair. She now had it wrapped in a piece of paper and safely tucked into the cup of her bra; until she found a more suitable place for it. Down in the kitchen the inmates were busy scrubbing pots and peeling potatoes. Sister Philomena called to two of them.

"Lilly! Peggy! Will you please go back to the laundry and help sort out the Tuam and Ballinalsoe baskets? These new girls will take over here."

Then turning to Bridie she said,

"What's your name?"

"Bridie."

"Bridie! Will you come with me please, and I'll show you what to do. Girls, I'll be back in a moment."

Sister Philomena led Bridie down to the steam room where she was shown what clothes to iron, and half an hour later the three new inmates were shown where they'd be sleeping, by Sister Stanislaus the Ward Sister.

There were three large dormitories up stairs: St. Teresa's, 'Our Lady's and the 'Sacred Heart'. Bridie and Josephine were going to sleep in 'Our Lady's while Noreen Donnellan was going to be sleeping across the corridor in the 'Sacred Heart'.

On their return they were given tea and bread in the kitchen and taken on a guided tour of the laundry by Sister Philomena. They were shown the large industrial Calendars; the rows of galvanised wall sinks for hand-washing; as well as the steam room, the ironing room, the recreation hall upstairs, the church tucked away neatly at the back of the main building and the convent.

During their dinner break, all the girls in the laundry went outside to absorb the fresh air and sunshine. Bridie was amazed at the crowds of people huddled together in little groups, nattering here, there and everywhere: and all of them clad in long white calico gowns and silly looking white caps. Apparently these were new uniforms, or so the girls told Bridie. Some girls were walking around by the perimeter wall, linking each other in two's and three's, while some of the nuns walked around behind them with their rosary beads in hand, or knelt at 'Our Lady's Grotto' in prayer. Two or three elderly penitents were tending the nuns' graves, and looking after the flowers in and around the walkways. But Bridie had eyes only for her comrades. She wanted desperately to compare notes, but above all to make friends with the two new girls. Josephine Finn waved wildly when she spotted Bridie and rushed to join her, dragging fourteen-year-old Noreen Donnellan, with her.

"Oh God, what do you think Bridie? The kitchen's horrible; I'm not staying here. What are you doing?" asked Josephine with urgency.

"I'm in the ironing room, ironing shirts. I don't mind ironing, but the girl I work with has been here ten years and was never out once. Not even for a day, and she said some of the girls were here an awful lot longer," answered Bridie with even more urgency, as Noreen stood listening and looking all around her.

"We work with two oul' ones. They hardly spoke to us. Did they, Noreen?" asked Josephine, turning to her young friend.

"No. They seem to creep or shuffle about the place. I was afraid to ask, how long they'd been here. They looked like zombies to me. To tell you the truth I think they're a bit gone in the head," said Noreen Donnellan.

"And one keeps forgetting where she leaves things," added Josephine."

"Why don't you ask if you can come over to the ironing room with me?" suggested Bridie.

"Do you think it would work? They'd never let the two of us out of the kitchen," said Josephine, doubtfully.

"Well you could try," suggested Bridie. "Tell them you worked with me in Tuam."

"But I didn't, and I'd be no good ironing."

Then, Bridie spotted her work-mate and called out, "Julie, these are my friends that I was telling you about: Josephine and Noreen; they came in with me this morning."

Suddenly, another group of girls came rushing to their side, asking excitedly "Are ye the new girls?" "Where are ye from?"

They were wondering if they knew this one or that one, a brother or a sister or a cousin. Did they know the village? How far away from it did they live? But when Bridie inadvertently said she didn't really know anyone or any of the named villages because she'd only been free herself a few short months, they all looked away in silence before hanging their heads. These long-forgotten inmates craved news of the outside world. Did their mothers or fathers really know where they were? Where was the father of their child who caused them to be put in there in the first place? Even more important where was the child, who like Bridie's, had been forcibly removed from their breast at dawn and was now living only God knows where? Some of the girls, who were forcibly parted from their brothers or sisters as teenagers, were beside themselves for news of their relatives. Were they married, or living even? Did the new girls know anything at all?

No. Bridie and company knew nothing. Looking at their sea of anguished faces, Bridie felt as if she was betraying each one of them. If only she knew someone in Gort, Mountbellew, Boyle, Strokestown, Belclare – or Tuam even. But no, she felt so utterly useless that after coming into this strange place from the outside world, she could not answer a simple question.

"Bridie! Do you know my brother, Billy? Billy Reilly, from Tuam? He's real tall, good looking, with blonde hair. Billy Reilly! Every one knows Billy! He goes to midday Mass in the Cathedral every Sunday…."

"No. I don't think…"

"But you must. You must know him. Everyone knows Billy!"

"No. I don't. I'm sorry."

"But I thought you said you came from Tuam?"

"Well I do…I mean… I did. But I was only in St. Mary's Home for unmarried mothers and before that I was in St. Joseph's school in Clifden."

"Oh! So you're…you're… one of us!"

Then a small spectacled nun, head down, walked slowly by

clanging a little bronze bell, to round up her troops and get them back to work.

Lining up four abreast they filtered through the narrow doorway, each lost in a sea of self-doubt, loathing and pity; before fanning out in the corridor to go and work in the wash room, the steam rooms, the ironing room, the dormitories, dispatch room, the bakery and the kitchen.

For some at least, they were mid-way through their first full day working in a lovely new job in Galway.

* * * * *

It was almost two weeks later, as she made her way back to 'Our Lady's Dormitory, that she felt the first real pangs of loneliness. Standing behind Sister Stanislaus, as she unlocked the dormitory door that housed fifty penitent inmates, Bridie slowly made her way to her bed, beside the steel barred, painted window, and flopped down with sheer exhaustion. She had been on her feet since seven o'clock that morning. It was now half past nine of a fine July evening, and everyone was already in bed, or about to get undressed: Bridie being one of the last, had ironed scores of shirts, not to mention numerous other bits and pieces. She never wanted to see another shirt as long as she lived, she told herself. She was even too tired to think and when she did, all she could think of was, how was John Paschal? She realised she had spent thirteen months nursing her only son and now she felt as if someone had severed part of her body. To think, her son, her own flesh and blood had been snatched away from her – despite her best efforts. Now, she didn't even know if she would ever see him again. When she thought of his smiling, cheerful expression and his fancy quiff, which she had so lovingly trained, she reached into her blouse and pulled out a small pouch, which she had stitched on to her sacred heart scapular and which held the precious lock of golden hair. She kissed it good night as she had done every night for the past week.

Soon she heard faint footsteps approach her bed and when she turned her head she saw it was Josephine Finn; over for a chat. Bridie was too tired to talk. Any night other than tonight, Bridie thought, but she didn't like to say anything to Josephine, who was now sitting at the foot of her bed. As she did so, somebody from the other end of the dormitory whistled loudly, but Bridie and Josephine decided to ignore the taunts, as to respond to them would only create mayhem, as they had seen happen during the week.

"How did you get on today?" asked Josephine.

"Oh God, 'twas shocking," she yawned. "I was standing there like a statue all this day. Ironing! Ironing! And now my feet are killing me."

"But at least you have someone right, to talk with. I'll go mad in that kitchen. I will, I swear! I'll go mad if I don't get out of there. Three times I've asked Sister Philomena if I can go and work with you and all she says in her squeaky clean wouldn't-put-a–finger in a fanny-voice, is 'Patience dear, patience.'"

Bridie meanwhile was looking straight at Josephine and thinking how really beautiful she was with her faintly freckled face, crowned with a mass of blond hair, which now hung in ringlets about her shoulders. She was imagining what she must have looked like as a child, and then she was away on another train of though herself; playing with John Paschal in the nursery at St. Mary's. But when she thought she heard Josephine saying something about being stuck in this place, she sat up in bed, because she knew she'd get no peace, until they were both exhausted from all the yapping.

Josephine was saying, "Bridie, you're not listening. What am I going to do ? I don't want to be stuck in this place forever."

"I don't know," answered Bridie, who after a momentary pause had a brainwave and asked her friend, "How are you getting on in the kitchen anyway?"

"How do you think; I hate the sight of the place."

" I know. But I was just thinking," whispered Bridie. "If you started making a mess of things in the kitchen they might think you were no good and move you some other place."

Josephine's eyes lit up and she exclaimed loudly,

"Yes, yes! That's it!. That's it!." And with that she sprang from the bed and proceeded to the centre of the floor where she whirled and twirled like a ballerina, singing;

Somewhere over the rainbow,
Skies are blue,
And dreams that you dared to dream of,
Really do come true...

But then an ageing cranky inmate woken from her slumber, put paid to Josephine's song.

"Would you ever shut up and let a person get some sleep?"

But she in turn was instantly drowned out by a chorus of, "Ah Grumpy, leave the girl alone. You're sorer than a boil on a bear's arse; let the girl sing?"

With that, everyone started to laugh and two or three of the more brazen ones jumped from their beds and began pulling the bedclothes off Grumpy Moran's bed.

"Take no bleedin' notice of that rip," said Molly from Dublin as she sat crocheting on her bed, "If you want to sing love, you sing."

And for a time it seemed as if pandemonium would reign as everyone started shouting and throwing pillows or pulling at each other's bedclothes. Suddenly the appearance of Sister Stanislaus, bursting through the door, vigorously swinging her bell brought proceedings to a halt.

"Girls!" she exclaimed, "I'm ashamed of you. You're behaving like a gang of hooligans."

The silence was deafening until Molly piped up. "Sister how do you spell that?"

The dormitory erupted into peals of laughter again, as one or two of the more brazen inmates tried to intimidate Sister Stanislaus; but she was too alert for them and soon locked the dormitory door for the night.

Bridie felt elated that her friend Josephine had such a beautiful voice and together with the other girls, tried to cajole her to sing again. But she merely ignored their pleas by saying,

"Goodnight."

And then the lights went out, leaving the inmates screaming as they grabbed each other and tried to find their beds in the semi-darkness.

Soon everyone was fast asleep, except Bridie. She knew she'd had a bad day, and judging by what her work mates were saying, she would have many more to come. She also knew she couldn't keep going like this with no hope, no plan, and no future; with nothing to look forward to. The tales she'd heard of life in the Magdalene Laundry were too frightening to even contemplate. She began to twist and turn in her bed in an effort to erase them from her mind: trying instead to devise a master plan. Whatever about anyone else, she would try to look after herself from here on in, she decided. And the sooner she decided the better.

The small bronze bell made a heavy clanging noise as Sister Stanislaus, shook the instrument vigorously. Jesus! exclaimed Bridie. That bell has the most irritating tone I ever heard. I swear that bitch 'Stanalaus', gets pleasure out of wakening everyone at this hour of a morning.

When Sister Stanislaus had left the room, Bridie, turned over and curled up beneath the blankets. She felt so tired and so wrecked that she didn't want to ever get up again. It's only seven-thirty and everyone's getting ready for work already. She felt very apprehensive about effecting her plan so quickly, but she decided she'd better get up anyway, and when Josephine Finn came by her bed and asked,

"Are you ready?"

She jumped up and grabbed her soap and facecloth from her bedside locker.

As the two of them left the dormitory, they could hear and see other girls in the corridors fighting over towels. This ritual was repeated on an almost daily basis, as the inmates tried to procure fresh towels from wherever they could. Several girls had already been beaten black and blue by the nuns, when it was discovered they had helped themselves to a nice range of hand towels sent to the Laundry for cleaning, which resulted in everyone being afraid to convert even a small silk handkerchief for their own use. Down in the washroom, Bridie was once again struck by the appearance of the worn out elderly penitents, as they went about their ablutions in a silent robotic fashion. Their grey haggard unsmiling faces, a stark reminder to all that sooner or later, life in the Magdalene Home laundry takes its toll. For a brief moment Bridie stood in the queue and watched two inmates from, 'Our Lady's, dormitory, turn in unison from the wash basins and press a towel to their thin wan lips, and amble out of the wash-room, oblivious to those around them. Bridie wondered, if they had ever been kissed, somehow she could not imagine it. She knew by now that they would shuffle back to their dormitory and get dressed slowly, then go to Mass and receive the Blessed Sacrament, have their breakfast and never say a solitary word to anyone. Bridie found out from some of the inmates that these women were only in their forties; and it sometimes frightened her to even look at them, before glancing at her own reflection in the washroom mirror, as everyone kept commenting on how pale and tired she looked. It was a relief to Bridie to know she had a plan of action in place, for her eventual freedom this morning. When Josephine and Bridie had finished washing they returned to their Dormitory and got dressed for work before making their beds. Then Bridie turned to Josephine and said,

"You go on downstairs, I'm staying here."

"Why! Are you sick or something?" asked a startled looking Josephine.

"No, no. It's something I have to do. I'll be down later."

"But Sister Stanislaus will notice, and you might be punished," said Josephine.

"I don't care," said Bridie. "I just want to be left on my own for a while. I'll be down later, I promise. But don't say anything to anyone."

When Josephine went out and Bridie was left on her own, she looked about the large dormitory-room and thought it had a surreal atmosphere about it; despite the fact it had a large statue of the 'Sacred Heart' at one end of the room. For a moment she thought it could be classed as a hospital, with its fifty odd beds, but on closer inspection she thought it looked more like a prison with its heavily barred, painted windows. And when Bridie pictured Sister Stanislaus with her numerous dangling door keys by her side locking all the dormitory and intermediary doors, she suddenly felt frightened. She walked tentatively towards the door in case it should be locked. It wasn't. For what seemed a long time she hung around listening for any approaching sounds and when she heard the intermediary door in the corridor being unlocked down stairs and the mouse-like movements of the Sister's garments, she scurried back to her bed.

'Sister Stanislaus came in and said, "What's this Bridie? You're late…. and have not received the Blessed Sacrament this morning. Is something wrong?"

On hearing these placid words Bridie thought perhaps she should abandon her plan. Maybe she was being foolish, that no good would come of it. But then how would she explain her absence. She'd better say something. Now was her chance.

"No Sister. There's nothing wrong…except…."

"Except what?" demanded Sister Stanislaus.

"I don't know if I'm ever going to see my baby again."

"Aw, come Bridie, don't be silly. That's all in the past now. You'd do well to leave it all behind you. You're starting a new life for yourself here, and you have an awful lot to look forward to. Look at all the wonderful friends you've made. Friends anyone would be proud of. So come on down now and have your breakfast: I won't say a word to anyone."

But when Bridie heard the words, 'Don't be silly,' 'That's all in the past now', she felt such heart ache, that John Paschal's existence didn't even merit a care or a thought to anyone but herself; she knew she had a fight on her hands. "I'm sorry Sister, But I refuse to go to work until I know when I can go and see John Paschal," she said, looking Sister straight in the eye.

"That's all very fine for you to say Bridie, but when the Reverend Mother hears about this she will not be very pleased. Do you realise you may be deprived of your privileges? Being allowed to sleep in a dormitory of your choice and not have to scrub linen all day long, is a perk I'd be very slow to lose", said Sister, authoritatively, while pushing her pale white hands into the deep folds of her long black sleeves.

Bridie stared at the floor for a long time before meeting Sister Stanislaus's eyes again, but said nothing.

"Well, are you coming down with me or not?"

"No Sister," replied Bridie, realising she had now taken a stand and would have to see it through.

"Fine. In that case you give me no choice but to report your disobedience to Mother Superior," said Sister Stanislaus, turning quickly on her heel and out the door.

But she very soon returned to inform Bridie that the Reverend Mother wanted to see her in the office, right away. Bridie followed Sister Stanislaus, down the long corridor, feeling somewhat elated that she was at last making a stand for herself.

When she went into the Reverend Mother's office, the hard-faced Mother Superior looked at Bridie, with disdain, as Sister Stanislaus remained standing next to Bridie, like some prison guard. When the Mother Superior spoke, it was with a gruff voice.

"I understand you have a problem Miss Rodgers."

"I...I don't really have a problem."

"Well then, what are you doing here?" she growled. " I thought you said she refused to go to work?" said Mother Superior looking directly at Sister Stanislaus.

Bridie spoke up promptly when she realised she was losing ground and was being pitted against Sister Stanislaus.

"I refuse to go to work Reverend Mother, until I know when I can see my son Paschal, or if I'll ever be allowed out of here,"

"I see," said the good Mother, starting to tidy up her office desk: ignoring Bridie. "So we have not one, but two requests from you Bridie Rodgers. Is that correct?"

"I want to know how my son is?" said Bridie changing the emphasis slightly.

The Reverend Mother stopped work instantly and looked at Bridie. She knew she was dealing with a novice, so she availed of the perfect opportunity to get her full contingent back to work.

"But why didn't you just come out and say that? I could have told you: your son was fine. I was speaking only yesterday to Sister Hortense, and she informed me that your son is thriving. He's just fine. You have absolutely nothing to fear," she lied.

"Now, can you be a good girl and get back to work, please because I'm afraid we're very short-staffed this morning on account of the nuns retreat."

Bridie knew instinctively that she had said the wrong thing. She couldn't very well make a demand now, after what Mother Superior, had said. Her son was fine and that was all that mattered.

"Thank you," she said rather tamely as she stood up and was escorted all the way down the corridor and back to work by Sister Stanislaus who uttered not one word.

Down in the ironing room there was an air of excitement, with everyone wanting to know where Bridie was or what happened to her. When she returned and told them what she'd done, Julie Murray said,

"You were silly to bother your head a grá. Sure that wan wouldn't take a blind bit a notice of an'thin' any wan said. Sure she's only an oul' cod," she added as she began carefully folding up another ironed shirt. "You should have told us *f*what you were planning; and we'd have told you *f*what to do."

"But what else could I do?" asked Bridie, somewhat perplexed.

"Sure if we'd known, we could have gone and supported you and…and…."

"That's right," chipped in Lilly MacAlastair, "You were lucky the Superior Ass didn't put you on a starvation diet. At least if we were with you, they couldn't starve us all; because then there'd be no work done. Mr. Hehir, the van driver, he said, the one thing the nuns hated was the prospect of a strike. That they have to have the clergy's laundry done, no matter what...."

"And besides, they'd have no money for the Bishop," added Julie.

"Money? For what Bishop?" asked Bridie, feeling really annoyed that she knew nothing, and that no one had bothered to inform her.

"The money they charge the hotels, in Ennis, Gort, Kilrush an' ever'fwhere," said Julie. "Sure they make a fortune," she continued, "and give it all to Bishop Frown. He comes here then at Christmas and we all have to kneel down and kiss his oul' ring...an' the devil...stuck-a-thin-him."

"Yes," agreed Lilly, "And we like a right shower a eejits polishing his size ten shoes and washing his smelly oul' underwear all year."

"Sure glory be to God Almighty, Bridie, where's the sense in that? 'Tis him should get down on his two bended knees and kiss our ....our.... feet" continued Julie good-humouredly.

"Our arses, more like," corrected Lilly.

"Oh My God will ye stop it!" cried a disgruntled Peggy Neary, as she began pounding down the heavy steam iron, trying to press her own religious views on all and sundry. "Ye know well it's all for the good of the Catholic Church. That some day, please God, we'll all get our reward in heaven."

"Reward, how are you?" echoed Julie. "If you ash me, we're livin' in hell already 'cause none of us can get out," she tittered.

"May God forgive you, Julie," snapped Peggy Neary

"You'd want to watch who you're talking to Bridie, around here, 'cause the place is full of spies," said Lilly MacAlastair, tipping a wink at Bridie.

"And what's that supposed to mean?" bellowed Peggy, suddenly wheeling around and feeling threatened.

"Oh Peggy we don't doubt you for one minute, but it's strange how the last time we planned to go on strike, the nuns knew more about it than we did," said Lilly, matter-of-factly.

"But that had nothing to do with me Lilly, I swear to God, cross me heart and hope to die," said Peggy, making a fleeting gesture of a cross on her chest.

"But fwhy do the nuns always give you nice clothes an' ever'thin', an' we're left wearing nothin' but oul' rags?" added Julie, mischievously

"It was a bloody parcel! From home! I already told you..."

screamed Peggy defiantly, as the sound of the dinner-hour bell reverberated through the laundry, "…If I told you once, I told you a thousand times, 'twas a parcel!" reiterated Peggy, as her laughing colleagues were already scrambling out the door.

"Bastards"! swore Peggy, as she finished folding and putting away another freshly- ironed shirt. "Just ye wait till I tell Mother Superior, just ye wait," she mumbled.

* * * * *

Bridie, was feeling somewhat down, after another long day at work and wanted desperately to be alone with her thoughts. After carefully considering the chapel as a quiet place of refuge she decided instead she'd hide behind Our Lady's Grotto out in the laundry grounds. Surely there wouldn't be anyone there at this hour of an evening, she thought. All I want is a quiet moment to get away from everyone and have a fag in comfort.

She began by walking casually around by the perimeter wall of the enclosed grounds and peered through the heavy iron, barbed-wire gate leading to the nunnery field where two of the young penitents and a nun were turning out the cattle again after they had been milked. She then stole up by the back of the grotto and stood leaning against the stone wall, well away from the prying eyes of the nuns in the convent and took out the butt of a Woodbine cigarette she'd found in the pocket of a shirt. After a few wholesome drags she was surprised by the unexpected appearance of her friend, Julie Murray.

"Oh! there you are! An' I searchin' all over for you. Sure I was wonderin' fwhere you'd gone," said Julie. "Fwhat are you doin' here? fwhere'd you get the fag?"

"Oh, I found it somewhere," said Bridie, annoyed at being discovered.

"Come on and we'll walk around to the front of the grotto, 'cause the nuns can see ever'thin' outa-them-windas, and if they see us hidin' behind 'Our Lady', they'll think we're up to something. The best place to talk, is the nuns' graveyard. Sure they think we're praying for them then, the oul' eejits," she tittered, as they both started out.

Bridie had earlier in the day witnessed a relay of penitent women, under the directorship of the Mother Superior, pluck the neat pastures of grass that grew between the rows of headstones. So there was nothing else for them to do now but pray, pray, pray; and Bridie didn't feel much like praying. Not now anyway. Bridie and Julie both stood facing one of the graves, so that anyone looking out of the convent windows would think they were a pair of religious zealots. Bridie admired Julie's cuteness and regretted not having thought of the idea herself.

"Bridie, do you know *f*what it is, I'll never stick it. Kneel down there now," she ordered, "until you hear my confessions."

"Well, you've stuck it ten years," said Bridie, kneeling down and joining her hands as if in fervent prayer. "Look at me I'm only here a few weeks. Do you think we could ever run away or climb over the wall?"

"I don't know! Sure you'd want to be mad in the head to stay here a grá. And madder again I'm thinkin' to get away. "Only one young wan managed to get clean away. And wan died in a laundry basket. Sure scores-a-girls-tried, but them oul' raps a nuns cut off their hair and left them black and blue. God forgive me Bridie but I hope them oul' nun's rot in hell. Oooh! And to think some a them girls had such beautiful features", she lamented. Then turning to look at Bridie she continued, " Do you know *f*what it is, Bridie, I think I must be going mad. I really think I am."

Bridie was so taken aback by this remark she could say nothing but began to stare quizzically at her friend for a brief moment, because she didn't want to dwell on such horrible thoughts.

"Ten years! Sure that's enough to drive anyone mad," added Julie, as if to reinforce her argument

"But you're not. You're not," said Bridie trying to reassure Julie. "You're just upset, that's all, and you have every right to be. You're here a long time. But why are you in here any way? You never told me and I didn't like to ask" she added hesitantly, feeling that she could converse more openly with Julie now that they were friends.

"We better keep movin' and keep walkin' 'cause them nuns hate to see two friends together," said Julie.

When they were out of the graveyard and walking silently by the perimeter wall, Julie, stopped abruptly, glanced around and whispered,

"Bridie, I have to tell you something awful. Promise me you'll never ever tell a sinner, because if the nuns knew about it, I'd never ever, be-let-outa-here."

Bridie felt privileged at that moment, at the thought that she was now going to be entrusted with some terrible secret.

"Julie, you can trust me. I promise," she said with all the sincerity in her heart.

"Oh I was a silly girl! A silly, silly girl!" lamented Julie. "Sure I had no sense!" she began to whisper emotionally, as they both started to walk, slow unified steps, their arms neatly folded, their heads bowed in contemplation, along the winding circular path that zigzagged its way around the scenic grounds. "There was twelve of us in family, an' then Daddy died. I was very young then; around thirteen or fourteen, an' I hadn't a coat or a gansey to put on me back."

As she spoke, she pulled out of her sleeve a lovely silk handkerchief, that was trimmed in red lace and that had the letter J boldly embroidered in one corner, her very own creation; and began dabbing her eyes with it.

"An then I saw a beautiful red coat hangin' in a shop winda, an' you know Bridie, I dreamed-a-that-coat, night noon an' morn'."

Suddenly she stopped and turned to Bridie sobbing pitifully.

"I ran into the shop an' stole the coat. I'm a thief Bridie! I'm a thief! I'll never get out of here now. Oh what am I going to do!" she cried distressingly as Bridie, looked embarrassingly around in case anyone saw them.

But the only ones around were two nuns reading from a prayer book the other side of the grounds. Bridie, surprised by this admission of guilt, linked her friend by the arm and said,

"It's all right! It's all right! No one knows and besides, you're not a thief. You only took that coat because you were poor. I'd have done the same myself. I swear. And anyway, it was a long time ago. How did you come to be here?" asked Bridie, trying to change the subject.

Julie, drying her tears, mumbled

"The Guards were called and said I'd have to go to jail. But the priest stopped them. He said I was too young an' told my mother she'd be better off without me: that he knew a place in Galway that'd soon smarten me up. So he put me in here. For four years, he said, an' I'm here since. Sure they must plan to leave me here forever. I'll never get out now. Never ever," she started to cry again.

For the very first time, Bridie saw the enormity of her own predicament within the confines of the Magdalene Laundry, and was stunned into a bout of prolonged silence.

Julie meanwhile, began to wish she hadn't told Bridie anything as she was now ignoring her, not having said another word.

When finally they returned to the dormitory and were locked up for the night, Bridie lay awake for hours and hours. She couldn't sleep because the whole spectre of her life began to unfold like some long forgotten horror story. The memory of her childhood in Connemara, the beatings at the hands of Mrs. O'Malley in Conly House, the forcible separation of herself and John Paschal, and her removal to this house of refuge from which no one can escape.

She was terrified the way her future seemed to be shaping up. As things stood, she surmised she didn't have a future. But the most horrible thought of all then entered her head like a bolt out of the blue; the sayings of Madge Courtney, or 'mad Madge' as they liked to call her in Tuam. A fearful chill crawled up her spine at the thought that Madge's words were a prophecy. 'We're fallen women' she had said, and 'Fallen women are put away for life. 'This is the worst place in Ireland that a woman can be. You can be in jail a grá for stealing a hen or new bicycle and be out after six months.'

If the guards had put Julie Murray in to jail that time she'd be out by now, thought Bridie. 'But here it's for life because we're all mentally deranged.'

Oh God, thought Bridie, that must be what's wrong with Julie! Didn't she say that very thing this evening? I think I must be goin' mad!

God, maybe she didn't steal a coat at all! Maybe she imagined it!

Bridie's already tired and worn-out body developed a cold sweat as the words 'We're all mentally deranged,' echoed over and over again in her head.

'We're all mentally deranged.'

'We-are-all-mentally-deranged.'

'We're mentally deranged'.

Did Madge mean all the girls in Tuam? Or did she mean Tuam and Galway and where ever else groups of women were locked up?

She threw down the covers from her saturated body and tried to peer into the dimly lit room as a faint ray of moonlight filtered in through the painted windows.

Jesus we must be all mad, that's why they lock the doors, and put bars on the windows, and paint them: so we can't see out and no one can see in. If I got sick now, would they let me out? I think I'm going to die this minute. I really do. I must have a fever. Why am I so hot?

And if this place went on fire, we'd all burn alive, cause no one can get out. Julie? She's here ten years. Ten Years? Oh God! What am I going to do? What hope have I? And the old women, they're here all their lives. They don't even send them home when they die. They bury them here. That must mean, I'm going to die here in the Magdalene. Oh God! Oh Jesus, Mary and Holy St. Joseph, please come to my aid this night, she cried softly, as she crept out of bed and made her way down the dormitory amid the sleeping, snoring heads to seek solace and comfort with Julie. But when she reached Julie's bedside she was shocked to discover somebody else was sleeping with Julie, and a strange sickly feeling came over her; yet somehow she managed to prevent her jelly-like legs from folding beneath her. She didn't want to talk to Josephine Finn who was nearby – who was asleep anyway- because she didn't think she'd be able to understand. She made her way slowly back to her own bed and lay down once more. She asked herself was this whole thing a nightmare. She had thought things were bad in St. Joseph's when she had no mother or father, or brother or sister. She thought things were bad in O'Malley's, when she felt the weight of the broom across her back; and she'd never ever forget the pain in her heart the day her son was wrenched from her breast as she lay sleeping. But this: 'the worst place in Ireland that a woman can be'.

In desperation, she clutched her rosary beads and she tried to say the rosary. But however hard she tried, her mind could not get away from those haunting words; 'The worst place in Ireland that a woman can be'. So she made a pact with God that she'd say one 'Our Father', one 'Hail Mary' and one 'Glory be to the Father' that tomorrow would bring her a better day, and with that plea ringing in her head, she fell into a deep, deep sleep.

* * * * *

Sister Philomena came in hurriedly through the swing doors of the ironing room and requested Julie and Bridie to go with her to the storeroom.

"The new girls must have got them mixed up somehow, because several items of precious altar cloths from the Bishop's residence, have gone missing as well as some of the sheets from Ennis," she explained, as she stood among the stacks of linen cloth.

"I want you to check all the codes and see if you can locate them. Then put them into a basket and take them over to dispatch."

"Yes Sister," replied Julie and Bridie, delighted to be away from everyone. A welcome break from their normal everyday routine.

It's the perfect time thought Bridie, to find out, who's sleeping with Julie.

All morning, the thought that Julie had another close friend was distressing Bridie. She had to find out right now, who it was before the thought cracked her head.

"You know Julie, I couldn't sleep a wink last night," said Bridie as they both started checking the mountains of folded altar cloths and clean white sheets, that had the codes and initials, neatly hand sown into the corner of every item.

"Thanks-bit-o-God, I slept like a log,"

"So, I went down to you late last night to have a chat: but there was, somebody else with you." said Bridie.

"Fwhat do you mean, someone with me?" replied Julie, going through the layered folds of material to find the initials.

"There was someone with you."

"Someone with me? Fwhat are you on about?" said Julie, stopping to look quizzically at Bridie.

Bridie, knew by Julie's face that she was as puzzled as herself and began to think that perhaps she herself was imagining it all.

"I went down to have a talk with you because I was having the most awful nightmare about this place...but when I got to your bed..." hesitated Bridie.

"Fwhat are you on about?" said Julie, pulling out one of the missing cloths with a vengeance.

"There was someone sleeping in your bed; so I didn't say anything," said Bridie, delighted that she had the courage to confront Julie.

"Arrah, you must be ravin'!!," said Julie, continuing to stack one neat pile of linen on top of another.

"I'm not raving! Far from it!" answered Bridie, emphatically. "I couldn't see who it was in the dark, but there were definitely two people in your bed."

"Sure there was no one in bed with me. An' anyway, isn't it me own business who I sleep with," she frowned. After a momentary silent recollection, she rejoiced, "Arrah it must be Harry! I brought

Harry back last night," she laughed. 'Twas Harry you saw."

"Harry? Harry who?" asked Bridie, horrified that Julie might have sneaked in one of the delivery drivers, although she couldn't see how that was possible because you couldn't even smuggle in a packet of cigarettes into the laundry without the nuns knowing about it.

"Harry! Me teddy bear! Sure he's as big as mesell. I call him Harry after a fella I knew. Some of the girls *ashed* me weeks ago, could they borrow him for the night, and he's been doing the rounds ever since. I had to bring him back from 'St. Teresa's dormitory, because Margaret Sherry was trying to keep him. Sure the poor devil's worn out doin' the rounds, but I have him back now and I'm keepin' 'im." She tittered.

"God, that's a good one!" laughed Bridie with relief. I thought it might be Noreen Donnellan, or Josephine Finn, I was killed wondering.

"No, a stóre, 'twas only Harry. Lord if he was real, wouldn't it be wonderful," she paused dreamily. "I'd tie him to me bed and keep 'im forever. But sure *f*where's the use in talking. I'll soon be eleven years here now, and no one cares!" she sighed. "No one cares!"

Bridie watched Julie shuffle over to the storeroom door where she listened attentively for a moment before returning to the centre of the room.

"If I tell you a secret, will you promise to keep your mouth shut?" whispered Julie.

"Of course I will! Why wouldn't I." promised Bridie, wondering what else Julie had done and if she herself would be able to cope with all the secrets.

"I'm going to try and get out of her because I don't think I can stick it another minute."

"Get out!" exclaimed Bridie in amazement.

"Yes. I'm going to run away. Climb over the wall, or some thin'. Any thin' to get away from here."

A surge of excitement brought a sudden flush to Bridie's cheeks, that something was about to happen and that she herself might be part of the plan.

"When are you going?" asked Bridie, holding a set of priests' vestments in her hand in case Sister came in quickly and caught them talking.

" Sure I haven't the foggiest, but I remember wance, 'twas months and months ago, I was walking down the corridor and I happened to look down the nuns corridor and didn't I see the big door at the front of the grounds wide open. You could see straight out on the road. Sure I should have ran I suppose, and got away: because I'd be afraid to try and climb over the wall. It's awful high the other side and I might get kilt."

"Oh I know," said Bridie, recalling how frightened she was it might collapse on top of her the very day she first came to the Magdalene. "Would it not be easier to escape across the nuns field at the back? Maybe we could then catch a train or something," suggested Bridie.

"Sure the only time we're out there, the nuns walk beside us while we're on retreat, saying the rosary an ever'thin' and if we as much as whisper a word: them trumps 'ill give wan a skelp across the back of the head that'd knock you kicking. Sure they nearly kilt me wance, because I started titterin' an' everythin'. Some ould eejit was standing on the railway embankment shoutin' over at us. 'Ah, Jaysus, will you look at the seagulls, and the oul' penguins. Look at the penguins', he was saying. Sure we were all in stitches and the next thing I got such a clatter across... the"

The sound of sandaled feet across the floor alerted the girls.

Sister Stanislaus came in cheerfully exclaiming, "Bridie, a letter for you," handing her a small white envelope. "Put it away now and don't open it until you've finished your work," said Sister Stanislaus, with an air of authority.

"Oh thank you Sister. What a lovely surprise," said Bridie' studying it for a split second before slipping it into her pocket and wondering who could possibly have sent her a letter. It must be only a note it feels light, she thought.

When Julie saw Bridie getting a letter and she there only a few weeks, she was immediately full of despair, as no one ever wrote to her, except her own sister, Kay. Otherwise known as Sister Rosario who was a nun in America, and who only ever wrote to Julie at Christmas.

"Sister Stanislaus! Are you sure there's no letters for me? 'cause I never seem to get an'thin' from an'one."

"Julie dear, you know there are never any letters for you. So why do you keep asking? If there's any letter you shall be the first to know," said Sister gliding out the door, rosary beads clinking at her side, with a small handful of letters held tightly to her breast.

Julie turned to Bridie after a momentary pause, and whispered,

"Aren't you going to open it?"

"Do you think I should?"

"Sure it's your letter, Bridie. They can't take it off you."

Bridie took out the letter and quickly tore it open as Julie stood guard at the storeroom door. She pulled out a small square photograph of a child sitting on the grass. Bridie immediately kissed the image of her son.

"Oh Julie! My prayers have been answered," she sighed, as she held the photograph for a moment to her bosom, while raising her eyes to heaven in appreciation of the power and glory of the Almighty.

She checked the envelope again for some form of correspondence but there was none. Not a word. Then she turned over the photograph and read aloud, 'To Bridie, best wishes from all in St. Mary's, xxx'

She could barely conceal her glee at having got a picture of John Paschal, yet, was mystified at the lack of any correspondence and when she turned to Julie to show her the photograph, she saw she had her back turned and was making believe she was busy folding clothes. Bridie, knew it was not the time as she could sense Julie was being torn apart at not having received any letter.

After a while Bridie said, "Why don't you come for a walk this evening, and we'll talk about your plans."

Julie turned round and placing an armful of clean fresh linen along with what Bridie had already sorted, mumbled,

"Plans me arse! Sure I'm sick of plans. They never work," she said, dismissing Bridie's suggestion before going over to the door once more to peep out.

When she came back she said, "If you're ever caught by the Guards they leave you black and blue, and then the nuns give you the works *f*when you're brought in. They cut off all your hair and ever'thin'. Sure I'd look like a *convent,* an' ever'one laughin' at me."

Bridie, herself laughed at the word *convent* and knew Julie was trying to say convict, and the idea of seeing Julie; hair cut to the scut with a ball and chain around her ankle appealed to her own sense of humour.

"Sure besides, *f*where can I go? Me mother mustn't want me. If I wrote wance, I wrote a score a times and as for the rest-a-the-family…" she sighed, "Only God knows *f*where they are now. So, there's no use in plannin' a grá. No use. 'Cause…we've all supped with the devil."

A few days later, as Julie was sent from the steam room to help out in the kitchen, she chanced to look down the short corridor leading from the main hall and noticed to her dismay that the huge laundry van was just pulling out on to College Road, and that the big oak door was wide open. For a split second her heart pounded in her chest at the prospect that escape was so tantalisingly close. She stopped in her tracks and looked furtively around to see if anyone was watching. The coast was clear. She ran like an alley cat up the short corridor leading to the Mother Superior's office, crouched down beneath the glass-panelled door and scurried out into the yard. She ran across the front grounds leading to the main exit and in an instant found herself out on College Rd., where she momentarily froze, before deciding to turn right and go straight into the city. Running as fast as she could, she thought she'd surely choke, gasping for breath, as on and on she ran and into the fair green in Eyre Square. She glanced quickly round, but no one was following her. She stopped in disbelief at what she had just done. I'm free! I'm Free! Free at last, she gasped as she turned again to face into the city after spending nearly eleven years as a penitent in the Magdalene Home laundry.

Chapter Seven

The Reverend Mother, was busy in her office making phone calls and writing letters when she happened to raise her head to seal an envelope and thought she saw what looked like a blip of white flee pass the bottom of the window in her office door. Moving quickly, she went to the door in the hope of apprehending one of the nuns listening or spying on her. But when she opened the door there was no one there. Then she thought she caught a brief glimpse of a white calico gown disappearing to her left out on College Rd. She didn't know who it was, or if she were imagining it, but the speed at which the thing moved told her it must be one of the girls in the laundry – escaping. She rushed out and was halfway across the grounds when the driver suddenly appeared ready to slide the heavy oak door back into position, but not before he was grilled and reprimanded by the Mother Superior.

"But I was in the front of the van, checking the delivery dockets. I didn't see anyone," he said.

"Seamus, if I find out one of my girls has gone missing, then your career as a van driver will be in the lap of the Gods. You're to report to my office on your immediate return. Have I made myself clear?"

"Yes Sister," answered a puzzled-looking Seamus.

Sister Antonia could scarcely believe that one of her inmates would run out the gate. They didn't have the brains, the guts or the courage, she thought, not after the way I dealt with them last time. That must be what a year ago or more, but now someone had undoubtedly escaped, perhaps two or three: my God, what will the Bishop say if he hears about this. She moved quickly and went back into the laundry where she ordered an immediate head count, and after a considerable delay, it was ascertained that one Julie Murray was missing, so she phoned Eglington Street Garda Station.

"May I speak with Sergeant Ruane, please, it's very urgent."

The Duty Officer collared Sergeant Ruane as he was about to go out the door. "…She says it's very urgent, Sergeant."

"Women!" he grumbled, as he grabbed the phone.

"Sergeant Ruane speaking."

"Good morning Sergeant, I'm so glad to have got hold of you. I hope I'm not inconveniencing you in any way. But unfortunately one of my girls has gone missing. I think she's gone straight into town…"

"Sister Antonia! What a surprise. I haven't seen or heard from you in ages… It sure has. It sure has… Now what's this about one of your girls? … What? … Missing? Are you sure?"

"Yes, I'm sure Sergeant, and remember she 's no push over; she's a bit of a wild one. Her name's Julie Murray. She's from Kilmaine, and will probably try to go home, … About twenty-five, I'd say, of stocky build, with shoulder length fair hair, but she may still have it pinned up beneath her cap"

"Leave it with us Sister, we'll see to it, she won't go far."

"Sergeant, you're an angel. I'll ring you later to see how you're progressing."

When Bridie heard that one of the inmates was missing she could not in her wildest imagination have visualised Julie Murray absconding, despite the fact that they had discussed that very subject only days earlier. But after the inmates were all shepherded into the various departments, and a thorough search was carried out, it was indeed confirmed that Julie was missing. Bridie became very despondent that her friend, Julie Murray, could do such a thing with out giving Bridie the opportunity to escape with her. She didn't know whether she was happy or sad that her friend had managed to escape. She felt that Julie had cheated her in some way. That she had all along concocted some well-laid plan to go it alone, or with the able assistance of someone on the outside. But who'd help her? Maybe it was one of her brothers? Her sister? Her mother? No. No. Not her mother, anyone but her mother, thought Bridie.

Julie Murray wandered back out on to Shop Street for the umpteenth time. She didn't really know where she was, but thought that the buildings looked vaguely familiar. First she thought Moon's shop was on the right hand side of the street and now it seemed on the left, and *there, was* Lydon's lovely restaurant again. There must be more than one of them, she thought. And the smell of their freshly baked scones and the sight of their strawberry tarts in the window made her ravenous with the hunger.

She moved on down the street, but kept looking over her shoulders.

She had to continuously dodge into shop doorways, as she saw several nuns from her own Sisters of Mercy order making street collections. Her greatest fear was that she'd be spotted by one of them, so she decided to take to the side streets again. She kept asking herself where she'd go, because she couldn't stay in the city. Someone was sure to see her. If only she could get away. She didn't have any money except a half a crown, but that was hidden in her dormitory locker and of no use to her now. Worse still, she had no food and no clothes. If only she could change out of her white gown she might not be recognised. She took off her cap and after careful consideration decided she'd catch the bus to Kilmaine. But every bus she saw appeared to be packed with tourists bound for either Salthill or Mervue. If she found the right bus she'd tell the driver she'd lost her purse, or better still she'd say her mother was meeting her at the bus stop, then when she got near home she'd jump off and hide. It was her only hope. She could not go down to the bus station as it was too close to the 'Magdalene', and wild horses would not drag her in that direction. She'd keep walking and walking until she found the right bus.

Sergeant Ruane made up his mind once and for all that he was going for a bite to eat. Since coming on duty it had been one hurried cup of tea after another. In the meantime he'd added another name to the city's growing list of missing persons. He had already issued the latest description, that of Julie Murray, to his men on the beat. Strange, he thought, that she hadn't yet been sighted in or around the bus or rail terminals. It was four hours since she'd been reported missing. But he was going for a feed now no matter what, he told himself.

He was making his way towards the outer door when the phones started hopping again. God! He muttered as he fled the station, crime! It gets worse everyday.

He was about to cross the road on his way to his favourite eatery when something interesting caught his eye. It looked like a young nurse had walked right by Garda Headquarters. He stopped in the middle of his stride to ogle her as she made her way through the throng. A sturdy piece, he thought by all accounts. But not at all like the starched uniform of the 'Come-to-bed' nurses he knew so well from the Regional Hospital. She wasn't a nurse, so she must be a chemist, or a bakery assistant. No. He wasn't convinced. Yet, she had such a shapely rear, he wished he could have caught a better glimpse of her, to see if he fancied her.

Watching her progressing down the street he thought she didn't seem to be going anywhere in particular, just ambling about. Perhaps she's on her lunch break. But the way she was looking up at the buildings, it was as if she was never in town before. He was in two minds whether to pursue her or not, in the hope that if she proved any way attractive, he might be able to set up a date. But the sudden ear-splitting sound of a brazen cyclist's bell made him jump out of the way. The ringing of the bell jolted his wayward mind into a broad sense of reality. He immediately set off at a fast pace down the street. As he was about to catch up with her he got a strange notion. Would it ever be your one from the 'Magdalene', the missing 'Mag.'

Now he too just ambled along behind her, convincing himself that it was indeed the missing 'Mag.' The frayed hem of her long white gown and shoulder length fair hair as good as confirmed his suspicion. His heart skipped a beat at the prospect that he himself might be the very one to apprehend her. If he managed to do so, it would be a considerable feather in his cap. He decided he'd use the same ploy he always used when chatting up his women. Either way, the sight of the Garda uniform worked every time as far as females were concerned. "Excuse me madam. Excuse me," he called out.

Julie Murray wheeled round when she heard the male voice directly behind her. She stared transfixed. A Guard! A bloody Guard! she thought. She was about to plead, *I didn't do anythin', I didn't do anythin'*, when the officer said,

"Haven't I seen you somewhere before? You wouldn't be Julie Murray from Kilmaine by any chance?"

When Julie saw the smirk on his face and heard him mention the word 'Kilmaine', the awful nightmare of that fateful day when she stole the coat came back to her in a flash. He would arrest her now and throw her into jail. The thought of that made her turn and run for dear life.

For a moment Sergeant Ruane stared in awe, then his brain slipped into top gear, and he pursued her down the street at an almighty rate. Christ, it's her! It's her! It's the missing bloody 'Mag' he mumbled excitedly to himself.

As he caught up with her he reached out, grabbed her by the collar and said, "Not so fast 'Maggie'! Not so fast!"

Julie Murray, terrified of being put into jail, reacted instinctively by sinking her teeth into the Officer's long bony fingers.

"Bitch! You poxy bitch!" barked Ruane, giving her the full force of his good hand into the side of the jaw. "If that's how you want to play it 'Maggie', then I'll give you plenty of it," he shouted, grabbing her forcefully by the collar, as she was about to stumble to the ground.

In an instant he had her arm twisted up behind her back, and gave her a good kick in the arse as she screamed in agony. He then began to lead her back to the station. Julie unable to plead for mercy, just screamed with the severity of the pain as several onlookers stood watching in bewilderment as the city's enforcement officer successfully apprehended his prey.

When Julie realised she was now inside a Garda Station, she did everything in her power to escape. The thought that she was going to be sent to prison as a thief was too much for her. Several times she sought to break free and each time she was met with a blow of a heavy truncheon.

When Sergeant Ruane felt that she had calmed down sufficiently, he relaxed his grip on her, only to find she again tried to break free: But was again subdued by a few more blows to the side of her body. Soon a small number of newly recruited officers had gathered round to look at her, as their leader boastfully outlined his recipe for success.

"As you can see, this is a perfect example of how we should all go about our duty as members of this force. Keep your eyes open! Keep your wits about you! And I can guarantee, you'll keep one step ahead of crime!"

When the Reverend Mother received a phone call from Sergeant Ruane, informing her that he had apprehended Julie Murray, she was overcome with joy. She would not now have to inform the Bishop that one of her charges was missing. But she felt somewhat disappointed when the Sergeant informed her, that as he himself was very busy right now, 'his officers' would be returning Julie Murray to the Magdalene Laundry in the 'Black Maria'. She recalled instead his last visit to her office when she distinctly felt the flush of excitement on seeing his handsome features. She wished for nothing more than to see his rugged face again, as she lay back momentarily in her comfortable oak throne. It was what, six months ago. She remembered vividly him standing right beside her, in his impeccable uniform with its gleaming silver-crested buttons. The mere closeness of him gave her a thrill beyond her wildest imagination, and when he gently placed his peaked cap with its sparkling Garda Síochána emblem on her desk and accepted her offer of a nice cup of tea, she felt as if they were sharing in some strange symbol of power. It must be something to do with the coming together of Church and State, she thought: the combination of their uniforms; an Officer and a nun. We were so close to each other, she sighed. They say opposites attract; Male and female; one soft and pliable, the other big and strong… hard as…

The phone rang. Interrupting her dream forever. She let it ring for a moment; praying it would stop. But its incessant ringing tone killed her passion instantly. She grabbed the offending object with distaste.

"Mother Superior's office."

"The delivery driver has gone without the Ennis shirts, what will I do?" a voice asked.

She paused, "One minute, I'll be down right away." Drivers, she sighed. Stupid, bloody drivers."

When Julie was led in handcuffs out of the Garda van and into the care of the Magdalene Laundry she could not believe her luck. She went meekly down the long corridor, escorted by the Mother Superior, Sister Stanislaus and Sister Philomena. She was brought into a small room, occasionally used as a storeroom and told to sit on a chair. She already knew the awful punishment that awaited her, so she made up her mind, that she would take her beating like a man, no matter how painful; rather than give satisfaction to the Mother Superior who was instructing Sister Stanislaus to cut off Julie hair.

If there was one thing the Mother Superior relished it was the power she had over her entire flock. She had learned a long time ago that supremacy was the only rule to guarantee an orderly house; and was proud to have inherited this trait from her father who ruled their home with an iron fist. Many is the time she had witnessed her mother go down on bended knees and beg for mercy when his favourite shirt wasn't ironed or his dinner wasn't on the table when he came home from a cattle fair, after a few well-earned pints. When he threatened to break loose, she herself would hide in the broom press beneath the stairs, and watch as her father removed his broad trouser belt and beat her mother. In no time at all everyone would be running hither and thither at his beck and call. And later when she'd emerge mouse-like from her hiding place, her father would ruffle her fair hair and give her a few sweets from his coat pocket as an acknowledgement of her having supported him.

Consequently, she too was very proud to have inherited that trait and had succeeded in turning the Magdalene Home into a virtual fortress, and it was her intention to keep it that way.

When at last Julie emerged from the torture chamber, it wasn't the fact that she'd been beaten within an inch of her life – despite the pleas of Sister Philomena – that pained her most, it was the sheer humiliation of having had her hair cropped. As if that wasn't bad enough, she then had to get down on her bended knees and join the nuns in prayer, by offering up five decades of the Rosary for her own intentions, so that God might grant her the wisdom to see the errors of her ways.

It was late that balmy August evening when Bridie, Josephine and the rest of the gang returned to their dormitories only to find Julie Murray, the supposed escapee, sitting crying on her bed.

"Julie! We thought you had escaped," they cried.

But Julie could not speak. She didn't know if she could ever face them again, because she knew she had let them all down by upsetting the cosy little arrangement they all had of living and working together. Worse still, she felt like some hideous monster when the girls all gathered around her, some of them tittering at her grotesque appearance. She knew she looked awful as she had stolen a glance at her savaged features in the mirror. She had a badly swollen jaw, a black eye, and a naked skull, not to mention a multitude of other marks on her body that no one would ever see. She felt as if part of her inner being, her self-respect, had been torn away. Worst of all she could not restrain her hands as they continually explored the flat contours of her bony scalp while her lower lip quivered uncontrollably.

For a long time, Bridie Rodgers and Josephine Finn, sat beside Julie, trying to ward of the many inquisitors surrounding her bed and when at last dusk fell and all but a few of the inmates had gone to their beds, Bridie held Julie's hand.

" Remember Julie, we're your friends! We'll always be here. It doesn't matter what the Guards or the nuns do to you, they can never take your friends away from you."

"*F*why is it… I have such misfortune?" she babbled. *F*why is it?"

"Shush…pet," said Bridie, as she gave Julie's hand a gentle squeeze. "Some day, please God we'll all be free: don't ever forget that. I met a man who told me, that in the end I'd win, and that I'd be very lucky. And do you know what, Julie?"

"What?"

"I believe him, because he was the nicest person I ever met. His name was Gerald. I'll never forget him and I know that some day his words will come true."

While all of this was going on, Josephine Finn was sitting, listening and thinking to herself, there's something about Bridie Rodgers. What it is I don't know. And when Julie Murray suddenly seized the back of Bridie's hand and kissed it, Josephine was filled with some powerful emotion that somehow galvanised her own flagging spirits. If ever she was going to test her own mettle it was now, she told herself while as the same time feeling so useless at being unable to offer any consolation to Julie the way that Bridie had. After what she had just witnessed, she knew she herself needed consoling more than anyone else and the only way she could get it was to give of her voice, and in return receive the admiration of those around her. Besides, these inmates needed each others support and friendship as assuredly as she needed theirs

"Listen," she said, standing up to face the few remaining friends who had not yet retired to bed, "There's too much gloom around here. Feck the nuns and feck the laundry! We should all stick together, and not let the nuns get the better of us. What we need is to keep the faith. Smile! Smile! As Judy Garland would have sang... *smile though your heart is breaking*.'"

"Oh Josephine! Please! A song," intoned Bridie.

"Oh please, please! *Somewhere over the rainbow*, begged Lilly MacAlastair, joining in the growing pleas to help lift their spirits. They'd give anything to hear Josephine give a haunting rendition of her favourite song.

Josephine could not look her friends in the eye: to do so would be to drown forever in their glinting sea of sadness. Instead she turned and began to walk slowly away as the quivering, faltering tones of her favourite song rent the air.

Somewhere over the rainbow way on high,
There's a land that I heard of once – in a lullaby,
Somewhere over the rainbow skies are blue,
And dreams that you dared to dream of,
Really do come true.
Somewhere I wish upon a star where the clouds are far behind me,

Where trouble melts like lemon drops away above the chimney tops,
   That's where you will find me,
   Somewhere over the rainbow,
   Blue birds fly,
   Birds fly over the rainbow,
   Why then, oh why can't I?
   Tears. Happy little blue birds fly beyond the rainbow,
   Why oh why can't I?

Hours later Josephine still lay awake in her cosy bed, happy in the knowledge that she had enthralled her audience. It was the first time, she thought, that she was truly happy since she'd been put into the 'Magdalene Laundry. She was beginning to despair of ever getting out, to nurture her dream of becoming a great singer. But now she could begin to believe in the lines of her own lay. Some day, somewhere, I'll be back with you Cathal, my one and only love.

Chapter Eight

It was almost ten o'clock in the morning and Sister Stanislaus was on her way to supervise the cleaning of the 'Sacred Heart' dormitory, when she thought she heard the swish of clothing and sandaled-feet behind her. On looking round she was met by a breathless Mother Superior.

"Sister, I'm so glad I caught up with you. I need to speak with you urgently."

Sister Stanislaus, sensed that the Reverend Mother was in one of her moods or that something was amiss as she replied,

"Yes?"

"Could you please come to my office in ten minutes?"

"As you wish, Reverend Mother. I'll show the girls what to do, then I'll be down straight away."

"Thank you Sister," said the Mother Superior as she hurried back down the corridor.

Trouble, thought Sister Stanislaus. I smell trouble; either she's in trouble or I'm in trouble. With a supercilious look she watched the quickening gait of the Mother Superior as she disappeared around a corner.

When they pulled up a chair to face each other in the office, the Mother Superior said,

"Sister, I may need to call on your support tomorrow. That 'Murray One', the escapee; did you know she has a sister, who's a nun in California? Well, seemingly she's home on holidays. What harm, but she phoned me late last night to say she's coming in to see Julie tomorrow."

"A sister? A nun?" feigned Sister Stanislaus in reply.

Sister Stanislaus knew that Julie Murray, had a sister called Kay, in America who was a nun; because Julie was forever giving out about her, how she'd never write to her, except maybe at Christmas. Sister Stanislaus got a great thrill out of this, believing she had far superior knowledge of the penitents in general than the Reverend Mother ever possessed.

But as she watched the Reverend Mother lean towards her, across her office desk, hands joined together as if in prayer, she began to feel guilty for having denied any knowledge of Julie Murray's Reverend Sister.

"Coming to see her! Tomorrow!" she exclaimed. "But what are you going to do?"

"What are we going to do?" echoed the Mother Superior, emphasising the word 'We'. "I've spent the whole morning praying for guidance. I thought perhaps you might be able to throw some light on the subject and come up with some idea to stall that lady. "

"You'll have to say she had some kind of an accident – working in the laundry," suggested Sister Stanislaus, relishing the prospect that the Mother Superior might have landed herself in hot water.

"Are you suggesting we break the eighth commandment?" she smiled vaguely as her chubby fingers danced on the desk. "Remember, 'Thou shall not bear false witness against thy neighbour'. Bearing that in mind, whatever excuse I come up with must stand on its own merits in the eyes of God and man.

"Yes," bowed Sister Stanislaus, struggling to acknowledge her Superior's undoubted wisdom. "But what are we going to do? We could postpone the visit," she blurted out, as a brain wave took hold of her and she awaited its favourable reaction.

After taking the idea on board for a few seconds the Mother Superior, said, "No! That would be to postpone the inevitable. In any case, I gather Sister Rosario hasn't got the time, and I haven't got the patience."

After careful consideration she added, "I think I'll have to leave it," and stood up promptly, which signalled that the meeting was over. "I'll probably think of something. But I need to know Sister that I can count on your support tomorrow, whatever I decide to do. You do realise that under no circumstances must Sister Rosario be allowed to see Julie in her present condition."

"I understand," replied Sister Stanislaus, meekly, because she knew to disagree with anything the Mother Superior said, could lead to her being transferred to some enclosed order; where prayer commenced at 4 a.m. and where promotional prospects were non-existent. One must abide by the rules, and even my own individual will must be sacrificed, for it is the will of God, that I obey my superior, she thought.

At least here in the Magdalene Home she was a 'Ward Sister,' looking after the welfare of one hundred and fifty penitent women in three large dormitories, St. Teresa's, Our Lady's and the Sacred Heart. As well as that she could read her breviary every night while quietly pacing the corridors, and still be privy to the goings on in the women's dormitories. Many is the snippet of information she gleaned, which helped prevent the penitents going on strike and lead directly to a strengthening of security within the Magdalene Laundry. So all in all, she thought, it was always best to agree with the boss. And although she didn't always agree with some of the ill treatment meted out to the workers, she felt she had to go along with it.

Because of Julie's physical condition, Bridie knew she would not be escorting her friend on their late evening walk of the enclosed grounds, so she decided instead to slip away quietly into the chapel where she could have a quiet think for herself. As usual three or four nuns from the Convent knelt close to the altar in silent prayer. As Bridie tip-toed into the second last pew, they all got up to leave: their heads still bowed reverently in prayer as they passed by: and Bridie wondered how on earth they could devote their entire lives to constant prayer with nothing to look forward to: no husbands, no children, no freedom. But then on the other hand she thought, the church was such a peaceful place of worship it must surely be good for the soul, which I suppose is the reason I'm here myself. But as she studied the beautiful glow of the red Sanctuary lamp she realised that wasn't the real reason she came here. Oh yes, the photograph of John Paschal? Who could possibly have sent that now I wonder? Sister Hortense? Mad Madge, or the other girls? I must write and thank them. But whom do I thank? If I write to Madge or one of the other girls, I could be getting one of them into trouble – unless it was Sister Hortense herself who sent it. And according to the girls here, no parcel or letter ever goes in or out of this place without the nuns knowing exactly what's in it. And if they don't like what's in it, it gets the bin. Funny, I always thought it strange how there was no letter or anything with that photograph, even a few lines. Lilly said, that's probably why it was signed 'Best wishes from all in St. Mary's', so that the Mother Superior wouldn't actually know who sent it. I'll bet you anything it was Sister Hortense, thought Bridie. Didn't the Mother Superior – or Super Ass herself as they call her – say to me, 'your son is doing fine.' What did she say again? 'I was speaking only yesterday to Sister Hortense and she informed me your son is thriving.'

Strange too, how Sister Hortense was talking about me and John Paschal on the phone, if one could believe that rap. God I must write now and thank her for sending the photograph. That's what I'll do. I'll write and thank Sister Hortense and I'll sign it, 'from, all the...' No, I'll sign it, 'Best wishes.' No, No...I'll say 'All the staff...' No, no, no. Why am I making such a mess of it? Just say, 'Many thanks for the beautiful photograph of the baby.' That way no one will ever know who sent it: except Sister Hortense I'll also say, 'please write soon again, with best wishes from all in the 'Magdalene'. There, that's it. I hope I can think of that now. That's it. That way if it *was* Sister Hortense, only she will know and write back again. But how will I address it? I'll say,

To Sister Hortense, and all the girls

Bon Secour Hospital

St. Mary's home,

Tuam, Co. Galway

There, that's it. And how about writing to Gerald in Conly House, while I'm at it? I can't very well write to Mr & Mrs O'Malley: and besides I wouldn't write to that bitch. God forgive me. And If I write to Gerald and she finds it, then he's in trouble. If the Mother Superior here finds out I'm writing to a man – a married man at that – then I'm really in trouble. Lord God Almighty! Is there no way out?

While she was thinking these thoughts, she almost jumped out of her skin with fright when one of the Sisters suddenly appeared and whispered in her ear.

"Sorry, but we must close the chapel now."

Bridie, nodded agreement, and smiled humorously to herself, God I'd better leave quickly, while there's still a way out.

* * * * *

Midday Angelus bells rang out across the Cathedral City as Julie Murray's sister, Sister Rosario arrived at the entrance to the Magdalene Home. A small petite creature, she was still swathed from head to toe in the cool climatic white which enabled her to cope with the searing heat of the scorching Californian sun. She was escorted by one of the Sisters into the lavishly furnished parlour to meet the Mother Superior of the Magdalene Home, Sister Antonia.

The Mother Superior extended a limp fleshy hand, smiled graciously and said,

"Sister Rosario Dear, it's so good to see you. You must be exhausted after all the travelling. Have a seat and I'll get one of the Sisters to fetch us a nice cup of tea."

"Thank you Sister," bowed Sister Rosario.

The Mother Superior then went across the corridor and gave whispered instructions to one of the young novice Sisters, before returning to join Sister Rosario, in the parlour.

"How was your flight? Did you have a nice trip?"

"It was wonderful. I flew into Dublin on Monday, and then I went by bus to Arklow, where I had arranged to meet with an old friend of mine who used to work in the Franciscan Order. We used to have such wonderful times together," smiled Sr. Rosario. "Then my friend drove me up to Howth where we stayed overnight with some more friends. And this morning I travelled down to Galway."

"How sweet. Did you come on the train?"

"Yes. I caught the 8.30 from Westland Row Station, and only for some kind gentleman I would have had to stand most of the way down, it was so overcrowded. And of course it was late arriving."

They were settling down nicely, discussing current affairs when there was a knock at the door.

"Sister! You're a topper," said the Mother Superior, as the young novice Sister left the silver tray on the large mahogany table.

As the Reverend Mother began pouring out the tea she asked,

"And what, Sister Rosario, may I ask is the nature of your own particular vocation in California?"

"Our Order, The Sisters of the Most Holy Rosary, takes care of deprived children; particularly those from the ghettos, where as you probably know there's a large population of ethnic minorities."

After listening to Sister Rosario for some time, the Mother Superior pushed her empty cup to one side awaiting an opportunity to intervene.

"How interesting that we should both lead such similar lives. And of course you're correct, it's not an easy task: what with all the responsibility and everything. And believe me Sister Rosario, some of the adults under my present stewardship can be far more demanding than any group of children. Especially as none of their relatives seems to give a hoot about their welfare; saving yourself and one or two others."

"Oh yes! It's so sad, isn't it. And how is my sister Julie getting on? I hope she doesn't cause you any trouble. I'm so looking forward to seeing her after such a long time."

"Hmm, I'm sure you are and I can well understand. But you know, she's been through so much. But Julie is a fighter, and given plenty of time and with God's help, she'll come through," said the Mother Superior, with a deeply furrowed brow, that already had Sister Rosario moving uncomfortably in her chair.

"You mean, she's not well?" suggested Sister Rosario, fearing she might have misinterpreted what the Reverend Mother had said.

"Oh. I'm so sorry. Please forgive my ineptness. How could you? How could you have known of her illness? Perhaps I should have warned you on the phone. It's just that I'm loath to convey bad news to anyone. I'm afraid your sister Julie has been through a horrid time this past while and is in no condition to see anyone."

On hearing this, Sister Rosario turned visibly pale, before leaning back in her chair as a horrid memory from the past came flooding back to her. How many years ago she'd written to the Magdalene Home and enquired about her sister's welfare, with a view to having her brought out to join her in South Africa, as a lay worker. But according to the Mother Superior, she was then something of a rebel who required constant care and attention and which in hindsight probably explained Julie's long rambling letters to her, which never ever seemed to make any sense. And now it seemed as if nothing had changed, nothing at all.

"But why didn't somebody tell me?" asked Sister Rosario, shocked by the news that her sister was still a problem after all these years.

"Unfortunately you didn't leave any forwarding address dear. And if I remember correctly you were working in South Africa at the time." said the Mother Superior with suppressed glee. You do know she suffers from Schizophrenia. Which means she's prone to conflicting ideas and emotions,"

Sister Rosario, felt at that moment as if she had been betrayed. Betrayed by the Reverend Mother. Betrayed by her very own sister, and by the whole world in general. She reached for the crucifix attached to the long crystal Rosary beads that hung round her waist and made the sign of the cross, whispering,

"Lord, protect us from all harm."

"Amen," replied the Mother Superior, duplicating Sister Rosario's religious rite.

Recovering her composure Sister Rosario added," I'm sorry Rev. Mother: how was I to know Julie was causing you so much pain and suffering? Please accept my humblest apologies and convey my deepest gratitude to your 'Sisters of Mercy' order, for their due care and devotion in looking after her. And to think… I was contemplating taking her out of here, and bringing her to the States with me. But I figure that's the end of that now. Is there any possibility, that I could see her… for a few moments?" suggested Sister Rosario, as an after thought.

The Reverend Mother, thinking she was already over the worst sensed a direct challenge to her authority on hearing this request. In order not to lose any more ground, she told, herself she must remain calm and collected.

"Oh dear. How kind of you to suggest helping her in that way. I'm sure she would have loved the idea of joining you in the States, to start a new life. Regrettably Sister, she is no longer in a fit state to see anyone. Besides, it would be too upsetting – and believe me I know – for a family relative; a loving caring blood sister, such as yourself to see her now. As you undoubtedly remember; Julie was once as pretty as a flower, and perhaps it is God's wish that you should remember her so. Were I to allow you in to see her now, I know full well that you would go away with a heavy heart and like I've already told you, I'm loath to convey bad news."

Then, lowering her voice to a whisper she continued, "The Doctor suggested she be put into a mental institution, for her own good. But after careful consideration I sought instead the advice of an expert Counsellor in Dublin, and he informed me that with time and careful medical attention she could make a good and complete recovery; particularly in her own natural surroundings. And were I to let you in to see her now, just think what it might do to her already disturbed mind."

Julie Murray's sister, Sister Rosario began to rise ever so slowly from her chair. She had heard enough. Close to tears, she extended her small delicate hand to the Reverend Mother, Sister Antonia. "What can I say? Words fail me: except that I'll remember you all in my prayers. I'll write on my immediate return to the States and you can keep me posted on her condition."

Before leaving the Home via the small exit door Sr. Rosario turned to the Mother Superior once more, and taking the Reverend Mother's hand, she inclined her head graciously and said,

"Thank you so much for all you've done and may God bless you."

Then she quietly melted into the city, vowing never to return to the Home. Her mother it seemed was right all along, Julie had brought nothing but shame on the entire family, and Sr. Rosario's long held belief that Julie had been unfairly treated by her mother, was now blown to smithereens by this latest revelation. There was nothing she could do for her now, but remember her in her prayers. In fact, she thought it only right, that she should remember all of the 'Maggies' in her prayers. For it seemed to her, they were all in urgent need of divine intervention.

Chapter Nine

It's Sunday, and there's a distinct air of fulfilment wafting its way through the marbled halls of the Magdalene Laundry. Faces seem brighter as they gather to converse in huddled groups at the top of the great wooden staircase, or in one of the huge dormitories of Our Lady's, St. Teresa's or the Sacred Heart. They reminisce and tell jokes and there's the added lilt of laughter.

Julie Murray is happy because she is the proud possessor of a span new half-crown, given to her during the week by Sister Stanislaus on behalf of the Mother Superior who let it be known that she was a tremendous worker and deserving of special recognition.

When Julie heard her name being called out in the long corridor she was at once filled with dread that she must have done something wrong. But when Sister Stanislaus, gently pressed the large silver coin into her hand and whispered, the Reverend Mother would like you to have this; for your hard work and dedication, she stared at Sister Stanislaus for a moment before blurting out,

"Does...ever'one...Do we all get one?"

"Shu! Don't be silly. It's for you dear: you alone, because you deserve it. And remember you're not to tell anyone. Promise me you won't say a word."

"I promise."

But of course Julie told everyone, eventually, and soon they all looked at each other as if to say 'but what about us?'

In spite of this however they were all happy: because it was widely rumoured that a film was now going to be shown at Christmas, which was only just around the corner.

Bridie too was pleased; more so because everyone else seemed happy and despite one's best efforts at always grumbling, these things have a habit of rubbing off on one another.

Earlier in the evening Bridie had returned from walking a lonely furrow in the picturesque grounds. Of late, she had taken to wandering off on her own more and more in an effort to find peace and solitude. But she was not alone; for walking in front of her were other penitents, quickening their step, so that they too could retain some semblance of privacy. Likewise, other girls drifted in and out of Bridie's wake, for there was no other way. From morning till night they worked, ate and slept together, seven days a week, three hundred and sixty five days a year. At night they were caged in congested dormitories, which made them sick of the very sight of each other. If only they could be alone with their thoughts they might see a way out of their terrible dilemma. Likewise, Bridie was constantly at war with herself for her indecisiveness in confronting the nuns in relation to her son, John Paschal. Several times she had written to Sister Hortense in Tuam to enquire about him, but no response had been forthcoming. She chided herself for going about things the wrong way. Perhaps she hadn't put the right address on her letters; But surely to God they'd get there anyway – that's if the letters ever left the Magdalene, in the first place. Who knows? But what she did know was that she was thoroughly fed up, and tired of being a nursemaid to Julie, Josephine and a host of other girls who found themselves in a similar situation. For some strange reason Josephine Finn, in particular, thought Bridie could wave some magic wand in relation to her and Cathal Swanick. But no, she couldn't. She couldn't cure everyone's ills.

So for that reason alone and to help retain her own sense of sanity, she made up her mind once and for all that she was going to confront the Mother Superior tomorrow morning and demand her freedom. The least the Reverend Mother could do, she figured, was to allow her out on a short visit to see her son John Paschal. She felt she had had enough of their authoritarian ways; besides she was tired writing to the nuns in St. Mary's and getting no reply. It was time she tried some other way, only this time she decided, she'd be a lot cuter and less formal than the last time. First thing tomorrow morning she'd stay behind in church until all the penitents were gone, and then she'd confront the Mother Superior and hopefully shame her in front of the other sisters into letting her out to see John Paschal. She had thought long and hard about telling her close friends but had decided that it was too personal a matter, and that no good could come from enlisting their support.

Now as a group of her friends sat nattering around her bed in Our Lady's dormitory, prior to going to bed, she pushed the thoughts of freedom from her head as one of the girls claimed excitedly, that she could hear the faint sound of music. Instinctively, they all fell silent, before rushing headlong towards one of the tall windows. And in a matter of seconds four of them were crammed tightly up on the narrow window-ledge trying to peer out through the tiny spy-holes they had previously scratched on the painted glass of the stoutly-barred windows; which, afforded a panoramic view of the city's roof-tops. They all listened attentively to try and discern the source of the music. Some were of the opinion that it was just fairground music, provided by Duffy's or Fossett's Circus in Eyre Square. Others were adamant that it came not from the city fairground, but from the Hangar or Seapoint ballroom way out in Salthill, because the music was so faint.

"It must be the Hangar ballroom," said Josephine Finn, "because it sounds like a waltz to me...Oh! I know what it is; it must be a dance somewhere. They'd never play that kind of music in a fairground or circus, it would be too slow."

"I think you're right," said Bridie, struggling to maintain a toehold on the cramped window-ledge, as she clung desperately to Josephine's shoulders in order to catch a glimpse of the twinkling city lights. "Oh I know what it is now," she added excitedly, "It's *Danny Boy*, I used to play it on the mouth organ when I lived out in Clifden"

"I didn't know you could play," interrupted Lilly MacAlastair somewhat delighted. "Will you play it now? I'll run down and get the mouth-organ, and we'll all have a bit of craíc," she added excitedly as she jumped down from the window-ledge and ran down to where she knew she had a mouth-organ gathering dust, at the back of her bedside locker.

Meanwhile, Josephine Finn, disentangled Bridie from around her shoulders and eased herself gently down from the window ledge because she didn't really want to be reminded of *Danny Boy*. The very name was enough to remind her of her own *Danny Boy*, Cathal. She was remembering how the one night she had been allowed to dance the night away at the village carnival, she had met Cathal Swanick. Yet this harmless act was enough to ignite the rumours which spread like wildfire through the whole parish, how she was doing a line with young Swanick, a direct descendant of the wealthy Protestant landowners who had driven Josephine's ancestors off of their land three generations ago for non-payment of rent. Josephine was not even aware who the good-looking gentleman was when she first laid eyes on him, but had very politely accepted his offer to buy her a mineral after a flurry of dancing. She remembered all too clearly her Grandfather's vivid description of the painful evictions when she was growing up. But, due to it being such a sore subject – as far as her mother was concerned – it was deemed better to sweep the whole thing under the carpet and let bygones be bygones. Besides, all that was years ago. How was she supposed to know that the gorgeous fella she met at the dance was related to the tyrant Landlords. As far as Josephine was concerned, he was a perfect gentleman. But when she continued to meet Cathal by devious means, her cantankerous father and in particular her Grandfather threatened to have her sent to Australia, where she would be forced to live with her equally cantankerous aunt. Are you mad, he bellowed over and over again, They took possession of our cattle and land and drove our people to the very edge of extinction; and for all you know Josephine they are now planning to take possession of you, our only daughter. I swear to God Josephine, if you as much as look in that man's direction one more time, I'll have you put away for life.

Josephine kept her promise and for all of four weeks restricted her movements. But when she met the lovely Cathal, purely by accident, while out shopping in Tuam they were drawn to each other like magnets. They both slipped quietly into an adjoining alley, on the pretext that they were parking their bikes: and in an intimate hurried conversation they considered how best to overcome their particular dilemma and met up again. But before they could develop any worthwhile plan they were interrupted by the unexpected appearance of their local village postman who soon relayed the message to all and sundry that Josephine Finn and Cathal Swanick, was still an item. So that by the time her father got to hear the news, the story had grown out of all proportion and she stood accused of far more that she was ever guilty of. As a result she was immediately seized by her parents, with the blessing and aid of the Parish Priest who had her sent to the women's home in Tuam, from where she was quickly transferred to the more secure Magdalene Home Laundry in Galway City.

Now, Josephine was beginning to have grave doubts about 'her Cathal'. How come he hadn't been to see her or come to her rescue? Or was he too, under some sort of family pressure to have nothing to do with a Catholic: any Catholic?

"Josephine a grá, will you sing us a song an' stop your oul' day-dreamin' while we're waiting on Bridie; sure that wan's as slow as Christmas," said Julie Murray in an effort to get a bit of entertainment going.

Josephine shook her head and smiled dryly, saying, "I'm not in the mood, some other time."

Instead she knelt on the floor with the other girls gathered around the bed, as Bridie tried playing the mouth organ. For a long time she struggled for the correct air to *Danny Boy*, but somehow she seemed unable to concentrate, as a strange sensation began to gnaw at her conscience, slowly seeping it's way through her entire body. It took hold of her the minute she threw her arms tightly around Josephine's shoulders to peep out of the window. It was an overwhelming desire to relive her worst moment when Peter took advantage of her in the hay. And as her lips slid rhythmically over the metallic instrument, she wished with all her heart, that she could instead respond to his hot passionate kisses by pursing her lips along his stubbled jaw. For a mere second she closed her eyes and thought 'God, I'd give anything right now to feel that awful hardness in his body again'.

"Bridie! Bridie!" interrupted Julie, "*f*what are you at? You're pure useless. Sure I thought you said you could play that thing"

"And I can. I can…. if only you'd give me time. Arrah, here, play it yourself. I'd rather talk," replied Bridie angrily, as she threw the mouth organ on the bed.

"Ah go on, go on. Play it. Play something. It doesn't have to be '*Danny Boy*'," the girls pleaded.

"No, I won't," answered Bridie, emphatically.

For a few moments there was a strained silence. Julie knew she had hurt Bridie's feelings and put a stop to whatever fun they might have had. So she decided she'd better say something to relieve the tension, quickly.

"I wonder what it's like to go dancing in the 'Hangar Ballroom', would that be the same as a Carnal?"

"You mean a Carnival…?" corrected Bridie quickly, anxious to show she knew a thing or two and to get a dig in at Julie.

"That's *f*what I said," cut in Julie.

"No you didn't, you said 'Carnal'. It's not 'Carnal' it's car-ni-val"

"Sure *f*what does it matter? A Car-a-nal is a Car-a-nal," replied Julie blushing and trying desperately to say the correct pronunciation.

"No. No, I don't think it's the same," said Lilly MacAlastair, intervening to ward off a row amongst her friends because she knew Bridie and Julie were very loyal to each other, and she didn't want to think their friendship could be threatened over a stupid little word like Carnival, that was supposed to mean fun or happiness or something.

"No, I'll tell you" continued Lilly, " the Hangar and Seapoint, are fierce big dance halls like, and Carnivals or Caranals" she laughed "are big tents that are put up out in the country for country people. But I'm not too sure because I was never at a Carnival."

"Well, I was," said Julie, delighted to inform all and sundry, now that the tension had eased. "Sure me older sister used to go ever' year that it came to our village. She used to work in the ladies cloakroom and she brought me with her wance, when I was fourteen. Sure 'twas fierce excitin' and ever'thin'. Talk about people," she added dreamily, recalling the glorious atmosphere.

Josephine Finn meanwhile, was sitting sideways on the floor, her head resting on the backs of her hands the other side of the bed. She was watching Julie's every nuance, and listening to her every word. But when she heard Julie describe the music, the twirling, rhythmic dancers, in her own tin-pot way, and how some of the older girls were bold enough to put their arms lovingly around the men's shoulders during a slow dance, she quietly stood up and walked away, to go and hide in the lavatory, because listening to each descriptive word of Julie's was like a hammer blow to her chest; chiselling away at her heart. She didn't want to be reminded of what it was like. She knew only too well what it was like to have somebody sweep you romantically off your feet, as they waltzed you round and round until you were delirious from the thrill of it all.

What, she was wondering, as she made her way down the dormitory, her head hanging in distress and her arms folded tightly across her bosom; what if Cathal Swanick was at home at that very moment getting ready to go to some dance: and him there standing preening himself in front of some gilt-edged mirror in the Big-House? What then? And what if, in her absence, he had arranged to meet some other girl at the dance? What if at the end of the dance he offered to buy her a drink and then they made their way to a discrete corner to hold hands, while siphoning bottles of Clada orange? What then?

On reaching the seclusion of the lavatory Josephine Finn, rushed headlong into the cubicle and slammed the door shut, threw herself down on the hard wooden seat and buried her head in her hands, crying aloud, "No! No! No! He wouldn't."

But despite her best efforts at suppressing her emotions, her ruby red lips quivered uncontrollably and the overflowing tears rained down her pale cheeks as she begged Cathal to come and take her away: to rescue her from that place of horror, occupied by gangs of lecherous looking women and dark ghostly creatures of the night, masquerading as the Sisters of Charity.

Bridie in an effort to drive the wanton thoughts from her own head asked Lilly, because she was from the city and was a good bit older than the rest of the girls, what one would have to do or say to meet a nice fella at a dance. But the minute she opened her mouth to ask the question she knew that wasn't what she had meant to say at all. She meant to say something that would get the thoughts of men out of her head, once and for all and in particular the thoughts of Peter. But somehow she couldn't drag herself away from the subject.

Lilly's eyes lit up at the prospect of coaching her friends, as they lay all around her, while they in turn eagerly awaited her response.

"Well it all depends, Bridie. Sometimes it's very easy and sometimes it's very hard to meet the right one. Half the time the men are drunk and slobbering all over you. That's the worst time, because they start mauling you, just because you refused to dance with them. And the smell-a-drink: sometimes, it'd knock you kicking. But then again you might see a real nice looking fella, and he'll ask everyone to dance but you – and you after refusing half the country while waiting for him, only to be told by some smart Alec 'that you'd make a lovely statue if only you'd brought along an oul' Rosary beads.'"

Her admirers tittered knowingly, and settled themselves like Cheshire cats around a warm fire, as she went on.

"….No, the best thing I found, was to stand at the very front of the crowd; that way you can keep an eye on the fellow you're after, and he can see you. But whatever you do, don't move out of that position – even if it means crossing your legs – because then he won't know where to find you."

All of the inmates laughed, as they warmed more to Lilly's favourite subject.

"An', if you did get wan," asked Julie brazenly, would you go outside with him the first night, or tell him you'd see him again?"

"Oh, you'd have to go outside the front door at least, because if you didn't then you can be sure some cheap hussy would come along and whip him right from under your nose. The golden rule is that if some poor eejit asks to buy you a mineral, then that means he'd like to take you home – only because he thinks you're a right good thing. But what ever you do, don't let him out of your sight; not even to go to the toilet. If you do, and your fella is left standing around on his own and another girl happens to sidle up to the bar: next thing your buckeen is weighing her up and she's weighing him up and before you can say 'Jack Robinson', the two of them will have slithered down to the other end of the hall and the next bloody thing she's sitting like a peacock on the bar of his bike, the two of them going hell for leather out of town and ready to climb into the nearest hay shed…."

Bridie's heartbeat quickened considerably at the thought of climbing into a hay shed and having some fella kiss her passionately before nibbling her ear and making her go all wobbly at the knees. She could feel herself blushing now at the mere thought and prayed that the other girls didn't notice her.

Julie too, was starting to remember her rare romantic interludes of a Sunday afternoon at the village cross down in Kilmaine, where all the young girls would gather and wait for the lads: who usually came from miles around, tearing down the dusty roads on their bikes at wicked speed; showin' off and tryin' desperate to impress ever'one.

"Down ƒwhere I lived, we used to meet at the 'bridgeen' ever' Sunday …", intimated Julie.

"That's right," piped up one of the younger girls. "We used to do that too, and some of the lads would chase us across the fields…"

"Wait a minute a grá 'till I tell ye me story, about this fella," continued Julie, mad to get her spake in now; to reveal the saucy details. "There was this fella I knew an' he'd give the girls sweets an' everthin' if they'd lift up their skirts and let him have a look. He was a biteen wild like. But sure all the girls were mad after 'im. God forgive me, but I was always prayin' he'd ash me like 'cause he was gorgeous lookin'. But then one day ƒwhen he got me on me own, an' the others were messin' over the road, he ashed me like, but ƒwhen I said no, he said something awful…"

"He asked you what?" interrupted Lilly, in an effort to absorb the juiciest details.

"What do you think?" quipped Bridie, laughing at Lilly's concocted innocence, "To lift up her skirt of course!"

"Sure! Wasn't it awful," acknowledged Julie, blushing at the thought that she was now divulging her innermost secrets. 'But what the hell', she thought as she continued. "Anyway, ƒwhen he ashed me, I said no, an' do you know ƒwhat he said? He said he'd pull the knickers off me. Sure I got afraid an' started to run for dear life: over the road and him after me; like a…like a… a wild jackass. I ran across a big field, an' him still after me. But then I think he must have seen somethin' 'cause all of a sudden he stopped like. God! If only I'd had the good fortune to fall in the long grass," She tittered heartily before adding, "I should have let him catch me I suppose, 'cause some of the girls reckoned he was a great kisser. Lord, I'd have given an'thin' to see ƒwhat he was like. An'thin'."

"Troth he might have given you more than you bargained for. Men! Oh they're all the same! laughed Lilly, heartily.

Then recovering her composure she continued, "But do you know what they say? And I think 'tis true: that the women are worse than the men! I had this friend, once, out in the country. She was about eighteen, and she was telling me that her friend, Mary, was stone-mad after this fella who used to go fishing beside this bridgeen, every Sunday. Seemingly, all the girls were mad after HIM, and they used to write dirty messages on bits of cigarette boxes and throw them down at him, hitting him on the head and everything; and do you know, he used to read everyone of them. But he'd never ever ask anyone of them for a date, or arrange to meet them at a dance or anything. Then this girl, Mary, well she hung around one Sunday until everyone else was gone. She was trying desperate to get your man to meet her at the dance. And do you know what he said to her and he looking straight up under her skirt? He said, 'I'll meet you at the dance if you take off your knickers and throw them down to me now.' And on the virt' of my oath, didn't she up with the skirt and off with the knickers and threw them down to him: and he never again as much as bid her the time of day after that. So now; where would you be going without a bell on your bike?"

"God! I don't believe it. She actually threw down her knickers at some fella?" queried Peggy Neary, in disbelief and disgust. "That lady should be in a mental hospital; she couldn't be right in the head."

"Arrah, what are you talking about? She's probably sounder in the head than you or me. She's still out there, and we're the ones that are locked up," replied an angry Lilly.

"I hope they landed on his nose, at least he could use them as a handkerchief," added Julie mischievously; because she knew it would horrify Peggy.

"Oh Julie, that's disgusting. How could you say such a thing?" cringed Peggy, springing to her feet and blessing herself, before walking away from her foul-mouthed colleagues.

"Are any of ye hungry?" asked Lilly, jumping from the bed and rummaging under the bed for her slippers.

"You know… I'd love a cut of bread. Do you think is it too late to sneak down now?", asked Bridie, who had no sooner asked than the sound of the bedtime bell came echoing along the corridors.

That meant they had just fifteen minutes to get ready before the lights went out and the dormitory doors were locked for the night. Not enough time for them to sneak down to the kitchen, or across to the rear of the nun's convent, in search of scraps of food.

"Ah well, we'll have to do without it," sighed Lilly as she slipped her bare feet into a pair of tatty slippers, and the rest of the gang dispersed to their own sleeping quarters, saying, "Goodnight girls."

"Goodnight."

"Oh dear, oh dear," yawned Lilly. "I'm as tired as a dog." Then gathering the bright red cardigan about her, to ward of the late night chill, she added, "The end of another long week. And as usual it's a penny for our thoughts Bridie; another shilling for the Bishop, and a lifetime's penance for our sins."

Bridie said nothing, because she was remembering now. Remembering how she had a date with destiny in the morning. Hoping desperately to talk her way to freedom. It was all or nothing now; all or nothing, she thought.

* * * * *

She was in the midst of a long queue as the priest gave out the Blessed Sacrament; her head bowed and her hands reverently joined together as if in prayer. But prayer was the last thing on her mind. Bridie, was trying to say the, Morning Offering, reverently. *Oh My God, I offer up to you all my thoughts, words, actions, sufferings of this day For thy greater honour and glory, through Jesus Christ Our Lord, Amen.*

Thoughts? Words? Actions? Sufferings? They were nothing but a jumbled up heap of words, circling around in her head, she thought. How can I possibly offer up to you all of my suffering? I would, she thought, and gladly if only I could get out of this place. All my thoughts, how can I control my thoughts? Words: Are they the same thing? Dirty words? Impure thoughts? It's the work of the devil himself; egging us to commit sin: at least that's what the priest keeps saying to me in the confessional.

Bridie raised her eyes to scan the length of the queue. Only three more to go before it was her turn to receive Holy Communion, then she'd go back and kneel down and accept the priest's blessing. And then they'd all file out past her on their way out, leaving her to succeed or fail in her mission to leave the Magdalene laundry, forever.

She looked up and saw the priest looking fervently into her eyes as he held up the Sacred Host, saying piously,

"Corpus Christi."

"Amen."

She opened her big gob to receive the precious wafer and her parched mouth tried desperately to swallow the flesh of Our Lord. But it stuck like glue to the roof of her mouth, and no amount of licking, or coaxing could shift it, until it slowly dissolved into a thousand fragments and disappeared down her parched gullet.

The early morning Mass now over the inmates were filing past, wondering why Bridie Rodgers, was still showing off; gone all religious like, with her head buried in her hands. 'She's not right, *that one,* thought Julie Murray. But I'll soon show her.

She gave Bridie a strong playful puck as she passed by and whispered,

"Get up out-a-that, you oul' amadán and don't be makin' a show of your sell."

But Bridie, remained still, and when she thought the last of the girls had gone out, she turned her head and stole a glance at the church door and saw Julie staring back at her.

For what seemed an eternity, the seven nuns prayed on in silence at the front of the altar. Even the priest had come out from the Sacristy, having already removed his vestments and extinguished the altar candles. Despite all the waiting, Bridie didn't think she was ready to put her well thought-out plan, into action: even when she saw the nuns rising from their pews before they each went down on their knees and bowed before the glowing tabernacle. Now they were gliding down the centre aisle as if they were mere shadows; and led as always by Sister Philomena, who stopped to inquire if Bridie was all right.

She nodded, she was, and then rose hurriedly to follow the nuns out.

The nuns were moving at such speed down the gravelled path, Bridie had to almost trot after them before calling out.

"Mother Superior…I mean Reverend Sister."

The fleeing angelic-looking sisters froze in their tracks before craning their veiled heads to look back at Bridie. But before Bridie could make up her mind what to say, the Reverend Mother signalled with a wave of her hand to the rest of the nuns to go about their business. Then, turning to look at Bridie, with a sour, tainted expression, she snapped,

"What is it?"

"Please Reverend Mother, I want to leave the Laundry…for good. I have to be with my son, John Paschal."

The Reverend Mother's shoulders trembled slightly as a result of the early-morning chill, and she buried her hands deeper into the black folds of her sleeves, before replying,

"Why aren't you down in the Laundry? You should be working by now instead of gallivanting around the place. Does Sister Philomena know about this?"

"No Sister, I thought …."

"This is neither the time nor the place. Now please, go back to your work. I'll deal with you later."

Without any further ado the ageing Mother Superior turned and was gone. For a moment Bridie stood in bewilderment, her anger mounting that she had once again failed in her quest to flee the laundry. Not only that, but she felt so belittled by the Sister's response, *'I'll deal with you later'*.

Was that a threat or did she mean she'd discuss the whole subject at a more convenient time? Would that be today or tomorrow, she wondered as she turned and trudged her way back to the laundry to begin another long day. I swear that lady must be in league with the devil; egging her on to torture the living daylights out of me, she sighed, as she entered the rear door of the giant washroom to the heavy sound of washing machines and trundling laundry baskets.

It's twelve noon and Sister Stanislaus informs Bridie Rodgers that the Mother Superior wishes to see her, right away. Bridie makes her way apprehensively down the long corridor. She knocks tentatively on the glass-panelled door. Mother Superior raises her bushy eyebrows from behind her desk and beckons her to come in. Bridie pushes open the newly painted green door and in response to another gesture sits down awkwardly, waiting for Sister to finish writing her letters.

The Mother Superior then adds her seal of approval to her great work, by promptly licking the large envelope with an even larger, grotesque tongue, before stamping it authoritatively with her ample fist. Then, turning to Bridie she said,

"Now Miss, to get back to this morning, what exactly did you hope to achieve by interfering with my devotions to Our Lord?"

After a lengthy, strained silence during which they both sized each other up, Sister repeated, "What did you hope to achieve?"

"I wanted to ask you if I could leave the Laundry," said Bridie.

The Mother Superior, acting as if she hadn't heard the reply, blasted loudly, "Don't you ever interfere with my devotions again, be it morning, noon or night. This is a religious…."

"I'm sorry Sister," muttered Bridie, interrupting the Reverend Mother.

"I haven't finished," said the Mother Superior with a vicious glare as she sat bolt upright, wringing her large blue hands in an effort to increase the blood circulation.

"My good lady, you only ever speak when spoken to. As I was saying," continued the Mother Superior after a momentary pause, "this is a religious institution, where we the Sisters of Mercy continuously pray for the sinners of this world. We have here a convent and a church, which is supposed to be a place of refuge for girls – such as yourself- who have fallen by the wayside. We cannot pray for God's guidance if we do not abide by the rules of his Church, two of which, incidentally, you broke this morning, thereby committing a mortal sin. You caused me to break my perpetual vow of silence, whilst attending church. Secondly, you committed a sin of disobedience, by being absent without leave from your place of work whilst under the care and supervision of Sister Philomena."

On seeing Bridie's obvious shock and look of bewilderment she asked smugly, "Shall I go on?"

"No, Sister," answered Bridie, embarrassingly, while looking deep into the Mother Superior's eyes trying desperately to detect a glimmer of hope, but there was none.

"I'm sorry Sister, I didn't realise...", said Bridie, already feeling sorry for apologising because she didn't want to, but somehow the words had just slipped out. If anyone deserved an apology she thought, it was herself.

"That's part of the problem, Bridie. You young girls never seem to realise anything...until it's too late...Now what was is it you wanted to speak to me about?"

Bridie had been thinking what she'd love to do, if only she had a scissors handy. She'd cut Sister Antonia's snow-white veil and black habit from around her head and upper body and expose her naked breasts, so all the penitents in the laundry could have a good laugh at the Reverend Mother, going around half-naked.

But now she was being jolted into a response by the Reverend Mother's 'anyway what was is it you wanted to speak to me about'?

Bridie swallowed hard, trying to summon up the courage again, after what had happened to her earlier in the day, she said,

"I want to leave the Laundry... for good so that I can get a job and look after my son," she slowly added, thinking the latter would impress the Reverend Mother.

"Oh dear," the Mother Superior began wearily, as if she'd already heard that request a thousand times. "You already have a job, one that you can be absolutely proud of. Besides, you know it's both wrong and sinful to desire that which we cannot have. You, of all people should know that. We reiterate it time and time again in our schools; of which you are supposedly a past pupil. Have we not made it abundantly clear to you time and time again, that all contact between mother and child is strictly forbidden once the separation has taken place?"

Bridie, unable to speak, stared open-mouthed at the Mother Superior. She began to realise for the first time the enormity of her predicament and that there was no way out.

The Reverend Mother seeing the look of despondency written all over Bridie's pale complexion leant forward to press home the point once and for all. "Sooner or later, you Bridie Rodgers will have to accept the fact that you will, never ever see your child again. It is God's will that he be taken from you and placed in a safe environment. It is also God's will that you, spend the rest of your life here in the service of God; for you have the potential to become a consecrated penitent, happy to spend the rest of your life helping others, thereby atoning for the terrible sins of your past."

On hearing the Reverend Mother say, 'sooner or later you will have to accept that you will *never ever* see your son again,' Bridie thought her heart would surely stop and break in two.

The words pierced her body like poisoned arrows. But when the Reverend Mother added '...thereby atoning for the terrible sins of your past', she could take no more. A force more powerful that anything she had experienced since leaving St. Mary's, was closing in around her chest and squeezing the life-blood from her body. She sprang from the chair like a demented woman, screaming.

"No! No! No! It's all a pack of lies." She turned and ran for the door; wrenched it open, before glaring viciously back at the Mother Superior, who was already standing up. "I'm going to see my son...now...one way or another and NOBODY will ever stop me."

Slamming the door behind her she ran down the corridor, ready to race out into the yard, around to the front of the building and out over the wall. But as she ran, she slowed down and thought better of it. It wouldn't do to end up like Julie Murray. She must not give the Mother Superior the pleasure of beating her senseless should she fail to get away, she thought and as for Sergeant Ruane, there was no way she'd accept the kind of punishment he had meted out to her friend Julie.

Mother Superior's initial reaction on seeing Bridie bolt for the door was one of elation. She knew she had killed all desire in Bridie, to be reunited with her infant, stone dead. She was extremely proud of her ability to subdue even the most hard-hearted penitent. There was only one way to do it, she thought, and that was the right way; while they were still young and new to the Home. But when Bridie turned on her from the relative safety of the doorway and cast that piercing look of hers, she thought she felt a tremor of fear enter her body, like no other. Not only that, but she felt as if that look had pierced God's armour which was her religious habit, her sacred veil; her protection. Her first instinct on hearing Bridie, warn that she would see her son again come what may, was to demand that she apologise for her behaviour forthwith, but somehow she lacked the power. Instead she slumped back into her great oak throne, and came to the conclusion, *that Bridie Rodgers one,* was an out and out brat: A brazen bitch. But she'd get her come-uppance one of these days. On further reflection the Reverend Mother was of the opinion that perhaps Bridie was mad. In that case corrective action would have to be taken. I'd better go down to the laundry now and see what's happening, she though: that lady's dangerous, I know she is.

Bridie, who was unable to face her friends in her present state of mind, headed straight for the lavatory; where she could hide for a few minutes, to gather her thoughts. Instead, she found herself burying her head in her hands, trying desperately to expel the veiled image of the Reverend Mother from her head. It was saying, "Sooner or later you will have to accept that you will never see your son again. Sooner or later you will have to accept...." Bridie banged her clenched fists off the cubicle door as she said aloud, that woman is pure evil. I swear to you God, she's pure evil. She's the devil incarnate. After a few moments she tried to pull herself together by pleading with God: Get me out of here now and I swear I'll never ask another thing. All I'll ever ask in life is to be reunited with my son. He's all I have in this world. Please, please don't take him away from me now, because deep down in my heart of hearts I know I've done no wrong. Answer my prayers please and I promise to be a better Christian. I'll do the nine first Fridays. I'll never ever call the nuns names again behind their backs...

Bridie's religious pleadings however were brought to an abrupt halt by a gentle rap on the lavatory door. She did not answer but stayed quiet as a mouse, thinking it must be Sister Stanislaus, who probably saw her going into the lavatory. Worse still, it might be the Reverend Mother herself. A second knock came, this time more aggressive.

"Is that you Bridie?"

Bridie stood up. The voice was unmistakable. She was relieved it wasn't Sister Stanislaus demanding to know why she was gallivanting, but at the same time annoyed that Julie and the rest of the gang could never ever let her have a bit or privacy. There was just, no mercy.

She opened the door and made believe she was adjusting her dress as Julie stood there staring at her, her mouth open,.

"Are you sick?"

Bridie stepped out past Julie and walked away mumbling sourly, "No ! I'm not sick, but everybody else is."

She went straight into the ironing room and sat down on the nearest linen basket, followed later by Julie who stood beside her asking,

"*Fwhat* wrong with you? Did your wan give out to you or *f*what?"

"There's nothing wrong with me, now will you shut up and leave me alone and get out of my sight?" said Bridie, raising her voice so that the other girls in the room stopped working to look on inquisitively.

"Don't you tell me to shut up I know there's somethin' wrong. No need to take it out on me. Sure I can see there's somethin' wrong because you look like a ghost."

"Arrah, I'm sick of ye telling me how I look," answered Bridie aggressively as she jumped off the basket and began pacing the floor, her arms folded tightly. "I'm pale! I'm sick! I'm thin! And now I'm like a ghost," complained Bridie, throwing her hands in the air. "Well you'd be like a ghost too if 'her royal highness' told you that you could never ever see your son again."

"Is it the Reverend Mother?" asked Julie, lowering the tone of her voice as Bridie sat down again, trying to control her own thoughts. She just wished that she could run away or hide away in some hole in the ground, and not have to be answering so many stupid questions.

"Who else! But that bitch; the Reverend Mother."

"But Sure a grá, you should have told me *f*what you were plannin'…" suggested Julie, feebly, "and not be keepin' it a secret."

"Ah shut up, it wasn't a secret and I wasn't planning anything. You're a nice one to talk. You ran away yourself and didn't tell any of us," retorted Bridie angrily, as more of her comrades gathered around to hear and see what was happening. They knew it had to be some disturbing news in order to get Bridie so agitated, for she was normally very quiet – much too quiet and civil, they often thought, for her own good.

"What's wrong?" asked Lilly MacAlastair coming to join the little circle that was forming around Bridie.

"They just told her, she'd never ever see her son John Paschal again. Sure them raps don't care," added Julie, trying to sound sympathetic.

"Wash, wash, wash, 'til our hands drop off, that's all them bitches ever want."

"And more money for the Arse-Bishop," added Josephine Finn emphasising the word 'arse'.

"I know," said Lilly thoughtfully, 'tis terrible. They won't let any of us OUT to see our children, or the little ones IN to see their Mothers.

You know I think I'd rather be in jail, I would, honest to God, I 'd much rather be in jail than have to live in this kip for the rest of me life. At least if we were in jail, we'd know how long we were in for.

The words had no sooner left Lilly's lips than the Mother Superior and Sister Philomena appeared at the door. The girls turned abruptly and began to fan out, slithering away back to their posts, save Bridie who remained sitting defiantly on a linen basket.

"Girls! What's the meaning of this! What's going on around here?"

But the girls were already beavering away on their ironing boards.

"Girls!" bellowed the Reverend Mother, "Come here at once!"

The penitent girls looked from one to the other before collectively deciding it was better to go forward.

"Now, what's the meaning of this? What's so important that it requires all of you to attend a meeting with Bridie Rodgers, who's quite obviously the ringleader of this little charade. What is it?" asked the Reverend Mother, as the penitent women stood before her, their heads hanging in shame, having been caught so unaware.

"Girls! Look at me while I'm speaking to you! And show some respect."

Slowly they raised their eyes, as one or two of the other inmates in the adjoining room looked on in glee from behind the relative safety of a curtain.

"Now which one of you prime lassies said, 'they'd rather be in jail than in this kip?"

The girls were stunned at the Reverend Mother's sense of hearing. Even Bridie, who remained tight-lipped, was amazed that she had picked up on every word of their conversation.

"Girls," repeated the Reverend Mother, this time in a more measured tone, but with a touch of venom in her voice. "I repeat, which one of you said you'd 'rather be in jail than live in this kip'?"

The penitent women remained silent: each afraid to own up, because they knew it would bring swift retribution. While telling the Reverend Mother, who it was that made the offending remark might earn one a much lighter sentence than the guilty party; it did nothing at all for one's standing in the ranks of the Magdalene women. To split on a friend or colleague was considered the lowest of the low and usually resulted in that person being continually shunned and treated as an outcast. Like Peggy Neary who was loathed by everyone because she was the nuns' pet and told on every one.

"So you've all decided to become model citizens by taking a vow of silence; how interesting," said the Reverend Mother, sarcastically.

"So, we shall see how long it will last. Perhaps you'd all like to offer up your continued silence as penance for your sin. All of you from this moment are forbidden to partake of any food or drink. Sister Philomena, will take charge of the fast and when you are ready to talk she will be only too happy to inform me of your repentance."

On hearing her name being mentioned as the enforcer of this rule, Sister Philomena cringed with embarrassment. She couldn't understand why she was being used in this way. As a novice she had spent years listening to her superiors in the Seminary preaching the language of God, learning to carry oneself in God's own likeness while absorbing the language of respect and common decency. Learning to move about at all times with dignity and decorum, only to end up being sent here to the Magdalene Home to witness the Reverend Mother herself behaving like a bully. She remembered her first day here all too vividly. She was appalled at the inhuman way in which the inmates were treated. They all had, what appeared to be, that wayward look of despair about them, she thought, and their dormitories stank of stale body odour, perfume and cigarette smoke.

Now she was being asked to be a party to their punishment by her Superior. She must not allow herself to be used in this way, she thought. She'd better say something otherwise the girls would think she was agreeable to the whole thing. She needed time to think but was afraid to contradict the Mother Superior as she had already chastised her earlier, for failing to carry out certain instructions to the letter of the law.

"As you wish Reverend Mother, I will lock them in their dormitories now," replied Sister Philomena, knowing that by suggesting such a thing she would at least be saving the penitents the ordeal of having to work, while at the same time giving herself the opportunity of smuggling some food in to them later.

"On the contrary! Sister Philomena! They shall pay for their disobedience by continuing to work right here in the Laundry where I can keep an eye on them " replied the Mother Superior.

Bridie, on hearing that her friends were going to be punished, because they dared to enquire about her welfare, jumped off the basket and came forward. At that precise moment she didn't care for all the nuns in County Galway, so she brazenly piped up,

"Rev. Mother, I don't think it really matters who said what because I refuse to do any more work until I know when I can see John Paschal."

The two nuns who'd already turned to make their way out of the room, stopped and turned back to look at her in amazement, while Julie Murray took a few hesitant steps forward and squawked, "Yes…I think she should be allowed to see her son…ƒwhen she wants."

Then Lilly MacAlastair added fuel to the fire, saying, "Yeah! She should be allowed to see her son."

The Reverend Mother's temper rose to boiling point at this direct challenge to her authority. Moving quickly forward she slapped Julie Murray hard across the face. "How dare you interfere with my authority!"

Slap! Slap! She went again, before Josephine Finn, who couldn't believe what she was seeing, rushed forward to support her friend by lashing out at the Reverend Mother, striking her in the face, but she only succeeded in knocking her veil sideways as she screamed, "How dare you hit my friend like that…you bitch!" as she lashed out again and again with her tiny fists.

"And how dare anybody stop me from seeing my son," bellowed Bridie, as she came swiftly to Josephine's aid.

The Mother Superior, seeing the fire burning in Bridie's eyes, knew she was out for more, 'in for the kill' as it were. Bridie was far too dangerous she thought. A troublemaker for sure, she surmised. She recognised all the signs, from her many years experience in the laundry. She could clearly see Bridie had the ability to lead others, which was the Reverend mother's greatest single fear in the running of the laundry. Bridie could start a strike as others had tried, down through the years. Fortunately, she had managed to outwit them on those rare occasions by planting an informer or two in their midst. Now she would have to submit to them, for the time being because of their superior numbers, and resort to her favourite tactic of 'divide and conquer'.

Throwing a glance in Sister Philomena's direction, she could see she had remained perfectly still; with her hands tucked into the neat folds of her long sleeves as if nothing had happened. The Reverend Mother thought, how in God's holy name did that child ever come to take her final vows. She's useless. Pure useless; But craving her support, which was not forthcoming, the Reverend Mother managed to recover somewhat before responding to Bridie and the rest of the inmates,

"Very well, if that's how you feel. Sister Philomena and I will let the matter rest for now; but rest assured girls, rest assured, I will deal with this matter later. Meanwhile, you can all go back to work."

Turning quickly she made her way nervously out of the room followed by Sister Philomena, knowing full well that the inmates had pulled off a major triumph by taking her down a peg, not to mention a physical assault on her person.

But little do they know, she thought, that they will be made to pay a heavy price for their arrogance: a very heavy price indeed: Particularly that... that... Rodgers Brat.

Sister Philomena, seeing that the penitents had rescued her from having to enforce the Reverend Mother's law, felt a warm glow of satisfaction that justice had been done. But little did she know that her Superior had other things in mind, when she invited her to have a cup of tea in her office, later in the afternoon.

"Thank you, for coming along Sister. Please be seated," said the Reverend Mother, before proceeding to bless herself and bow her head as they both joined their hands in prayer.

"In anim an Athair,

Agus on Mhic

Agus an Spirit Naomh, Amen."

"Blessed O Lord and these thy gifts which we are about to receive through Christ Our Lord, amen."

"Amen."

"Sister, I've just been thinking," began the Reverend Mother as she started to pour the tea out into her favourite pale, gold-rimmed china cups, "that you've been here with us for a while now. I know that it's a far cry from what you've been used to, teaching children I'm sure is so much easier. But I just wish you'd show a bit more co-operation with these unruly girls: show more interest in their overall welfare."

"I'm sorry, Reverend Mother, if I failed you in my duty," said Sister Philomena, resting her hands on her lap and hanging her head slightly while waiting to be invited to partake of her tea.

"Goodness dear, you haven't failed. Been a bit lax perhaps, but failed? No. Here, have a biscuit," added the Reverend Mother, pushing the small decorative plate in her direction, as she continued. "Failure is something we, the Sisters of Mercy won't tolerate in the Magdalene

Home. It is my duty as your Superior to teach you right from wrong. Now, tell me Sister, what do you think of Miss Rodgers?"

Sister Philomena, caught unawares, paused for a brief moment before lowering her head to answer.

"I'm sorry, I don't know her very well," she said deliberately, in case she'd be accused of being too familiar with the girls.

"Be that as it may, you saw her behaviour today. What did you think of that?"

"I thought perhaps she wasn't well, that she might be suffering from depression," answered Sister Philomena, knowing this might be what the Reverend Mother would want to hear, which was why she looked her straight in the eye while speaking.

"How very observant of you Sister. See! You have the potential to be a good analyst and counsellor. Certainly, Bridie Rodgers, is not well. However, it's not depression she suffers from, but *madness*" confided the Reverend Mother, as she leant forward to emphasise the point, "and *madness* in the confines of a refuge such as ours is highly contagious and must be stamped out immediately. Today was a perfect example of how a group of affected penitents could take over the entire institution: the church, the convent, the laundry, and turn the whole place into a lunatic asylum: a laughing stock. Therefore we must be constantly on our guard and watch out for their ulterior motives. It is God's will that penitents such as Bridie Rodgers, be sent to a secure Psychiatric Hospital as well as those of her friends who aid and abet her in her unreasonable demands. So I'd like you to keep a close eye on Bridie Rodgers in particular, and should she persist in her demands to see her son, then I shall have no choice other than to have her committed to Ballinalsoe right away."

Sister Philomena's eyes widened in dismay on hearing this proposal and it did not go unnoticed by the Mother Superior; whose sole purpose in outlining this course of action was that Sister Philomena, would convey this very real threat to Bridie Rodgers and her friends. For she knew, from close observation of her staff that Sister Philomena, was too meek and mild in dealing with her charges and figured she would inform Bridie, that she was about to be committed for the rest of her life. That message would surely take the wind out of Miss Rodgers's sails, because she's not stupid; not stupid, she thought

Sister Philomena left the Mother Superior's office determined to warn Bridie, that unless she toned down her demands right away, she might never ever see her son. Bridie, she figured, already knew that once a mother and child were parted, the chances of them ever meeting again were very slim indeed. What Bridie, didn't know was that once the mother was committed to a mental institution, then her chances of ever having a reunion were as good as dead.

After the penitent's resounding success in forcing the Reverend Mother to withdraw her threat of fast and abstinence against them, they were delirious with excitement. So much so that they did very little work, electing instead every few minutes to appoint a new *lookout* to guard the door so that they could revel in Josephine Finn's antics of singing and dancing and speaking openly about their plans for freedom. At the rate they were going, they figured they'd all be free in no time, because now the nuns were afraid of them. All one hundred and fifty of them would get together and if they weren't granted immediate freedom they would go on strike. But right now they were more interested in Josephine Finn's sense of humour, as she sang aloud while brandishing a pair of 'long-johns'.

"I've travelled about a bit in my time,
And of troubles, I've seen a few.
But found it better in every clime
 To paddle my own canoe.
My wants are small I care not at all,
If my debts are paid when due;
I drive away strife in the ocean of life,
While I paddle my own canoe.
(Chorus)
Then love your as yourself,
As the world you go travelling through,
And never sit down with a tear or a frown,
But paddle your own canoe."

The girls grabbed each other and twirled around the floor to the lines of Josephine's lay. Then Josephine jumped up on a linen basket – which threatened to take off across the room of its own accord if she didn't stop her jig acting – and began imitating the Reverend Mother.

"'I see you've decided to become model citizens by taking a vow of silence, perhaps you'd like to offer it up as a penance for your sins. Especially you Bridie Rodgers, full of butter milk and cream; or you MacAlastair, for the night you fooled poor Mick. Oh what a sight when you undid his fly and out jumped his little Dick."

Amid howls of laughter the *lookout* shouted, The Sister! Quick!

"She can go and kiss my arse," replied Josephine, loudly as she joined her hands and bowed her head as if in prayer.

"I think it's the Reverend Mother!" hissed the *lookout*. And for an instance all hell broke loose as they resumed hard labour. But it was a false alarm, brought about by a nervous *lookout,* mortified by their antics and afraid that a severe punishment would await them if they were caught again. For not everyone had confidence in the penitents new found sense of freedom: not everyone.

Chapter Ten

Having got over the initial shock of being told by the Reverend Mother that she would never ever see her son again, Bridie's thoughts turned to ones of escape. Carefully running the steam iron down the sleeve of a shirt, in the ironing room, she thought perhaps she should make a run for it, or climb over the wall. The thought both excited and frightened her, because deep down she did not believe that the Reverend Mother would ever accede to her request, so she would just have to escape. Managing to escape was one thing. Managing to stay out was another.

Well, suppose I managed to get out tomorrow or even next week, she thought to herself, what then? Where do I go? I have eight pounds altogether, enough to feed and clothe me for a while. But if I go to Dublin or England, which is where everyone seems to want to go, that'll cost me a fortune. And if I go to either place, I'll be too far away from John Paschal, she thought, as she started to sort out another pile of priest's vestments. Thinking of John Paschal again she reached into her blouse to pull out the small goatskin purse which hung around her neck and which contained the golden lock of hair and the only photograph she had of her son. For a long time she studied his jovial features; his bob of wavy hair, which she now held in her hand. She was mesmerised by the fact that she had a photograph at all, not knowing where it came from or who sent it because nobody in St. Mary's ever replied to her letters.

She resumed her ironing again and was trying desperately to plan her escape bid when Sister Philomena came into the room unexpectedly. She marched straight over to Bridie's table and began to inspect her work. And as she did so she looked furtively around before whispering to Bridie,

"I've come to warn you. You are in very grave danger as a result of what happened yesterday."

Continuing to inspect Bridie's work, she again glanced round to make sure none of the other workers could overhear her, before adding, "It's possible you may be taken away from here without warning and sent to a place far worse than here unless you curtail your demands, immediately. Do not under any circumstances ask to see your son again or get involved in organising a strike."

With those words ringing in Bridie's ears, Sister Philomena, disappeared almost as mysteriously as she had appeared.

Before Bridie could even begin to digest what 'a place far worse than here' meant the blood had already left her cheeks and she thought that at any moment she would faint. Struggling to maintain her balance she went over to her friend across the room and begged,

"In the honour of God, Lilly have you a fag? I've just had the most frightening news."

Lilly looked up at Bridie, in surprise.

"What's wrong with you? You're not yourself at all today," she said, as she rummaged in her pockets for a smoke.

"Oh God, I don't know, I think I'm in trouble. Won't you promise to come straight over to me after work and I'll tell you everything?"

"I will! I will! Don't I always," replied Lilly, as she handed Bridie, the crumpled blackened butt of a Woodbine cigarette. "Here! And don't smoke it all. That's all I've left," she added, as Bridie hurried away.

Lilly looked at the clock and thought what does that lady want a smoke for at this hour of the day. Won't we be finished working in another half an hour.

When she finished work she arrived back in 'Our Lady's' dormitory, and said to Bridie, "Well, what have you got to tell me? What's the big secret?" as Bridie and herself began removing their white calico gowns while awaiting the return of Julie Murray and Josephine Finn.

"The nuns are threatening to have me put away. Sister Philomena warned me this afternoon. She said they might send me to a place far worse than here if I caused any more trouble or asked to see John Paschal."

"Are you serious! said Lilly, looking at Bridie, in disbelief.

"As true as God is my judge! That's what she said. And I'm terrified she means it. What will I do if they send me to Ballinalsoe?"

"Ballinalsoe! Jesus they wouldn't send you to Ballinalsoe! Would they?" queried Lilly after dwelling on the subject for a moment, "But isn't Sister Philomena one of them? Why would she warn you? Why should she care?"

"I know Sister Philomena is one of them, but maybe she feels sorry for us. Did you notice she never lifted a finger to help the Reverend Mother yesterday; so she must be on our side. Why else would she warn me?" asked Bridie.

"Did she actually say, they'd send you to a place far worse than here?" asked Lilly.

"Yes," croaked Bridie, nervously.

"Oh Bridie, they wouldn't! They couldn't do that!" she said thoughtfully, as she sat down on the edge of Bridie's bed an air of despondency creeping into her voice at the very notion that the nuns held such power over them. "Ballinalsoe! You mean they'd send you to the mental, in Ballinalsoe?"

"I...I...I don't know. God they'd never send me to Ballinalsoe. Would they?" pleaded Bridie, as she began to feel terrified.

Lilly, seeing Bridie was clearly afraid of what might happen to her, tried to console her by saying,

"No, No! I don't think they would, not for asking to see your child anyway. Everyone knows that place is only for nut-cases."

But the minute Lilly had it said, she realised she was implying Bridie, was a potential nutcase. But at the same time she felt that the nuns and priests were capable of anything. Didn't they have poor Julie put into the Home because she was wild or something; Josephine Finn because she was in love with a Protestant and herself because she liked eyeing up all the talent. And if priests could put you away like that for nothing, then they could do anything, she thought.

Josephine Finn and Julie Murray returned from their hard day's slog, happy in the knowledge that they had come to the end of another long day. They were no sooner in the door than Bridie and Lilly, way laid the two of them and began to bring them up to date on the latest development. And when Julie Murray was asked on how best to cope with this latest threat she didn't know what to say. She wasn't really in favour of a strike, she said, because the nuns might find out I helped ye and then I'd be put away. She explained how she had escaped once and paid a heavy price for it. As well as that, the Reverend Mother now considered her a valued inmate and rewarded her from time to time with the gift of a half-crown.

"Sure how can we go on strike," she tittered nervously. "Sure fwhat can we do but keep going and pray to the Lord that some oul' eejit 'ill take us outa-here."

"The only way we'll ever leave here is in a bloody box," said Josephine resignedly.

"God almighty above," said Bridie looking aghast at Josephine. "That's it! We'll escape by hiding in one of the laundry baskets."

"Yeah, that's a great idea," said Josephine. "We could all go together."

"Sure that's been tried before ye oul' amadáns. And an'way, wouldn't we all smother. Wan young girl died tryin' to get out like that. They threw all the clothes in on top of her. That's fwhy I'd never try to escape like that," said Julie cautiously. "An' besides we'd be too heavy. The lads would notice the minute they tried lifting the baskets. An' the nuns are always watching out an' ever'thin' since wan young girl was caught kissing one of the drivers. Sure they were supposed to have sent her away to Ballinalsoe, because she was never seen again. Lord, I wouldn't mind kissing one of the men, if I thought I could get out" she added thoughtfully. "It's all right for you Bridie and Josephine, nobody would notice yeer scrawny arses lying in a basket, but sure I'd have no chance. It would take three men to lift me," said Julie, laughing at the idea of three men coming to her rescue.

"What's happenin'? What's all the excitement?" asked an inquisitive looking Peggy Neary as she approached them quietly out of the blue.

"Mind your own business! Now buzz off!" snapped Lilly, peeved that Peggy always appeared to eavesdrop on their conversations at the most inopportune times. But when Peggy insisted, by saying,

"Well don't let me stop ye," she really raised Lilly's hackles.

"Go on! Off with you! We don't want you around here..."

"Go on, buzz off!" added Julie, supporting Lilly, whom she knew hated Peggy more than anyone in the world.

"No, I won't! I can go where I like. It's a free country," said Peggy defiantly as she attempted to sit the other side of Bridie, because she knew Bridie would never interfere.

Suddenly, Lilly, who was facing Bridie, grabbed Peggy by the hair and dragged her screaming to the floor, and in an instant they were both kicking and leathering hell out of each other. Amid a chorus of whistles and catcalls, the two protagonists were locked together, each pulling the other's hair and screaming obscenities.

Bridie, Julie and Josephine jumped up to admire Lilly's efforts. The two assailants were still locked in combat and a large crowd of inmates was starting to gather round, when Sister Stanislaus entered 'Our Lady's' dormitory and began ringing her heavy bronze bell. But it was too late; the Ward Sister had caught them fighting, red-handed.

Looking solemnly around the large dormitory, Sister Stanislaus looked distressed, as she spoke haltingly.

" Girls; I have a sad announcement…to make." As again she rang the bell to get everybody's attention. Then looking directly at Peggy's and Lilly's she spoke with an air of disappointment. "Some of you are a disgrace to the good name of the 'Mary Magdalene Laundry'. It saddens me to say you're no better than a pack of wild animals." After a long pause, she looked around the room once more in silence, and inclined her head ever so slowly; and placing her left hand across her abdomen she said,

"I want you all to pray this day for the soul of Catherine Kelly, whom God has called to his side. She has just died peacefully in her sleep."

An audible gasp filled the air as each of the penitents in a chain-like reaction hurriedly made the sign of the cross and muttered aloud, "Lord have mercy," as their every thought and care suddenly vanished into thin air.

Sister Stanislaus, struggling to control her own emotions continued,

"Catherine Kelly was a loyal and faithful servant to the Sisters of Mercy. The Reverend Mother and I would like you all to join us in a night of prayer for the repose of her soul. May she rest in peace, Amen."

"Amen."

Bridie knew Catherine Kelly was an elderly patient who spent most of her life in the Magdalene Home Laundry. For some time she'd been confined to the infirmary ward and her death was not entirely unexpected. Yet the very thought that someone had died in their midst almost took Bridie's breath away, as she tried to listen to what Sister was saying.

"The Reverend Mother and the other Sisters will all be there to lead the prayers. We would like all of her friends and colleagues to organise themselves into little groups of ten; each to devote one hour of prayer at her bedside. Her burial will take place the day after tomorrow after twelve o'clock Mass, in the penitents' Graveyard.

Deo gratias."

Then, as she turned around about to leave the room, Peggy Neary, ran up to her and said,

"Sister Stanislaus, I'm so sorry about my behaviour. It was Lilly's fault. She didn't want me to mix with her friends. If there is anything I can do I'd be only to glad to help."

Sister Stanislaus pursed her lips thoughtfully for a moment, and replied, "How kind of you Peggy. Perhaps you'd like to offer up fifteen decades of the rosary for the repose of Catherine's soul."

Then seeing Bridie and Josephine standing together by the window, she went to them and politely asked, "Josephine, would you be so kind as to sing 'Soul of My Saviour' at the funeral Mass? And Bridie, I would like you to join in the choir, for the singing of 'Nearer My God to Thee."

The two girls could hardly believe their luck at being honoured in this way. They both answered in a subdued a tone,

"We'd be honoured, Sister."

And as Sister Stanislaus left the room, Bridie and Josephine felt a warm glow of satisfaction that for now at least the focus was on somebody else and not on them.

* * * * *

It was almost two weeks before Christmas. Bridie and Josephine were on their usual rounds, walking the well-worn path of the Magdalene grounds, discussing life's ups and downs, when Bridie unexpectedly said.

"I've never heard you talk about dreams; or do you believe in them?"

"Oh, I do! I do! I have dreams all the time. But they're usually horrible: about rows at home and everything. But worst of all, are the ones I have about Cathal. Imagine he never even wrote to me: never answered my letters: nor did my parents. Why did you ask?"

"Oh, it's nothing. It's just that I dream a lot too. But there are certain times when I believe in them, and I know that something good or bad is going to happen. You know my birthday is on the thirteenth and I dreamed a few nights ago that I would see my son on the thirteenth. But at the same time it seemed miles away. I don't know if it's the thirteenth of January or not. It can't be the thirteenth of

December because that's gone. So I was thinking maybe I'd see him in January. And you know, that's the second time I've had that dream since I came here. I don't really know what it all means, but I feel as if thirteen is my lucky number and that blue is my favourite colour. I don't know why I should dream about it but I did." said Bridie.

"Good for you! I don't seem to have a favourite colour, never mind a lucky number," replied Josephine despondently.

"Oh, don't be silly, everyone has a lucky number," said Bridie, giving Josephine's arm a reassuring tug, "but sometimes it's hard to tell. I don't know how to say this, even though it's the reason I mentioned it in the first place, but I had a lovely dream about you last night."

"About me!" intervened Josephine.

"Yes, and it was crystal clear, though very strange. You looked so beautiful – like an angel in fact."

"Ah go on, pull the other one!" said Josephine as she gave Bridie a gentle heave on the shoulder, and they started the short circle walk for about the tenth time.

"Honest to God, Josephine! Cross my heart and hope to die! You were in the Laundry singing away. But there didn't seem to be anyone around, and this man appeared and was watching you for a long time. There was like, clouds and things – a sort of mist in the background, with loads of nuns or angels praying for you. Any way this man, he was very clear to me. He said you had the voice of an angel and that he would take you away and that you'd become famous. Yet there was something peculiar about him. He only wanted you for himself. I was standing there at the side watching. It was as clear as day. I could even see myself in the dream, looking at the two of you. But the strangest part of it all was that I could also read his mind, and although he was admiring your singing and listening to every note you sang he was really looking at your body. He was desperate to have you for himself...."

"Oh Bridie! It sounds horrible! Stop it. You're making me nervous," squirmed Josephine as she began to feel the cold winter chill. "Why did you have to tell me that? Could you not have told me something nice. Like that it was Cathal Swanick or something."

"Ah no! It wasn't a bad dream or anything like it," said Bridie, sympathetically, as she gave the back of Josephine's hand a gentle pat. "I'm not very good at describing things. But I know it was like a prediction and I thought I'd tell you for the fun of it.

"Yeah, fun me backside," acknowledged Josephine fearfully, as they both considered going back in to the dormitory where rehearsals were taking place for the staging of the annual Christmas concert.

* * * * *

The religious festivities of Christmas were long since over; during which time the inmates had been shown a film for the very first time. Its historic showing and the penitents' enactment of it amongst themselves afterwards kept them going for weeks. But now it was back to the usual boring routine of cooking, sewing, washing, ironing and scrubbing for hours on end.

Josephine Finn, was one of the many inmates scrubbing the filthy shirt collars, spread out on their wash boards, in the deep galvanise sinks that lined one wall of the washroom. She was singing away to herself while entertaining her co-workers, when an inspector from the Department of Health paid a surprise visit to the Laundry. He was doing his rounds escorted by Sister Philomena when they both looked into the washroom from the safety of the screened doorway. Josephine was oblivious to the rhythmic scrubbing noise of the washboards and the suds that splashed onto the floor, drowning her sore infested feet. And as she struggled to balance another soggy heap of wet clothes on the trolley, Mr Fincock was immediately struck by her haunting rendition of *Danny Boy*.

"Oh Danny boy, the pipes the pipes are calling,
From glen to glen and down the mountainside,
The summer's gone and all the flowers are dying,
'Tis you 'tis you must go and I must Bide."

For a moment he stood with Sister Philomena, observing the girls at their station; they seemed so unaware of the distractions going on all around them. But when Josephine Finn turned towards him to place another heap of wet clothes on the trolley and he saw her face, he gasped, 'My God'! And when Josephine again picked up on the second verse he was forced to shake his head and utter,

"What a waste of talent."

Her beauty and demeanour, he thought bore all the hallmarks of a beautiful peasant girl, not unlike the portrait of 'The Connemara Girl', by Augustus Burke, which he recalled from the National Gallery.

Turning to Sister Philomena, he said,

"Do you mind if I speak to that girl, or who is she?"

"I'm afraid Sir, we're not allowed to let any of the girls speak to strangers; other than priests or doctors. But since you're here on official business, I'm sure it's all right. Please wait a moment, and I'll bring her over."

Sister Philomena went and brought Josephine over to meet Mr. Fincock. Josephine found it difficult to walk in her bare feet as they were covered in blisters due to the endless hours spent standing at the wash-tub where the soap-suds continuously splashed all over the floor. She and many of the girls had long since given up wearing any shoes or socks because the constant wetting made their feet to soft, causing them to develop nasty looking sores and blisters.

"Josephine, this is Mr. Fincock. He works with the Department of Health in Dublin. He'd like to have a word with you," said Sister Philomena, wondering what he could possibly want with a young penitent girl.

"Josephine, may I ask have you ever sang on stage?"

"No sir."

"Well I think you should. You have the potential to be a great singer. A star in the making I would say. Of course you'd need a little tuition…but that shouldn't create any problem."

Then he extended his hand and added, "My name is Bruce. I'm involved with the theatre in Dublin. So, Josephine, if you ever decide to come to the city, I might be able to get you into Theatre or something. Would you like that?"

Josephine looked questioningly at Sister Philomena before answering shyly.

"I don't know…."

"You know we have many fine singers here in the Magdalene Choir, and Josephine is one of our finest," said Sister Philomena.

"I'm not at all surprised," acknowledged Mr Fincock.

Turning to Josephine, he bowed slightly and said,

"Josephine, It was nice meeting you," as he again extended his hand.

Sister Philomena began to pray that Josephine would not be whipped off to Dublin to start a new career, or she herself would have some explaining to do to the Reverend Mother, for allowing them to be introduced in the first place. And now Mr Fincock was quizzing her about Josephine's lack of footware.

Walking back towards the Main Office Mr Fincock, remarked,

"For the life of me, I can't understand why a girl with such talent should be working here. I would very much like to bring her to Dublin – if that were possible" he added, as the two of them stood aside to let a mini-procession of linen baskets and trolleys trundle down the long corridor.

Sister Philomena who was holding her hands firmly to her abdomen, replied,

" I'm sorry Sir, but it's her family's wish that she remain here. And nobody has the authority to remove her from the Magdalene Home except her next of kin. As for her feet, we are treating them as best we can. She seems however to be allergic to all forms of foot ware. I will of course pass on your concern to the Mother Superior."

"Yes. I would appreciate that," replied Mr. Fincock as they both made their way to the office to sign the book.

After what she believed was a miraculous encounter, Josephine lived for months in the firm belief that one day Mr. Fincock, would return to whisk her off to start a new life in Dublin. So she sang every day in an effort to improve her voice: only to eventually accept that her saviour was never going to come to her rescue. And though she considered it daft at the time, she accepted that Bridie's prediction had materialized. A man indeed had come, but he was not the right one.

No, the right man for me, thought Josephine in the end is surely Cathal Swanick. Besides, he's taller and more handsome. Oh God!, Dear God! One way or another, I'll have to try and escape from here or I'll go mad.

And in an effort to keep her spirits high, she frequently sang her own songs, while perched precariously on a basket much to the amusement of her friends. Occasionally, the nuns would keep watch from behind a door or curtain and then try to subdue her because they knew she had the power to control and entertain her friends while keeping them from their work.

On rare occasions if the nuns felt that certain penitents were up to scratch as it were, they'd slip them the odd shilling or two. Later the money would be given discretely to the delivery drivers to buy cheap perfume, white socks, or cigarettes so that come Saturday night, the penitents would dress up and make believe they were at a real live dance in some famous ballroom while listening to Ceilí House on Radio Éireann.

Bridie never received any money. Her friends said it was because she was too proud to succumb to the Reverend Mother's petty games. She did however, receive two shillings on one or two occasions from Sister Philomena as a contribution towards gifts for her son's birthday, and although she never received any more correspondence from Tuam – save the one photograph – she continued to write to Sister Hortense and sent little gifts to her son.

Bridie, now entering her seventh year in the Magdalene as a penitent, and was beside herself for news of John Paschal. And it came as a major surprise to her when late one afternoon Sister Philomena whispered that she wanted to meet her later in the chapel, because she had some good news to convey.

"Bridie," she began "I've been down to St. Mary's in Tuam to collect an unmarried mother and I made inquiries on your behalf about John Paschal."

"Oh Sister! How is he?" intoned Bridie, placing a hand on Sister's arm in nervous anticipation as they stood whispering inside the Church door.

"He's fine! He's fine! I didn't see him. But I have better news. He's been boarded out to a good Catholic family, in a place called Williamstown. I managed to get the name and address. Here it is," said the Sister, handing Bridie a small slip of paper.

"Oh Sister!" exclaimed Bridie graciously, "my prayers have been answered. How can I ever thank you?"

"Remember me in your devotions," whispered Sister Philomena humbly, "For we are all sinners in the eyes of God. And I am guilty of breaking the commandments by flouting the Church's teaching on child separation. I need your word of honour Bridie, that you will not divulge a single word of this to anyone; otherwise I could be expelled from the convent. I've had a word with the retired Matron of St. Mary's, Sister Hortense. She sends you her kind regards. It was she who went into Sister Imelda's office and got the relevant information for me. Now listen carefully," she whispered softly. "To make things easier for you in the long term and to open up a line of communication, Sister Hortense, is going to officially inform you of your son's whereabouts. That at least will give you an opportunity to write to your son's guardians and to thank them for looking after him. Who knows, if you're lucky and his guardians are as responsible as I believe them to be, you may even get a reply. And please remember not to put them under any undue pressure. And I wish you the best of luck."

* * * * *

It was a bright summer's morning almost a year later that a letter finally arrived in response to Bridie's many pleading letters.

Corrolough,
Williamstown,
Co. Galway
10th May 1955

Dear Bridie,
Just a few lines to thank you for the parcel you sent to John. He is getting big now and was mad about the football socks you sent him. I hope you are keeping well as this leaves us all at present, thank God. The weather is broke again and we are busy at the moment with the turf and everything. I have no more news and will finish for now. God bless and write soon again.

Yours faithfully, Mrs. O'Brien

Also enclosed was a note from her son.

Dear Bridie,
Thank you very much for the big parcel. It was wonderful. I liked the lucky bags the socks and hankies and pencils. Good-bye for now, from your son Paschal.

P.S I almost forgot. I would like more lucky bags because our shopkeeper said he was out of luck and that I was lucky that I knew some one that had lots and lots of luck. Bye.

At twenty-five years of age, that letter was the first correspondence that Bridie had ever had from a living relative; her very own son. She read the letter over and over so she could absorb the joyous feeling of the last line, 'Good bye for now, from your son, Paschal.'

Wiping away tears of joy she did the rounds of her friends, showing them the letter. They were very pleased and that night they had a little treat in her honour. Scoffing large chunks of currant bread lathered in creamery butter, which they had stolen from the kitchen.

Julie Murray lay moping about on her own in the quiet of 'Our Lady's', dormitory. She was felling very depressed and was slowly coming to the conclusion that she'd never again see the sun shine on her horizon. It appeared to shine on everyone but herself, she thought; Especially Bridie Rodgers: who now had direct contact with her son and was forever writing to him. Where does that one get all the envelopes and paper? Sure 'tis a post office we'd need here. And as for that Josephine Finn, sure she's worshipped like a God, just because she can sing a few oul' songs. Even Noreen Donnellan, the oul' scallywag, managed to get workin' over in the nuns' convent: where she'll be smothered with tea and cakes and the devil knows *f*what. Sure that oul' carry on would sicken anyone, she sighed wearily.

And it was one of those balmy summer evenings, a few weeks later when children could be heard playing on the nearby city streets, that Julie Murray decided to make a desperate dash for freedom. Climbing over the iron gate leading to the nunnery field, she ran helter-skelter along by the boundary wall to the top end of the field: there, she climbed over a stone wall and down a steep embankment that led to the Galway to Clifden rail line, where she crossed over the tracks and made her way out on to the suburban city streets. She didn't really know where she was, but decided to keep going anyway to get as far away as possible. That, was the one thing they were all agreed on in the Magdalene. If you manage to escape, run as far away as possible.

Only when she'd made her way out into the country did the enormity of rash decision hit her. *F*where was she going to get anythin' to eat? Worse, *f*where was she going to sleep? It was dusk when she spotted a neat little haggard on the side of the road. And having had some experience of sleeping in the hay as a child she was happy to spend the night there.

Next morning she discovered an orchard in the adjoining garden and began stuffing herself with apples before wandering miles and miles over fields and laneways in an effort to get home. She was determined not to speak to anyone so that no one could betray her to the Guards because she knew they would be scouring the city looking for her. But the following day Julie was spotted by a farmer, fast asleep in his haggard. Eventually the farmer and his wife managed to coax her into their house. There she was given a hot meal and some fresh clothes to change into. They asked her where was she going. She told them she wanted to go to Kilmaine, but was afraid that she might be sent back to Galway.

As the farmer and his wife were in no position to take her in, they decided it would be best to notify the Magdalene Home. They knew very little about the Magdalene except that it was regarded as some kind of an institution for disaffected women. They were afraid to leave themselves open to a charge of assisting or harbouring an escapee, who was possibly a mental patient. So they sent word via the post office to the city. Soon two uniformed members of the Gardaí and a nun from the Magdalene Home came to collect her. But first they had to give an undertaking to the farmer and his wife that Julie would not be ill treated in any way.

Once more, Julie Murray was returned to the Magdalene Home laundry. She was about to commence her eighteenth year as a penitent in College Road, Galway.

Chapter Eleven

It was a Saturday morning and a worried frown masked Bridie's pale complexion. As a mother she realises she now has responsibilities to her son. So, she's trying to figure out her best tactic in relation to buying him gifts for his eighth birthday. It's already eleven-thirty and she hasn't yet had a chance to have a word with Julie Murray to ask her for financial support. They have had little time to converse since Julie's second escape bid. In Julie's absence, her bed in Bridie's dormitory was given over to a new penitent, and Julie on her return was transferred to St. Teresa's dormitory. And although Julie was not ill treated in any way on her return she still had her hair cut off as a form of punishment. Which Bridie thought made Julie more cantankerous in dealing with those around her. To Bridie however, she seemed as loyal as ever and they continued to meet whenever it was convenient.

As Bridie continued to iron a big heap of shirts, she asked herself what she should do in relation to John Paschal's birthday. I think I'll put sixpence on 'Mother's Pride' in the 3.30 race, she mumbled to herself. After all, she thought, hadn't she picked winners before by closing her eyes and sticking a pin in the long list of runners. 'Mother's Pride', somehow sounded like a good bet. She had read about it in last Sunday newspaper that came in with a heap of dirty laundry. And she recalled Gerald O'Malley's parting words to her in Conly House. 'Always take a little gamble in life.'

But what if I lose? My son will have little or nothing for his birthday, she sighed as she folded up another ironed shirt to add to the twenty she had already done. And today was supposed to have been such a quiet day on account of the Bishop's visit to the Magdalene, tomorrow. Easy me arse, she thought. It gets bloody harder by the day. If only I had five shillings, she mumbled, I'd buy him a pair of black patent shoes. No, they would be too dear. Maybe, I'll buy a nice pair of white socks, a shirt and tie, and some sweets instead.

Oh, and I mustn't forget the lucky bags. I have the two shillings Sister Philomena gave me, my own six-pence that I found in the lining of that coat and if I can get the two shilling I know Julie has, then I'll have four and six-pence altogether. I hope she comes in soon because today's the only day I can get the van driver to buy the things I want – if I have the money.

Josephine Finn and Margaret Sherry were waist deep in piles of bed linen from the City's hotels and seaside resorts. They were about to join Bridie across the room for a quick smoke and a chat when the portly figure of Julie Murray appeared at the door, accompanied by the Reverend Mother: looking to see if any department was understaffed.

"Girls, how are ye getting on?" asked the Reverend Mother in her dictatorial tone of voice.

"Bridie Rodgers! I thought you'd have those 'Inniscrone shirts', finished by now. Tomorrow is the Lord's Day and as you know we try if at all possible not to work on the Sabbath. Miss Finn, what are you tittering about? Is it that ye haven't enough work to do? After a momentary silent pause she added, "I think Julie, there's not a lot for you to be doing around here. Perhaps Sister Philomena, will find you something."

Bridie overhearing the remark knew her opportunity to talk to Julie was lost, unless she spoke up.

"Excuse me Reverend Mother, I wonder could I have some help? I'm not feeling very good this morning," said Bridie.

"What wrong with you?"

"I have a bit of a pain in me side."

A pain in your side! Are you sure it's not from tittering or laughing?"

"No, Reverend Mother." said Bridie.

"Perhaps we should all kneel down and say a decade of the rosary for Bridie Rodgers, who has a bit of a pain in her side. Will we do that Miss Rodgers?"

"No Reverend Mother, there's no need."

"There's no need! Well then let's be thankful for that. Who would you like to help you iron out your problems?"

"I don't mind Sister. Julie will be fine, if that's all right with you."

"Julie Murray? How very strange that she should be standing right next to me. How very convenient that ye two always seem to be together no matter where I go. Still, I'm glad that you didn't ask for His Grace the Arch Bishop, because he can't come in until tomorrow."

After a slight pause she added. "Girls, you have until about one o'clock to finish up here. Then it's down on your hands and knees. I want this place shining like a new pin for His Grace's visit in the morning. Go with her Julie and I'll see you later."

The very minute the Mother Superior left them all alone, an air of comic relief filled the ironing room as Josephine Finn jumped straight onto a linen basket and began to imitate the Reverend Mother by draping a large white sheet over her head, while holding it firmly beneath her chin as she began,

"Perhaps we should all kneel down and say a decade of the rosary for Bridie Rodgers, who has a pain in her fanny. Will we do that Bridie? No Sister, there's no need", said Josephine replicating the language to her own liking. "Well then who do you suggest might help you sort out the pain?" I don't mind, Sister, any oul' hairy 'Mick' or 'Danny' will do: If that's all right with you? How very strange. How convenient that ye two always seem to be together no matter where I go. Girls ye have, until one o'clock to get shagged. Now lets all kneel down and pray for Bridie Rodgers who has a pain in her fanny that can only be cured by a lovely boy called Danny."

Making an obscene gesture, Josephine suddenly breaks into a lewd rendition of Danny Boy.

"O Danny Boy, the pain, the pain is awful.
From tit to tit, and all the way down.
My knickers are gone and now my flower is waiting,
'Tis you, 'tis you, will come and I will sighhhhhh,
But come you back and shag me once again…"

Josephine's friends were so shocked at her powerful booming rendition, they ran to haul her off the basket before she got them all into trouble and then they burst into laughter at the good of it all. Still, some of them were terrified the Reverend Mother might have heard it and punish them later for the use of such filthy language. They were convinced she must have heard every word, especially seeing it was Saturday when nearly all of the trolleys were at a virtual standstill.

So they all knuckled down to work again in case the Reverend Mother paid a surprise visit.

"Oh dear, oh dear! I think that Josephine Finn's, for the birds" said Julie, spreading a shirt on the ironing board, "Anyway, how are you getting on? Have you much more to do?"

"Fine. I've only about another ten or twelve to do. We'll have them done before dinner handy enough," said Bridie, as she mentally prepared herself to ask Julie for the loan of her two shillings.

"You know Julie, I was praying all morning that I'd see you around as I wanted to ask you a great favour. I hope you don't mind."

"Not at all," replied Julie, manoeuvring her ironing board so that they could both have a nice chat while working together.

"You know it's John Paschal's birthday in another two weeks and I want to buy him a few things. I was wondering if you'd be kind enough to lend me the two shillings you got from the Reverend Mother. The few pounds I had when I came in, is gone already. What with gifts for Christmas and the odd packet of fags for myself I'm stone-broke. I'll help you with your own work when you're stuck and give you back the money the first chance I get."

"Sure I always give you ever'thin, an' then I'm left with not-thin."

"I know that dear," said Bridie "and I'm very grateful. But what can I do when the nuns never give me any money?"

"Sure why don't you try and be nice to them, like me? Then they might give you something too."

"Arrah! Do you hear what's talking? I'm working here, like a slave the same as you. And that's as nice as I ever want to be to them. I got two shillings last Christmas for a whole year's work, and nothing since. You know Julie, I think it's so unfair the way some people get paid and other people get nothing," answered Bridie clamping down the iron vigorously on a white shirt in suspended rage.

"No disrespect to you or anyone else Bridie, but sure didn't the Reverend Mother herself say I was doing the work of two people. And that's *fwhy I get the odd few bob." said Julie.

Bridie felt as if Julie was implying something so she stopped ironing for a second and said, "Julie, I don't doubt for one minute that you're the best worker in the Magdalene, but to be truthful I don't think that's why they give you the money."

Julie too stopped ironing to look at Bridie in bewilderment

"*Fwhat do you mean?"

"You know well what I mean. I think it's because they feel guilty about the way they've ill-treated you. If I was you I wouldn't take a red shilling off them."

"Sure, and you come beggin' me for money. Fwhat are you tryin' to say?" asked Julie, getting up on her high horse.

"Ah! For God's sake! Doesn't the whole world know how they treated you after you tried to escape: cut your hair to the bone and belted you around the place! A week later they're giving you money and telling everyone that the sun shines out of your backside. Great worker, how are you! Isn't it the same…."

"Wait a minute," interrupted Julie, trying to stem the verbal flow, but there was no stopping Bridie, now that she had the bit between her teeth. "No! No! It's the same thing with them other two up in St. Teresa's. Only the other day they belted them black and blue, for trying to get out. And from what I hear now the same two girls are being humoured with fine pieces of silver."

Julie, who was listening in embarrassed rage, suddenly turned on Bridie in earnest.

"How dare you, talk to me like that! Who do you think you are! Sure I should never have been in here in the first place: truckin' with the likes of you. At least I've a home and a mother; when you don't even know fwhere you came from. You have a child and you're not able to look after it. Sure only for the nuns you'd…you'd die with the hunger: you're like a beggar; you're always cadgin' off someone; every minute and hour of the day…"

"Well maybe I am always cadging," interjected Bridie. But at least I could never be accused of stealing anything…."

"Oh shut up! Shut up!" roared Julie picking up a heap of ironed shirts and flinging the lot at Bridie. "Here! Stuff your ironing; I never ever want to see you again," said Julie, as she stormed out of the room and the other girls looked on in embarrassment.

They were upset that two of their closet friends should end up squabbling with each other, particularly after Julie had come to Bridie's aid. They weren't sure what it was about. Josephine made up her mind she'd go over to Bridie to find out what was happening, but first she'd let the dust settle.

Bridie felt at that moment as if she could have cut her tongue, such was her remorse for having said such things to Julie and for having made such a mess of the whole thing. She turned her back to hide the pain of what she had just done. She felt so distressed she wanted to smash the iron against the wall; to never see an ironing board again: to be a thousand miles away from the nearest Laundry.

Instead she stood quietly pleading to herself, oh dear God and his blessed mother, what have I done? What in the name of God came over me, she sighed. What will John Paschal think of me if he gets nothing for his birthday? How can I ever hope to see him again when I can't even do that much right?

Josephine Finn, aware of Bridie's distress came across the room and slipped her arm around Bridie, saying,

"Cheer up Bridie. Don't let it get you down. You'll soon make it up again."

"Oh Josephine! I don't think I'll ever be right!. Everyone seems to be against me. The nuns if I haven't the shirts ready, and someone always wants the odd fag I sometimes manage to get off the van drivers. Even the Dublin gang blame me if I don't side with them and threaten the nuns."

"Shee! Calm down Bridie! Here's a chair. Sit down a minute. As I always say Bridie, feck the nuns, feck the clothes and feck everyone else," said Josephine authoritatively, as she placed a chair behind Bridie.

But Bridie refused to sit for fear one of the Sisters would catch her sitting down.

"What will I do Josephine? I worry so much about John Paschal. I could lose him, and then I'd have no one."

"Here! Sit down a minute and be quiet. I've a small bit of a Woodbine. Here! Have a drag; Margaret will watch the door, while I get a light."

"Margaret," she called. "Have you a light?"

Quick as a flash, Margaret darted across to them with a small American lighter she'd found in the pocket of a dinner jacket and handed it to Josephine. Then she ran over to the door to keep an eye, while Josephine said,

"Listen! You'll have to pull yourself together lass and not be falling out with your friends. We should all stick together and help each other. Anyway, what were ye fighting about?"

"We weren't really fighting. It's just I thought Julie would surely help me, that's why I asked her for the money. You know my son's birthday is coming up and I want to get him a few things."

"Your son will be all right. He's in good hands, and if he's not then there isn't a single thing you can do about it."

"Oh, don't say that Josephine. I'll have to send him something.

He's only eight."

"OK. OK, Calm down; we're all friends here, remember! Now listen Bridie, I've a lovely pair of white ankle socks: they're way too small for me: you can have them if you like. I was going to wear them for the Bishop's visit tomorrow. And anyway, if the truth was known he'd probably rather be looking at me oul' pink knickers, than at my white ankle socks anytime."

"Oh Josephine, you're terrible! Better not let Peggy Neary hear you," said Bridie cheerfully as she began to pull herself together.

"Isn't it the truth? They say some of them fellas can be as randy as hell. Julie Murray recons with the thick neck on some of them, they're fit to bull cows. Give me that fag 'til I have a drag before you have it all gone."

Bridie gave her the fag, which she inhaled quickly, before stamping it out on the floor and depositing it in a waste bin. Then Josephine, reached into her blouse took out her Sacred Heart scapular and said, "Here! You can have this six-pence. You know I don't really trust some of them bitches at my end of the dormitory, so I carry me money – when I have any – in my scapular," she continued, handing Bridie a shiny new six-penny piece. "Buy what you can and I'll help you make up some sort of a parcel for your young fella. We'll get one of the drivers to post it."

Bridie was so moved by Josephine's gesture she clasped Josephine's hand in hers, saying, "Thanks love, someday please God, when we got get out of here, I'll make it up to you. And that's a promise."

"Ah never mind. Isn't that what friends are for? I know you'd do the same for me."

"Of course I would dear, and I will. Listen, you'd better go back to work before the Reverend Mother, comes back and catches us talking," said Bridie.

"Oh, I suppose so."

Then turning round, Josephine asked, with a less than hopeful look on her face, "Do you really believe we'll ever get out of this place?"

Bridie, joined her hands and raised her eyes, as she emphatically replied, "Josephine, as sure as God above is my judge, cross my heart and hope to die, I'm getting out of here and I'm bringing two of my best friends with me; that's you and Julie. We may have our troubles, but that won't ever stop me."

Josephine, smiled half heartedly and said,

" Lord God, Bridie, If only I had your faith. If only."

* * * * *

For what seemed like a lifetime, Bridie and Julie managed to avoid each other: their pride too great to acknowledge that their frail hearts were broken.

Bridie, recalled almost every night before she went to sleep the memory of that day when Julie broke down, while disclosing her terrible secret. She had kept her promise, never once, disclosing it to anyone that Julie was a thief, until that horrid argument over money came between them. She now wished more than anything to heal the rift between them but couldn't bear the thought of apologising over something she thought was totally unfair. The fact that she had to beg and scrounge to enable her to send a few things to her son made it all the more painful: while Julie who had no child, received regular gifts of money from the Reverend Mother. It was, she felt, as if the unmarried mothers were being punished for their sins.

Julie Murray too felt that she shouldn't apologise because as far as she was concerned Bridie Rodgers was too cocky and too proud to accept handouts from the nuns. Not only that, but she treated the nuns with contempt, except maybe that Sister Philomena one, whom she went out of her way to make an ass of, by claiming she needed her son's address. Anyway I'm fed up, she thought, listening to Bridie on about her John Paschal. Sure you'd think no one else in the world had a child but herself. I could have had one mesell, maybe if only I had let Harry catch up with me that day in the meadow. He would surely have kissed me, and who knows I might have ended up with twins. Wouldn't that be great, I'd have two and Bridie only the one. But the way she goes on and on about him; and them lucky bags: 'twould make you soft in the head. But sure where's the use in me talking. I have no child, and amn't I as well to be giving the money to her to buy him somethin' as waste it on fancy lipstick that poor Harry will never see: or that oul' rotten perfume that Josephine said would poison a stray dog. But I'll not apologise to Bridie. Never.

It was a week, to the day almost when Bridie and Julie met face to face for the first time as they entered the long corridor. They both dropped their heads simultaneously to deny the existence of each other, as their hearts pounded heavily in their chests. Every move they made all week was in dread of coming face to face with each other, and of how they might react.

But now, as they were about to draw near, the pain and remorse was excruciating. Bridie looked furtively around her to see if anyone was following. There was no one. She lifted her eyes just as they were about to pass each other, and to her dismay found Julie doing likewise. For an instance their eyes met and they froze in their strides, and for a split second they stared at each other before collapsing into each others arms as their proud hearts melted, and they whispered sorry to each other before kissing each other on the cheek.

"Listen, we'll meet after work," Bridie said excitedly, breathing a deep sigh of relief that their broken hearts were now partially mended.

* * * * *

It was several weeks later after a particularly violent fracas, during which the nuns had to forcibly subdue one of the penitents and have her sent to Ballinasloe Mental Hospital that Julie decided to slip quietly away of an evening to seek refuge in the Magdalene Laundry Chapel. She wanted more than anything to sort out her head, because she was becoming more depressed and disillusioned with life in the Laundry. She wanted so desperately to be alone with her thoughts, to see if there was any hope at all for the future.

Having entered the church, she had to make believe she was saying the rosary because there were two nuns walking up and down the aisle reading their breviaries. When at last they left her in peace, Julie stood up and began mooching around the chapel before stopping to look up critically at the crucifixion.

Walking to the front of the chapel she sat down in the front seat and gazed up at the figure of Our Lord hanging there lifeless on the huge cross. For a long time she sat struggling to control her thoughts, asking herself why she wanted to come here. Finally, she admitted it was because she wanted to

confront Our Lord; to talk to him face to face and ask him, Are you a real God at all? Are you? Sure sometimes I think you're a fake. If you're real a grá, why go on punishing me? Sure, haven't I suffered enough already? I've been here now for years and years. Do you know *f*what it is, I'm wore out saying rosaries, and prayers for the dead, and going to Masses an' ever'thin'. *F*what am I doin' it for? For somethin' I did *f*when I was a young wan. I'm thirty-three now, going on thirty-four. I'm almost nineteen years here; the best years of my life gone forever. 'Lord', she pleaded silently looking at the hanging, wounded limbs of 'Our Lord' on the cross; is it fair I've never known the love of a man, or will I ever know what it is to have children? There's Bridie, at least she has a son. She'll have someone when she grows old. All I seem to have is pain and sufferin'. Sure the pain of being called a hoor is shockin'. To think them young brats up on the wall call us hoors! Prostitutes! When I've never even had a man's thing in me. Oh the scourge of them brats, calling us hoors and Maggies. For the life of me I can't understand how Bridie can laugh. She thinks it's funny. Sure, she's not right in the head that one. An' do you know *f*what she said last week, that they reminded her of her son. Imagine! She said they reminded her of her son. They're only a shower of trumps says I, and do you know *f*what she said then, 'Julie they remind me of John Paschal.' Imagine! She said that. She said 'Julie, I'd give anything to see that much of John Paschal. Anything! Just to see the whites of his eyes, even his little hands clutching the top of the wall'. Imagine! Sure there must be somethin' wrong with that lady. It's shocking the way some people think. Prostitutes! I wonder are we really prostitutes? Maybe we are: different kind of prostitutes. The girls from Dublin reckon, prostitutes sell their bodies for sex, because they can get no work or no man. But by selling their bodies, it's a sort of a job, and that way they can have any man they want. I don't think I'd ever sell my body. I'd do it for nothing. Lord, I'd give anything to know what it's like. Just to do it once. Sure it must be the same as when I do it with me finger, only bigger. Some of the girls said 'twas smaller, but that anythin' was better than trying to do it on your own. Oh God! I'd give anythin' if only I had a man to love. Dublin Mary said, half the prostitutes in Dublin ended up in jail, because they were too rough and dirty. Maybe that means I'm a prostitute too. Sure amn't I locked up for years. God! Is that them trumps I hear at it again?

In the darkening silence of the chapel, Julie could hear the brazen calls of the carefree city youngsters as they lifted each other up on the high walls to shout obscenities into the Magdalene grounds. *Up the Maggies! Up the Maggies! I'll give you a penny a look, three pence a go. Show us your knickers, Maggie?*

Julie, rising from her pew shuffled her way to the centre aisle and threw her hands in the air, shouting aloud in her distressed state. Dear God, do you know *f*what it is, I'm sick-a-ever'thin! Sick-a-nuns! Sick-a-priests! Sick-a-this-stinking-place! Sick-a-pain! Sick-a-sufferin'! Sick-of-being a penitent woman with cramps in me belly! Oh God! Oh God, I'm so sick of it all. And I have such a pain in me side, and me back, and blood leakin' from me fanny. Oh God! Will the curse ever end? She put a hand inside her coarse knickers, beneath her sanitary rag. She could feel the drip. Her curse was in full flow. She took out her hand and smelled the red menstrual blood on her fingers. It smelled as it always did, vile and disgusting: a mixture of blood and urine, and God knows *f*what else, she thought. She pulled a clean handkerchief from the sleeve of her cardigan and stuffed it down her knickers, remembering the embarrassment of one menstruation years ago when she got up from the dinner table. Imagine! I left a pool of blood on the seat. Sure Lord, what could I do? I didn't think it was due for at least another day. I wonder did the other girls or nuns really know 'twas me? Sure I hadn't time to wear the rags, and that oul' bitch the Reverend Mother lining us all up again' the wall, askin' which of us soiled our pants, leaving the blood on the seat for one of the chaste nuns to sit on; thereby destroying her sacred image. Image me arse. I could feel my face goin' red because some of the girls were titterin'. I was full sure they were laughin' at me, until 'Dublin Mary' told the Reverend Mother to shut up. She said that we were only human; and that a small drop of blood never kilt anyone. Oh Lord, to see the two of them rearing up. 'Mary' said, that if the Reverend Mother didn't shut her gob, she'd put her fingerprints up her fanny and see how she liked it. Sure the Reverend Mother gave her an almighty clatter. Said, stop that vile and disgusting language at once, before I report you to the Bishop. How dare you use such foul language in God's house. It's just what I'd expect, coming from the likes of you. And 'Mary' screamed back, It may be vile an' disgustin', but 'tis the feckin' truth, you oul' cow. Well, the Reverend Mother ...I thought, she'd knock her head off. Sure they near kilt one another. God forgive me, but I enjoyed every minute of it. Especially when 'Mary' lunged at the Reverend Mother. They were like two cats fighting. Sure 'twas awful. And 'Mary' screaming at us to help her, 'For Jazzus sake, will yez help me and not be standing there like a bunch of gobshites.'

Oh, the language, sure 'twas awful. I never heard anything like it. I suppose I should have stood up for Sister Stanislaus and the Reverend Mother, but sure that crowd would kill one and I'd be worse off then. In a way, only for that Dublin crowd and 'Connemara Phil', them nuns would walk all over us. Sure we'd all be murthered entirely. That 'Mary' sure she must be as hard as nails. Wouldn't give in or not-thing. Then she made up some dirty ditties and went round shoutin' them out in front of the nuns. They had to get shut-a-her, in the end, because she got a can a paint out-a-the-store-room and painted wan-a-the-ditties on the wall. *Fwhat* was it again? Lord but 'twas great gas.

There was an oul' nun from Magdalene
Asked a Bishop to have sex in the pavilion
Said he, with a frown
It will cost half-a-crown,
For a Bishop's prick is one in a million.

Sure we were laughin' for a week after it. Do you know *f*what it is, that Dublin Gang would say an'thin'. Lord I wish I could write like that. But sure I'm good for nothin'. Look at Bridie writin', ever' day. *F*what am I goin' to do at all? And *f*what am I doin' here, *f*when I should be out the country, in a field with some gorgeous fellow kissin' me. And then he'd pull off me knickers and I'd open me legs and he'd roll over on top of me and squeeze me to death.

Sure it must be pure Heaven to be lookin' up at the sky and then to close your eyes and let him do it.

God, *f*what am I doin', sittin' here, thinkin' them horrible things? Amn't I supposed to be prayin' to Our Lord for my freedom? Oh Dear God, haven't I asked you a thousand times to let me outa-here? I'll ask you one more time, as I get down on my bended knees to let me outa-here.

Julie knelt down in the silent, semi-darkness of the chapel, as a wave of depression took hold of her. Lamenting her wasted years and how she messed up the wonderful opportunities presented to her when she managed to run away: twice. Only to be apprehended and brought back because she hadn't kept her wits about her.

Oh God! Dear God, I think I'm finished. Sure there's no hope, no hope now. I must be an awful sinner to deserve this. Daddy! Daddy! Please! I beg of you, if you're in heaven to ask God for my forgiveness.

Please ask him for my freedom. I beg of you Dad! Please, I beg of you! Do it for me, because if you were alive now I know I would not be here. Sure me mother must hate me. She must hate me rotten, because she never even wrote to me. Imagine. To leave me here, rottin' away. Please! Hear my prayers. Just once! Please! Please!

By now Julie's tortured face caused her to tremble uncontrollably. She manoeuvred her heaving body so she could lie down comfortably on the seat and bury her head in her hands and let the tears flow. Soon she could feel the warm moist droplets stinging her cheeks, as the soiled unkempt strands of her shoulder-length hair clung to her face, as if bathing her in a sea of self-pity, forcing her to close her eyes like delicate transparent veils shutting out the light. Only the echoing sounds of iron horse-hooves could be heard traversing the ancient city streets of Galway as it assailed the peaceful sanctuary of the convent chapel. From somewhere a robin appeared, hopping unobtrusively from one seat to the next, as Julie's troubled mind carried her away on a tidal wave of emotion.

It was a glorious midsummer's eve in the picturesque village of Kilmaine as strapping farmers sons pedalled furiously from the four corners of the parish, drawn like magnets to the distant sound of the carnival music that echoed over the warm landscape. Julie Murray stood nervously outside the huge white marquee waiting for her friend Josephine to arrive, but as yet there was no sign. She studied every lamp-lit bicycle pouring into town until her eyes began to sting from the constant glare. Men! Nearly all men she sighed, as she watched them arrive in twos and threes, throwing their rusty steeds over the nearest wall with gay abandon; before rushing head long into the dance, so as to have the best chance to shift the cream of the crop. She already knew her own prospects were dwindling with each passing song, for the girls would now be standing four deep in their new shifts and silk stockings. She started to say a silent prayer that Josephine would not let her down, or she herself would be left to live at home, like an ancient wall flower, for the rest of her life.

Suddenly, as if by magic, Julie found herself being whisked out of the mob by strong hands. It was Harry, whom she worshipped like a God that had come to her rescue. It mattered not one iota where he came from she told herself, she had him in her grasp now and she meant to hold on to him. Harry's sunburned face shone like a beacon.

His strong white teeth seemed to enhance his rugged complexion, giving him the appearance of a Celtic warrior and when he opened his mouth to speak and call her by her pet name "Pickles", she thought she'd pass out, such was her state of happiness.

"Pickles, I've never seen you looking so beautiful. It's great to see you again. Where have you been? I've not seen you in ages," said Harry as he began to wheel her around the dance floor, which was already treacherous from an overdose of Lux snowflakes.

"I'm in Dublin, staying with my aunt, but I just love to come home for the caranal," said Julie excitedly.

"I wish I'd seen you earlier, and we could have danced all night," said Harry with a broad smile that stretched back to his two sunburned ears.

The words were almost too much for Julie. In one fell swoop, Harry had managed to pluck her aching heartstrings, and at that precise moment she felt so delirious with pleasure she wanted to throw her head back and burst into song. '*I could have danced all night, I could have danced all night,* she began to hum dreamily to herself; the melodious words straining at the back of her throat. God, if only he'd slow down, she thought.

"Harry!" she cried. "Why are we going so fast?"

But Harry was oblivious as he waltzed her majestically to the strains of Victor Sylvester's famous brass band. Six uniformed musicians in navy pants and red dickey bows were swaying rhythmically, as they blew their gleaming saxophones and trombones, blasting the swirling mass of dancers into a state of romantic hysteria. There must be all of seven hundred people here, thought Julie, as Harry and herself, already perspiring heavily, took a deep breath during the short interval. She was aware of big shots' daughters wearing expensive dresses, which were crucifying their waists, dancing nearby. They wore pleated frills and ball gowns that swished up around their waists as they did a lightening spin on dainty legs. Their male partners, proud as peacocks, waltzed them round and round with strong, yet delicate movements, which made each couple look like fine porcelain figurines.

While gangly youths and ancient relics of bachelorhood stood all along the top end of the marquee, staring spellbound and toothless at the fleeting exposure of suspended stocking tops and naked flesh. Just when they were about to enjoy another show of leg the band would come to an abrupt halt and announce a short interlude where those not already committed to each other would return to their friends and await the next opportunity to meet a dream date before the night ended.

Julie Murphy counted her blessings as she led her prize-catch through the excited crowd, to the mineral bar on the right hand side where they siphoned bottles of Clada orange and agreed to leave after one more dance. Back on the dance floor, Julie slid her long slender arms lovingly around Harry's tall frame and rested her head against his chest, as they swayed gently to the music of 'Galway Bay'. For a moment she closed her eyes and began to recall her first meeting with Harry.

They had been childhood sweethearts a long, long time ago, and this now was going to be the happiest night of her life. For a brief moment Julie thought she heard someone mention her name or was she imaging it? Someone was calling her name.

"Julie Murray, Julie Murray." She glanced over her shoulder and saw a shadow at the door. A man in black wearing a white collar approached her as the crowd parted to either side of the dance floor. A sudden wave of fear engulfed her body as she recognised the Parish Priest, Fr. Gilhooley. He'd already taken on the appearance of a madman and was foaming profusely at the mouth as he started shouting at Julie while waving a huge black thorn stick.

"How dare you Miss Murray, destroy the good name of my parish and its people. I will not stand idly by and watch you cavorting and fornicating with some of Ireland's most respected citizens; thereby destroying their good name and character."

Instinctively, Julie turned to Harry for support but incredibly he had disappeared and every Christian in the place was now staring at her. Fr. Gilhooley, with a hideous crown of white hair and black teeth was closing in on her brandishing the heavy, blackthorn stick. Julie stood rooted to the ground unable to move. She let out a blood-curdling scream, but the people around her just laughed as Fr. Gilhooley grabbed her firmly by the wrist and brought down the weight of the heavy blackthorn across her delicate shoulders. She fought to get out of his grasp, but his hand was like an ever tightening vice, which made her scream hysterically. Just when she thought her wrist bone would crumble under the pressure and her bulging veins spurt jets of boiling blood she broke free from his grasp, but appeared to inhabit another vague planet.

For a few brief moments she lay in a warm saturated limbo as she tried to unravel the mystery of it all. Slowly ever so slowly, the stark reality appeared before her very eyes and what she saw was worse than death itself. For there was no Harry, no dance, no village carnival, but worst of all, there was no freedom. She stared transfixed at the dimly lit altar, where she knew she'd come to pray. Then a feeling of sheer hopelessness came over her when she realised it had all been an illusion: a vile deception. For there really was no Harry with that loving smile: only the wicked ghost of Fr. Gilhooley, somewhere in the distant past.

She dragged her heaving body into an upright position on the hard wooden pew of the tiny chapel and saw the spot where she lay sleeping was awash with her tears. She could again feel the teardrops welling up in her eyes but was powerless to control them, as they started to cascade down her cheeks. "Oh God," she sobbed. "I can't go on; I'll go insane. I'll kill myself." Raising her head to look at the tabernacle, she whispered, "God, I swear on my father's life, I'll kill myself if I can't get out of this place." Just then she heard the creaking of the heavy oak door. She looked round and saw Noreen Donnellan enter the Church.

"Julie! Are you all right? We've been looking all over for you."

But she realised the minute she opened her mouth that Julie was anything but all right. She'd been missing for over two hours. She could see that Julie had been crying over something

But Julie did not answer but stared transfixed as Noreen approached her in the seat. "Won't you come back with me now and tell me what's bothering you? I promise I won't tell a sinner."

Julie rose slowly to her feet and clung momentarily to her friend, before they both turned to shuffle awkwardly down the dimly lit aisle of the Chapel. The friendly robin hopped unobtrusively before them and out the wide door to freedom. A sure sign that tomorrow would bring a brighter day and a brand new dawn.

Chapter Twelve

Noreen Donnellan really began her escape bid the day she was transferred from slaving away in the big kitchen of the main laundry to the more peaceful surroundings of the nuns convent discretely tucked away to the rear of the Magdalene Home.

Over the years, Noreen had listened to her many penitent friends' – particularly Julie Murray and Bridie Rodgers – sad tales of woe in relation to their many brave attempts at escape. And she had come to the conclusion that they had all failed in their endeavours because of poor planning; but she never had the heart to say this openly to them. Instead she resolved to work extra hard herself and to align herself with some of the nuns. Furthermore, she let it be known that in time she wished to become a consecrated penitent. Such inmates were often regarded by the nuns as model penitents, who were prepared to give up their lives for the good of their fellow penitents and the Catholic Church. And now after eleven years of dedicated service in the Laundry, Noreen found herself transferred to the nuns' convent.

From Noreen's point of view the transformation was unreal. Gone were the hard days of continuously washing and peeling spuds for one hundred and twenty inmates. Gone were the endless hours of slaving over hot stoves, baking loaves upon loaves of bread.

Here in her new position she only had fifteen resident nuns to look after: a figure, which often rose to twenty or more particularly during the tourist season. Besides, she always had the assistance of the housekeeper and two elderly penitents to help look after the many visiting nuns and priests, who came from all over to pay court to the Sisters of Mercy Order of nuns in Galway. Everyone it seemed to Noreen, wanted to see Galway. If you came to Ireland on Religious Vocation and you hadn't been to Galway and seen the brand new Cathedral being built, then you might as well have stayed at home they said.

Noreen Donnellan soon realised that she was better dressed and better fed than at any time in her entire life. Furthermore, because of her good work and reliability she was often on the receiving end of little gifts of money; a shilling here, a sixpence there: with the odd two shillings or half crown thrown in for good measure.

In her first month alone, she had saved ten shillings and didn't quite know what to do with it. Later still, when she had gathered five pounds, she began to realise that with proper planning and that kind of money she could perhaps buy her way out of the Magdalene.

Soon she become something of a nuns' pet and being a trusted member of the convent staff, she was on occasion, invited to escort one of the nuns as they made substantial cash lodgements from the thriving laundry, into the bank once or twice a week. On very rare occasions, she was sent urgently to the nearby Post Office for envelopes and stamps. And it was during one of these hurried trips that she decided to open a Post Office account. Besides, witnessing all those people in the city streets, going around on their bicycles or hopping on the nearest bus as if they hadn't a care in the world, made her more determined than ever to work on a master plan. She knew she had to get away. She'd get one chance she told herself, and she'd better not make a hames of it. So every two or three weeks she continued to make lodgements to her account when she could, while at the same time making discrete inquiries about train and bus services to Dublin, Cork, Limerick and Sligo.

After ten months, when she considered she was ready to flee, she took full possession of her Post Office book, so that she could admire her handy work and prepare herself in earnest for whatever lay ahead. She took the precaution of hiding her savings book under her own bedside locker, secure in the knowledge that no one would ever see it. That was until one morning while she was otherwise engaged the Reverend Mother ordered her staff to rearrange the furniture in some of the rooms. She was overseeing this when she spotted Noreen Donnellan's Post Office book on the floor as she moved her bedside locker to one side. Noreen was soon summoned to the Superiors office in the main building to explain her actions.

"Miss Donnellan, I have in my possession a very interesting item. Can you confirm whether or not this Post Office book belongs to you?" asked the Reverend Mother, holding up the pale green book, which had Noreen's name clearly legible on the cover.

"Yes Sister, it's mine."

"And would you mind explaining to me how one of our supposedly forgotten, homeless penitents, in the care the 'Mary Magdalene Home', came to acquire the princely sum of nineteen pounds, ten shillings and sixpence?"

"I saved it," replied Noreen nervously, somewhat dismayed at this sudden turn of events.

"Yes, I can see that. But what I want to know is where did you get it?"

"Visitors, 'twas the visitors… mostly," added Noreen as she saw the Reverend Mother was studying her reaction like a judge might study a suspected thief.

"What? In ten months?"

"Yes, yes. Sister."

"You're telling me you managed to save nineteen pounds, ten shillings and sixpence?"

"Yes Sister, I swear by Almighty God, that he may look down on me this minute: yes in the ten months."

"And would you mind telling me why you saw fit to keep this a secret by hiding it under your locker?" said Sister, holding up the book.

"I was afraid it might get lost, yet."

"Afraid it might get lost?"

"Yet, yes Sister."

The Reverend Mother was watching her young housemaid like a cat might watch a mouse, trying her best to unnerve her. One false move and she was ready to pounce.

"Visitors mostly," repeated the Reverend Mother sarcastically. "Looks like I, should have been *charging them* for accommodation. Nineteen pounds, ten shillings and sixpence in fact!"

The Reverend Mother, didn't for one moment, believe Miss Donnellan. Nobody, she figured could possibly amass so much money in so short a space of time. Then leaning across the table she began a line of cross-questioning she knew would make Miss Donnellan feel guilty as far as her secret account was concerned.

"Noreen, is it true that you wish to become a consecrated penitent?"

"Yes Sister," nodded Noreen nervously.

"Prepared to dedicate the rest of your life in the service of God, by looking after the welfare of the poor penitent women here in the Magdalene Laundry?"

" Yes Sister. I've me name down already."

"Yes Noreen, I'm well aware of that, which is why I want you to give me one good reason why I should not confiscate this nineteen pounds, ten shillings and sixpence and have it sent immediately to help the poor, starving, black babies of South Africa."

This suggestion really shook Noreen. She had expected to be reprimanded, punished even. But this was the worst ever. After all her scrimping and saving she was about to be put back down where she had been all her life; destitute, both in mind and in spirit.

She kept her composure only because she had warned herself that major problems could arise. That sooner or later something was bound to go wrong, either inside or outside the Magdalene. It always did. Up to now everything had worked out so well for her. Which was why so many other penitents had failed. She had seen and heard it all so many times. Now she was beginning to see at first hand what it was really like to try and escape.

But Noreen figured she still had one ace up her sleeve: One desperate throw of the dice and that although it appeared entirely useless to show her hand, she had little choice, as it was part of the over-all plan. She wanted more than anything else to see the Reverend Mother's reaction when she dropped her bombshell.

"It's… it's for me pension. I'm saving for me pension. Yet…when I'm old, don't you know?"

"Pension! Pension!" exclaimed the Reverend Mother, as her two bulging eyes clearly conveyed the absurdity of it all. "What do you know about pensions Miss Donnellan? You'll be dead and long gone like myself dear by the time you'll need a pension! What a preposterous idea!"

For what seemed a long time the two women just sat staring at each other, like two bantam cocks.

"Who or what put that into your head?" asked the Reverend Mother in a subdued tone of voice as she sat back reflectively, in her great oak throne.

"'Twas some of the penitents: they were worried, don't you know that they'd have no money to live on…. when they're old, yet. They wouldn't be able to work. They said they might be thrown out on the street, yet, don't you know. But I'll have me own money," answered Noreen confidently; in the firm belief that for once the Reverend Mother had met her match: all the way from Winn-am-stown

"Upon my word, Miss Donnellan! If I didn't know you better and the fact that you're very highly regarded by the Sisters in the convent, I'd say there's more to you than meets the eye. But seeing as God has granted you the wisdom to see the errors of your ways, and that you're about to become a consecrated penitent, willing to devote the rest of your life to those less well-off than yourself… I'll give you the benefit of the doubt. Nevertheless, I'll take it upon myself to keep this book in my office for safekeeping. Should you wish to add anything to it, then you must first get my permission. And you are not: I stress the word NOT to leave the confines of this building unless accompanied at all times by one of the Sisters. Is that clear?"

" Yes Sister, 'Tis the best idea, yet. I'd be afraid it might get lost or stolen, don't you know."

It was days before Noreen could make up her mind on her next move. Whether to shelve her plans for the time being or to go ahead. She also had the added embarrassment of having to ask the Reverend Mother for her book every time she decided to put some money into the Post Office. But soon she hit on the idea of opening a second account and leaving the new savings book in the post office. Then when things had settled down again, she'd reconsider her plan.

She had five pounds in her new account when she approached the Reverend Mother early one Friday afternoon. She knew the Reverend Mother would be busy in her office finalising the weekly laundry bill.

The Reverend Mother, curt and to the point rummaged in her desk drawer for Noreen's book.

"How much are you putting in?"

"Two pounds, sister," replied Noreen.

"Who's going with you?"

"I don't know, yet. Probably Sister Margaretta."

"Here, take those with you and ask her to post them for me, and don't forget to bring your book straight back," said the Mother Superior, handing Noreen some letters together with the precious Post Office book.

Noreen breathed a deep sigh of relief once she had the book in her hand. She knew however she'd manage it, she wasn't going to let it out of sight again. At least not until she had her money safely in her hand; because she figured, the Reverend Mother might change the rules at the very last minute. She knew she was really up against it and she'd have to devise a way of getting all her money out without any of the nuns seeing her. And because she wasn't planning on having any of the nuns with her when she withdrew her savings in the first place, she came up with an instant, bold plan.

"Sister Margaretta, is it all right if I nip out to the shop, yet. I've to get some writing paper for Bridie Rodgers? She wants to write to her son. She axed me yesterday, don't you know, but I forgot."

"Yes, but try not to be too long."

Sister Margaretta had no sooner given her permission than she realised what featherheads they both were. Weren't they going to the Post Office shortly, and couldn't they have done the two jobs at once. She went quickly to the door, but Noreen had vanished.

Noreen slipped out quickly, leaving the front door in the convent slightly ajar so she could slip back in again. Once outside she ran down to the Post Office, and it seemed to Noreen about an hour before she came out with the grand total of twenty-four pounds, ten shillings and sixpence in her possession. She slipped the notes into the lining of her skirt and ran all the way back to the Magdalene.

"Where have you been Noreen?" What kept you?" asked Sister Margaretta, a concerned look on her face. "You know you're not supposed to go outside on your own."

"Sorry Sister, I forgot. 'Twas Bridie Rodgers kept me talking. She's thinking of becoming a consecrated penitent. She was axing could I go over and have a chat about it."

" Bridie Rodgers?"

"Yes…yes. She thinks she'd like to join."

"I wouldn't take that lady too seriously if I were you. By the way Noreen, your pronunciation of words still leaves a lot to be desired, despite all my teaching. You're supposed to say, 'Bridie was asking', not axing. Axing means to terminate something, although I don't think you'll find the word 'axing' in the dictionary," lectured Sister Margarita, as she folded up another pleading letter for funds for the Cathedral and sealed it in an envelope.

"Are you ready? Where are the Reverend Mother's letters? Oh good!" she added as Noreen held up the two letters. "You know we've to be back in time for Benediction, and you've still got to go to confessions."

Going back into the Post Office the second time, Noreen stood well back while Sister Margaretta completed her postal business. Then going straight up to the counter, Noreen nervously handed in her old Post Office book, which contained half-a-crown and lodged her two pounds. She had little choice but to make a lodgement in the presence of her minder, thereby covering her tracks should things go wrong.

On the way back to the convent, Noreen spoke to Sister Margaretta non-stop, as she was terrified Sister would ask to see her savings book, which had become the talk and envy of all the nuns in the convent since it had first been discovered.

With terrific agility Noreen managed to evade the Reverend Mother for the remainder of the evening, before going across the grounds to see her friend Bridie Rodgers. She wanted to see Bridie urgently, because now she had some startling news to tell her.

Chapter Thirteen

For once, some of the inmates, the unmarried mothers, the wayward lassies, and the destitute, were having a wonderful time. They were sitting in a large circle on the highly polished floor of the 'Sacred Heart' dormitory, recalling their happiest childhood memories; their worst moments.

Out in the corridors Noreen Donnellan was checking the dormitories, trying to locate Bridie when she came upon the little gathering unexpectedly. They too were delighted to see Noreen and invited her to sit down and join them. And as she did so she listened with interest to Bridie, who was in the middle of her spiel,

"… And I remember sitting on Sister Concepta's knee – she was the Reverend Mother out in Clifden – and she had the most beautiful voice I ever heard and was always playing the piano. One evening she sang a lovely song. 'Twas called 'Where the Flowers Sweetly Grow', and do you know, for the life of me I can't think of a single word. But I'll never forget Sister Concepta, she was so kind to me."

There was a brief lull; a silent pause from her audience as they tried to absorb the fact that there could be such a person in the whole wide world as a decent nun. But before anyone could cast doubt on her judgement, she continued. "And I know the worst memory of all was the day they took my son away from me. I'll never forget that pain as long as I live: and if I ever get away from here, the first thing I want to do is to be reunited with my son. Then I'd like nothing more than to meet a nice man and get married, and maybe some day, please God, I might meet my real mother and father."

"Sure don't we all. An' maybe if he has a biteen-a-money an' all, 'twon't go astray," replied Julie Murray, good-humouredly after a strained silence.

Again they all laughed,

Fair play to you Murray ye know how to look for a bargain down in Kilmaine, said one of the girls, whilst another intervened to ask

Bridie, was that the day she cut off her child's hair.

"Yes," responded Bridie proudly. "I still have it here," she said, reaching into her blouse to extract the precious item attached to her Sacred Heart scapular, which she had now guarded for twelve years.

"What are you going to do with it?" asked one of the girls, examining the lock of hair; trying to imagine that it once belonged to another human being: living somewhere out there in the big wide world.

"Nothing. I just want to keep it in memory of our time together. You know it would have to be something very special, something extraordinary for me to ever part with it. But I know a day will come when I'll give it away with a heart and a half, because then I'll have my precious son back."

"Anyone else?" asked Julie, looking eagerly around to see if anyone else wanted to join in the conversation.

"Noreen, what about you? You haven't said anything," urged Bridie.

Noreen only had one memory from her childhood; one that seemed to stretch over many years. She didn't really know if it qualified but was eager nevertheless to tell it, because now her recollection would carry greater significance for Bridie as her son was now being reared in Williamstown where she herself was brought up. So turning to Bridie she began, hesitantly.

"Well, when I was down in Winn-am-stown – that's where I was before I came here – there was this man; Tom Tully was his name, and he used to come to our house to help out with the ploughing and the harvest don't you know, yet. And the people I lived with were very mean. They'd leather the-hell- outa-me if I took as much as a graineen-a-sugar or a thing. I was always starvin' and I'd be wake with the hunger, yet, don't you know? And when Tom and the workmen would come in from the fields for the dinner, I'd be sent out to the street to hold the horses by the head, in the freezing cold. I hadn't a shoe to me name, yet. And Tom would say, 'Bring in that child there, outa-the-cold: the poor girleen 'ill be famished. That's no place for her in her bare feeten, yet. And when I'd come in, me mother and father – I mean the people that reared me – would be fierce jealous, yet, because Tom would stick a fork into a thick piece-a-bacon, cut it up and say, 'Here, take this a-gráeen and warm yourself up, yet. Then he'd make me sup a big mug a-hot-tay with loads and loads-a-sugar. He'd give me the whole dinner, so he would, yet. He had no children of his own, see. And he'd call me his little pet, yet. If I ever go back to Winn-am-stown, I'm going to see Tom Tully so I am. Now that's all I have to say, yet."

"He really sounds like a lovely man. I'd love to meet him," said Bridie, "And I'd tell him you were asking for him."

"You can, yet."

"I'm afraid I don't have very many happy memories," said Lilly MacAlastair intervening. "But I remember one nasty shopkeeper who was rotten to me mother, God rest her soul. Do ye want to hear it?"

"Go on! go on! yet," urged Noreen.

"Of course we want to hear it," answered Bridie, as Lilly hesitated because it brought back such an awful memory.

"Sure haven't we 'til eight o'clock in the morning," suggested Julie cheerfully.

"Anyway, there was this nasty shopkeeper" began Lilly, "I was only about ten or twelve at the time. Of course we hadn't two pennies to rub together, and you know at that time 'twas a great treat to get a couple of herrings of a Friday. If you could get two or three lovely fresh herrings, you were the bees' knees. Usually me mother would send me to the shop. But this evening we were both walking back from my aunt's house, as me father, God rest his soul, was only after being buried."

Some of Lilly's friends on hearing this let out an audible sigh, and they hurriedly made the sign of the Cross.

"Amen," nodded Lilly before taking up her story again.

"…Well we stopped when we saw this big box of herrings outside the shop window. And me mother pulled out an old newspaper she always had in her bag and picked out a decent lump of fish. And because that time they were all the same price – big or small – she started rummaging through the box for another good one. But I could see the shopkeeper looking out at us with a sour puss on him. So the next thing he comes out and says to me mother, 'Listen Mam, 'tisn't your husband's cock you have in your hand now. No matter how much you play with them, they're not going to get any bigger. So just take as many as you want and go'."

"Aw, what a thing to say," said Bridie trying desperately to sound sympathetic, but not fully understanding what it meant, as the rest of the gang began to gasp and titter and snigger before finally, they all broke down into peals of laughter.

Even Bridie had to succumb to a fit of the shakes, before normality was restored and Lilly could finish her story. "Let her finish. And what did your poor mother say?" asked Bridie, looking around at the smirking faces, while still trying to control her own mirth.

"Ah, me poor mother was mortified, and could you blame her? Well, she threw the herring back in the box and said, 'here, you can stick 'this one' up your arse, and maybe in God it will choke you'."

At this point the girls lost all control of their senses. They laughed like they hadn't laughed in years. Even Lilly herself had great difficulty trying to convey the point she was making: about her offended mother, coming home from the funeral.

"Ah no, 'twas an awful thing to say, and as young as I was I knew he had upset my mother something awful, because my mother cried all the way home. Anyway he's dead now the lousy bastard: I hope he died choking."

Noreen Donnellan, thought the girls would never stop talking and laughing. She was anxious to get Bridie on her own. She didn't want to make it obvious to the rest of the inmates that she had something to say to Bridie.

Bridie thought it strange how Noreen had just come along and joined in the fun. She had a feeling that maybe she wanted to talk to someone, so she kept a close eye on Noreen and as if reading each other's minds they both signalled with a flick of their eyes to move out.

Noreen Donnellan excused herself while Bridie offered to walk her to the end of the corridor. They started walking slowly, linking each other like sisters. Then when Noreen thought it was safe she turned to Bridie and whispered.

"I've something important to tell you. Promise you won't say a word, yet."

"I promise," said Bridie, wondering what was so urgent and why she had to always say that silly word, 'yet'.

"I'm leaving in the morning, with God's help. I've been planning it for two years."

"Two years!" said Bridie in dismay.

"Yes. I've saved twenty-four pounds and I'm going, yet."

"Twenty-four pounds!" exclaimed Bridie in astonishment. "But how?"

"Shush" urged Noreen putting her finger to her lips, as her small, child-like frame seemed to be dwarfed by Bridie, who was only about five foot five. "They'll hear us, yet."

"But how…?"

"Listen, I haven't time. I told Sister Margarita I was calling over to visit some friends, yet. They'll be expecting me back any minute. I'll tell you again, yet. If I manage to get away, I'm going down to Dublin, or England, yet. I'll write a letter to you and post it to Mr. Hehir, the van-driver. He lives across the road in 'Mary Magdalene Terrace', number 15. He'll pass the letter on. He doesn't know yet because I haven't told him. Say nothing to him for three weeks. If there's no letter, don't you know, you'll have to ax 'im."

"But how are you going to get out?" asked Bridie in disbelief, wondering if all this talk might be in Noreen's head.

"I don't know yet," answered Noreen shrewdly, not wanting to give her game plan away – even to a friend. Won't you say a prayer for me, yet?"

"Of course I will," answered Bridie. "I'll pray that everything will be all right," smiling to herself at the thought that Noreen was about to become a Houdini by vanishing into thin air.

God, she must be a biteen gone in the head, she thought. That lady would never manage to get out on her own. Their whispered conversation was curtailed at that point by the sound of the clanging brass bell as Sister Stanislaus entered the corridor and the penitents began fleeing in all directions back to their sleeping quarters. When Sister Stanislaus's back was turned, Bridie and Noreen hurriedly kissed and bid each other farewell.

"And don't forget to write, because I want to join you", was Bridie's parting whisper.

Noreen had made up her mind several weeks ago that if everything went according to plan, and when the time came for her to leave the Magdalene she'd tell only one person. Bridie.

She wouldn't tell any of the girls in the convent because like herself they were desperate to court favouritism; and although she wouldn't like to hear anything bad said about her work colleagues she didn't really trust any of them. She knew that like herself they had their own favourite Sister, and if she told one of them, they might just tell the nuns out of pure spite. Bridie was different, she considered. She was outside that circle. And although she knew one or two of the nuns didn't like Bridie, she was very popular with the rest of the penitents. But still, Noreen decided she'd not tell Bridie more than she needed to know. While at the same time she felt they had a certain understanding on account of having come into the Laundry on the same day. And now that Bridie's son was at this time being reared in Williamstown, they had even more reason to trust each other.

* * * * *

Noreen Donnellan rose at the crack of dawn, much earlier than usual on account of the fact that she hadn't slept a wink all night. She was full of apprehension and riddled with guilt that she was about to commit a major crime. In a few hours if she managed to get away, she'd be a wanted criminal sought by Sergeant Ruane, here there and everywhere.

She tried hard to reason with herself that she was entitled to her freedom, and at twenty-six years of age still had a chance to start a new life.

But her mind kept wandering back to the fact that she had told so many lies, making fools of the nuns by asking them to put down her name so she could become a consecrated penitent; prepared to dedicate her life to the service of God: and to looking after those around her.

After twisting and turning all night, she managed to convince herself that she was doing the right thing. If she didn't see it through now, she might regret it for the rest of her life. She knew failure carried a very high price. If she were apprehended, she'd probably be forever carrying out menial jobs like scrubbing floors all day, or washing up in the kitchen. She'd have her mouse like hair shaved off and be whipped within an inch of her life, by the Reverend Mother, whom she had fooled up to the white of her eye.

When she got up, she made a big pot of stir-a-bout, put on the fires, set the tables and did all the usual things before going to Mass: only this time she ate a big feed of porridge in preparation for the long journey ahead.

At early morning Mass she could hardly wait to carry out her last task; one for which she received special dispensation from the priest and nuns: that was to leave Mass directly after Holy Communion and return quickly to the Convent to make the tea. Seven small pots of tea she had to brew, regular as clock work every morning. So that when the Sisters returned from Mass, the tea was already on the table and everything was hunky dory.

Rushing back from Mass, Noreen attempted to make the tea but was so nervous she failed to complete her task fearing she would be too late for the train. Instead of finishing the tea she went straight into the Reverend Mother's private room and removed the spare key, which she had previously studied and which she figured matched those carried round by the Reverend Mother. Grabbing her own coat, she left all her personal belongings behind in her room, together with a hastily written note on her bedside locker.

Gone to Winnamstown for the day. See you this evening.

Making her way hurriedly to the reception desk at the front end of the laundry, where the public left in their washing, Noreen managed with great difficulty to open the heavy oak door out on to the street and locked it again behind her. She scurried like a rat across the street and into the station, where she knew if the Convent clock was right, the Dublin train would be leaving any minute: that's if it hadn't already left. The thought was unbearable.

Fortunately the train was still there. She had about five minutes to spare, she told herself as she queued for her ticket. Miraculously the queue disappeared as people fled with their luggage, and in no time she was doing likewise.

And as the Dublin train pulled out of Ceannt Station, she was filled with such elation on the one hand and fear of being apprehended on the other, she spewed her guts up before she even reached Athenry.

After what seemed like an eternity to Noreen, the train finally arrived in Dublin's Westland Row Station and from there she made her way via taxi to an address in Phibsboro she remembered from her youth. The woman of the house in Phibsboro was a distant relative of her foster-parents in Williamstown, whom Noreen suspected regarded her favourably. Noreen was going straight in the gate when she met the lady of the house coming out. After a lengthy explanation the woman turned round; put the key back in the door and invited Noreen into her home: where she quickly removed her grey coat and gave a deep sigh of relief: that after twelve years service with the Sisters of Mercy order of nuns in Galway, she was a free woman. At last!

Chapter Fourteen

Bridie read the letter and disposed of it immediately for fear anyone else might read it, particularly the nuns. As Noreen didn't leave a forwarding address, there was no reason to keep it. Noreen said, she would write to Bridie again when the dust had settled, and tell her everything. Noreen was in Dublin. But by the sound of things she might be going to England.

I just pray to the Lord that she keeps in touch, thought Bridie, because I need somewhere to go if I ever manage to get away from here.

Letters were something Bridie treasured above all. She wrote every single week to John Paschal and his guardians, Mr. and Mrs. O'Brien, pestering them to bring him in to see her. All of these letters had to go through the Reverend Mother's office unsealed, so that they could be censored before being posted. And Bridie was forever praising the nuns and saying how much she liked the place knowing the nuns would be reading them.

When the letter eventually arrived, the O'Brien's were well and truly convinced that Bridie Rodgers was a biteen touched in the head, because so many of her letters were incomplete, or had words blacked out. To Mr. and Mrs. O'Brien, many of the letters made no sense at all. Likewise, letters going into the Magdalene Home and meant for Bridie were steamed open and similar action was taken. Occasionally some of these letters were considered inappropriate and disposed of immediately.

For years, Bridie had been hankering for a visit from her son, but to no avail. Despite this she continued to write letter after letter, begging for a visit from her son until one summers evening her pleas got a rare mention in the O'Brien household.

They were seated either side of the cosy turf fire, each lost in worlds of their own. Edward was sitting quietly, smoking his crooked stemmed pipe while reading 'Treasure Island', courtesy of John

Paschal's school library. His wife Catherine or 'Kate' as she liked to be called was equally quiet, but with her knitting needles clicking rhythmically away while at the same time mentally plotting her next decisive move.

"You know, I was thinking, maybe we should hire 'Michael Kirrane' and bring that fella up to see his mother."

But Edward was a million miles away, although vaguely aware that his wife was rambling on about something or other. His only response however was to unknowingly grunt or groan for he hated to be disturbed while reading.

"...God knows, 'twould be an act of charity to get her off our backs. I'm not able to be writing anymore, and besides, I'm sick answering her letters and making excuses."

"Ah hmmm."

"'Tis all right for you and your 'Ah hmmm'. You never write anyway, not while you have muggins here to do everything for you...."

"Hmmm," sighed Ned, peeved that even in his own house he could never get a minutes peace without *herself* continuously be-draggling him about something or other.

"You know he's thirteen now. Another couple of years and he'll be gone from us altogether."

But still, Edward's only response was to raise the tempo of his reading to denote his heartfelt annoyance at her interference. His reading became an audible whisper in an effort to silence his wife's endless tongue, which at times he secretly thought was the length of the street.

Catherine knew that this change in his reading tone was a clear signal to her that she was winning her argument and that anything she suggested was more or less sanctioned by him. So she continued to gnaw at his subconscious in an effort to bring him to heel.

"....Of course we'll have to buy him a new suit: we can't have him going in there to that place looking like a tramp; what with his mother and the nuns looking at him and everything, he'll have to look his best."

Edward moved uneasily in his chair. His reading came to an abrupt halt. He removed his spittle-stained pipe and spat into the fire, saying angrily,

"I don't know in the light of Jesus how that tongue of yours can stick it!"

Catherine's knitting needles, which were going at a nice steady pace creating the sleeve of an aran sweater suddenly moved up a notch, and into overdrive, as she replied angrily,

"Arrah, God blast it! If one was waiting for the likes of you to do anything, one would be waiting a long, long time."

Edward, peeved at her accusation, stood up before turning his back to absorb a little comfort from the dying embers of the fire, asked her,

"And what's wrong with the suiteen he has?"

Kate stopped knitting and looked at him in sheer exasperation,

"Well, looked, you're the damnest man I ever met! Didn't I tell you before, that jacket of his, was too small. Isn't it like a little waistcoat on him, or don't you realise that he's a growing lad. And what's more, if we don't bring him in to see her soon, 'tis a brand new pair of shoes he'll need, on top of everything else."

"Well," replied Ned, with a resigning look, as he turned and spat into the fire again. "I don't care what you do; It's up to yourself," before deciding to put on his jacket and go out into the night.

Within days Mrs. O'Brien gave instructions to John Paschal – who usually spent his evenings playing football or gallivanting, as she liked to call it – to write and tell his mother Bridie that he was coming in to see her. Soon.

For years John Paschal had lived in a confused state of mind in relation to his mother in Galway. He couldn't understand why he had to go on writing to her, if she was his mother. Why couldn't he go and live with her? As far as he was concerned the whole thing was silly. Wasn't he already living with his mother, so how could he have another? Though there was a time when he thought he could vaguely remember running around with other children with one or two or three women looking after him. But then he thought that was probably another school. He wasn't sure of anything. And when he asked his mother, Mrs. O'Brien, why he had two mothers when everyone else in the world had only one, she told him he was too young yet. That he wouldn't understand. Maybe when you're sixteen, you'll understand better.

Sixteen! he thought. But I'll be an old man. I'll be living in Dublin or England or maybe America. Because I'm definitely not staying on the land, even though Ned would like me to. I'll go somewhere; where I can see the pictures every Sunday night, and maybe if I'm lucky, get a job, I'll play for Galway. There is nothing else in this world I want more than to play football for Galway.

But now he had more exciting things to think about. He was going to Galway to see his mother Bridie for the first time. He had to write and tell her now or Mrs. O'Brien would have his guts for garters.

> *Dear Bridie,*
> *Thank you very much for the lovely letter you sent me. I hope you are in good health as this leaves us all at present, thank God.*
> *The weather is good. We have the hay saved and some of the turf footed.*
> *Now close your eyes for a second, as I have some good news for you. Mammy said to tell you we are going to Galway to see you on Friday the 13th.*
> *That is all the news I have for now. Goodbye and God Bless, and write soon.*
>
> *From your son Paschal.*

He's in bed trying not to think about his visit to Galway. He wants instead to finish reading 'The adventures of Huckleberry Finn'. But it's no use. No adventure no matter how good could be as exciting as travelling by car to Galway city for the very first time. He had never been on a bus, train or car in his entire life. So he decided instead to curl up beneath the blankets and visualise Kirrane's gleaming black hackney car pulling into the street. Its hidden, powerful engine purring away beneath the bonnet, as a stream of white spasmodic smoke trailed from its chrome exhaust as it waited especially, to transport him all the way to Galway.

When at last the day came, he found to his great joy, that he was really on a holiday. He didn't have to do any of the usual farmhouse chores. No milking of the cows, no feeding of the pigs, no bringing in of the turf. Nothing.

"Eat up your breakfast now like a good lad and be ready to go when 'Kirrane' comes. We can't have you smelling like an oul' piss pot, and I after scrubbing the lard out of you," said Mrs. O'Brien.

Just when he thought he was fully kitted-out in his brand new suit, Mrs. O'Brien collared him and put a good lather of 'brylcream' on his head, to try and keep his hair in place: and not have it falling into his eyes. And to crown it all, as it were, she placed a triangular-shaped white handkerchief in the top pocket of his suit. When he looked at himself in the mirror he saw that this major white symbol transformed him from a well-dressed country gosun into a real townie and he felt awfully proud. All he could do now was sit by the window, and wait.

* * * * *

The sun shone its brightest as the car sped up hill and down dale. John Paschal sat in the back seat with his mother, Mrs. O'Brien, while her daughter Maureen, sat in the front with the driver. Paschal absorbed the fragrant smell of the highly polished upholstery, and he craned his neck to study the chromium-plated circular dials of the dashboard. They were doing fifty miles an hour, but not for long. Halfway past Tuam they met several herds of cattle, motor lorries and the longest nomadic convoy of gaily painted, horse-drawn, tinkers' caravans he had ever seen. This was indeed a breath-taking sight. There were hundreds of piebald horses, donkeys, goats and ponies travelling along the road. And bringing up the rear was a mini-parade of shawl-clad women and what looked like their chimney-swept husbands in corduroy garb. They were seated in the midst of their horse-drawn carts surrounded by leg-bound hens, ducks, and geese as the horses went clippedy-clop, clippedy-clop along the road at break-neck speed. Occasionally the chickens would flap their wings in a vain attempt to get away from the deafening sounds of whining horses, frisky, braying donkeys and wild-eyed, bleating goats. Then as Paschal knelt on the back seat of the car, looking back at the minuscule, fading spectacle, he was surprised to hear the driver say they were almost in Galway.

Meanwhile, Bridie fretted more and more each hour about her son's imminent arrival. Ever since she'd received John Paschal's letter and had its contents confirmed by the Reverend Mother, she worried about how he would react to her after all these years. Would she still recognise him? Would he accept her as his real mother? What if he wasn't nice to her, and wouldn't give her a hug? The whole thing might be too much for him, she thought. He might even get frightened and turn away. Besides Julie Murray, Josephine Finn, Lilly MacAlastair, Margaret Sherry as well as Sister Philomena and the rest of the nuns, everyone wanted to meet John Paschal. The way things were going she thought, she wouldn't get a look in at all herself. She had planned to give him something special. So when Sister Philomena gave her the gift of a few bob to mark the special occasion, she was very happy indeed.

Suddenly, all of Bridie's friends wanted to give him little gifts of their own; to mark the occasion. But Bridie was more worried about her hair, her clothes and her looks until Sister Philomena surprised her by bringing her into her office for a clothes fitting. Soon everything was arranged.

Bridie could not believe that a bright new day was about to dawn. She was almost too afraid to think about it in case something happened to spoil her happiness, that she'd get sick or that John Paschal would get sick, or worse still, get killed on the road before she could lay her eyes on him again.

Nervously she paced up and down the Magdalene grounds with her close friends. She had asked the nuns could they take time off, to be with her and to see John Paschal. It didn't matter anyway because all of the penitents were now on their lunch break, running around the place like excited school kids: most of them oblivious to Bridie's impending reunion with her son. Bridie prayed that the bell would soon go, so that they couldn't all gang up and gawk when Mrs O'Brien introduced John Paschal to her. She wanted only her friends to be with her, when the moment came. She was shaking like a leaf and asked Julie Murray for the second time, if she had any more fags.

"For God's sake will you slow down? Sure you must be eaten them," said Julie as they paced up and down the rear door of the laundry like a group of sentries. But despite Julie's outward show of good humour, she was struggling to come to terms with the fact that Bridie Rodgers was lording it over them all. She was thinking, *that one* gets her own way no matter *f*what. She can write letters galore to her son and no one will say a word to her. How she managed to swindle John Paschal's address out of the nuns I'll never know. An' now they're letting him in to see her if you don't mind. Sure that wan must be coddin' us all. There has to be some trickery involved. An' if I as much as try to run out the door or try to run away I'm near kilt: murthered so I am. Do you know *f*what it is, the people around here – especially them nuns – they're gone soft in the head. They seem to think the sun shines out of *that one's* arse. 'Tis not fair, so it isn't.

"God almighty, will he ever come?" asked Bridie, as she linked her friend Julie and they continued to walk behind Lilly MacAlastair and Josephine Finn.

Suddenly, they were stopped in their tracks the appearance of by Sister Philomena, calling aloud from the rear door of the laundry,

"Where's Bridie Rodgers? Bridie Rodgers! "

A surge of conflicting emotions shot through Julie's heart at the prospect of her friend's crowning glory. Look at her now, trottin' off, after the nuns every beck and call: off to meet her John Paschal. And all I'm left with is the devil; and all because no one cares. Sure there's no justice at all in this wide world. No justice at all, she sighed.

The nuns were trying to coach Bridie on how to behave, but she wasn't listening, merely bowing her head at every thing they said. She too was in a world of her own. She thought of all the days and weeks and months and years when she prayed for this moment. She remembered vividly how she had dreamed on countless occasions about seeing her son, on the 13th. Now it was about to become a reality. She knew it was the most significant number in her whole life. She was born on the 13th. Her son John Paschal was removed from her after the 13th month and now she was seeing him on the 13th day of July. She knew it was her lucky number and would always be so.

After a lengthy introduction with the various religious figures, John Paschal began to observe his impressive surroundings. The parlour room where Mrs O'Brien, Maureen and a group of nuns stood huddled together in whispered conversation was adorned with a beautiful array of antique furniture. Mini statues of St. Joseph, black St. Martin, and St. Anthony, adorned the massive Connemara-marbled-fireplace: while huge religious pictures hung on the walls and hanging there amongst them was a large blood stained Crucifix of Our Lord.

It was quite obvious to John Paschal that not alone could one not say a swear word to oneself while living here, one could not even think such a thing. These nuns were the holiest human beings he had ever seen. Their soft gentle voices proved their delicate minds could not withstand a minor swear word, let alone a real whopper, like he knew he was capable of delivering. He also knew from what his teachers had told him, that priests and bishops no matter how bad their behaviour in this life were sure of a place in Heaven. So naturally one only had to take a look at these nuns to know that they too would all march straight into the kingdom of Heaven. While mere mortals, like Mrs. O'Brien and everyone else had to work hard night and day, to redeem their souls.

John Paschal was, at that particular time, considering joining the priesthood, for that reason alone. But somehow the idea never took root in his head: no matter how many times he told himself he'd like to help the black babies of South Africa: where it seemed you could buy a dozen oranges for a penny. A Jesuit priest visiting their school had divulged this extraordinary secret to them. He begged them not to tell anyone or the whole country would be rearing to join up, to become priests, so they could all go on the foreign missions. He recalled, how he almost signed up there and then when the priest started describing the great problems they had with the vast quantities of grapes and bananas continuously falling from the tall trees, almost killing the natives. It seemed to John Paschal at that time as if everyone else and especially the priests had all the luck. And there they were now, before his very eyes, a bountiful bowl of ruby-red apples and mouth-a-peeling Transvaal oranges sitting majestically on the large mahogany table in the centre of the room; waiting to be devoured.

But his pangs of hunger were soon banished by a commotion at the door when a dark-haired woman, surrounded by a cloister of nuns approached him with outstretched arms, pleading,

"Paschal! Paschal dear, how are you?" said Bridie as she threw her arms around him and held him for a moment in a vice-like grip.

Paschal froze. He was unable to speak, even though Mrs. O'Brien had instructed him to be on his best behaviour. To say, 'yes ma'am', and 'no ma'am'. But how could he possibly do that now when a woman he'd never seen before was attempting to squeeze the life out of him. While a gang of dumbstruck nuns as well as Mrs. O'Brien and her daughter Maureen were watching him like hawks.

"Paschal! You look wonderful! You're so big! And you look so smart in your new suit and everything. Aren't you going to say anything?" said Bridie holding him at arms length.

Slowly, Paschal shook his head. No.

"Aren't you going to say 'Hello' to your own mother? Paschal! Paschal,! I'm your mother." teased Bridie again.

But John Paschal said nothing. Instead he dropped his head in shame and mumbled to himself, "No." All he wanted to do was run away. Because all eyes were still on him, as if he were guilty of some major crime.

"Won't you say 'Hello' to Bridie?" urged Mrs. O'Brien, annoyed that John Paschal wouldn't even open his gob; while at home, he'd talk the hind legs off an ass.

"Hello," said John Paschal out of the blue, because he knew he'd get the back of Mrs. O'Brien's hand and a right tongue-lashing when he got home if he didn't.

Aw!" exclaimed the nuns. "Now, can't he talk. Perhaps some day, he'll be a priest."

"Lord wouldn't that be wonderful?" added Mrs. O'Brien, proudly. "We'd all be blessed entirely," while at the same time she was deciding if this whole thing was such a good idea after all.

Inwardly she'd recoiled in horror when she heard Bridie say, 'Paschal! Paschal! I'm your mother!" Thinking to herself, you weren't much of a mother to him the day I rescued him from the home in Tuam, and you Miss not having a penny to your name, a bit to put in your mouth nor a pot to piss in. As far as I'm concerned, he'll only ever have one mother and that's the one that rears him.

After some time his new mother brought him on a tour of the picturesque grounds with their colourful array of shrubs and flower strewn pathways leading to a Grotto of the Blessed Virgin Mary.

It was only then, in reply to Bridie's many questions that he really observed his new mother for the first time. She was tall and thin. Thin as a wisp, with the most gorgeous head of black curly hair that was as sleek and shiny as a raven's wing. And when she spoke it was with a soft soothing voice that made him want to listen to her all day. She had beautiful big eyes with extraordinarily high cheekbones that gave her a Spanish look, he thought. And yet her face was as pale and white as the driven snow. This frightened him because he had never seen anyone so pale, except once when he went to a funeral with Mrs. O'Brien and he had to stand beside the coffin pretending to pray, but had looked instead at the hideous ghostly appearance of the body. In a way he thought, Bridie looked like that. She wore a long-sleeved silk blouse and a three-quarter length, navy, pleated skirt. She was so thin and frail looking he thought, she must be very ill, and that the place was some kind of a hospital. The word 'sanatorium' sprang to mind, but he didn't know what it meant. He had heard it used in whispered conversations at home, and was now of the opinion that this was such a place. But when his new mother put her arm about his shoulder and gave him a gentle hug as they walked around, he felt less afraid of her and her condition. But he still couldn't grasp what it was all about. It seemed as though he really had two mothers, the same as some of his school friends had two uncles and three aunts. He knew he had no aunts or uncles, but with this new addition to his family he couldn't wait to tell all his friends about it.

Bridie was at that moment endorsing his belief when she presented him with a small leather purse containing a brand new, pound note. He never had so much money before, and knew instantly that this was the same person who made all his birthdays come true at Christmas and Easter and every other day with her surprise parcels.

She was introducing him to all her friends, as they stood gawking in their long, white calico gowns and white hats, each of them giving him packets of sweets and bars of chocolate. And when Julie told Bridie he was the spitting image of her, her face lit up with a beaming smile. Then as Bridie made him wave goodbye to all her friends she led him back into the parlour once again.

"Paschal dear, I want you to know I'll be praying every day for your continued good health and happiness." she said, while giving him another long hug that he would never ever forget.

After supping lashings of tea from dainty china cups together with an assortment of cakes and biscuits, the visitors were soon back in their chauffeur-driven car, frantically waving their last goodbyes. But this time there was no excitement on the road. No cattle, no nomadic tribe to colour the horizon. Nothing. Only dark clouds gathering, as a strange silence filled the motor car, and a feeling of misconception and loneliness as John Paschal tried to comprehend the sudden appearance of a beautiful woman in his life, his mother.

Mother, he thought, why did you cry when I had to leave? And why does your face look so white? Why are you not like the rest of the people living out in the country? And why do you and all the other women in the 'Magdalene Home' lead such strange lives. Because of these and so many other unanswered questions, life for John Paschal would never ever be the same again.

Chapter Fifteen

As a result of Noreen Donnellan's successful escape bid, there was a serious rash of attempted breakouts within the Home. All of them failed miserably because the nuns were ready for it and constantly on their guard.

It was a fierce blow to the Reverend Mother's pride that one of her most highly thought of, in-house-residents, had managed to fool everyone – including herself – and got clean away. And unknown to Bridie Rodgers, her son's visit had almost come a cropper, as a result of Noreen Donnellan's successful escape bid. And were it not for the fact that the 'Reverend Mother' herself had given a personal commitment to her retired friend, Sister Hortense in Tuam, allowing the visit of John Paschal to go ahead, then she would have cancelled the whole thing, fearing it to be just another ruse: an attempt by Bridie Rodgers to escape.

The Reverend Mother came to the conclusion that when an ungrateful penitent brat, such as Noreen Donnellan, was prepared to raise her right hand to God and swear that she wanted to become a consecrated penitent, then the rest of the inmates were fit for anything. They deserved no mercy. The cheek of that brat, she thought. Imagine! Imagine leaving a note like that! Gone to Winnamstown. Winnamstown my foot! Why leave such a silly note if she were going elsewhere? Clearly she never meant to go Williamstown. Unfortunately it's too late now. I should have known she was up to no good: herself and her nineteen pounds, ten shillings and sixpence. God! What am I talking about? More like twenty-three or twenty four pounds I expect by the time she left. It seems my Guardian Angel let me down after all. I knew I should have followed my own instincts and asked Sergeant Ruane to check the trains and buses that morning just in case she got on. Me waiting here like a fool for her to return. No. The mistake I made was handing her the savings book. God! When I think of the embarrassment of it all: having to report her to the Gardaí and the Bishop as a missing person.

The Reverend Mother, was still contemplating while she finished her cup of tea and thought; I suppose I'm getting old, not able for this anymore. A few short years ago, I know what I'd have done; fleeced that lady good and proper and confiscated her little book. That would have taken the wind out of Miss Donnellan's sails; the ungrateful little brat. Oh, it makes my blood boil when I think of how good we were to that lady. And because of her, five more penitents thought they could make a run for it. But thank goodness, I was ready and waiting. Imagine if they broke out, I'd probably be transferred to Dublin or Cork. Sure where's the use in crying now. But I promise you the next one that tries to escape from the Magdalene is in for a rude awakening. I promise you that, she asserted while leaving her empty cup back in its saucer before taking up her pen again.

Peggy Neary came hurriedly out of the kitchen, carrying a small pot of Irish stew. She managed to slip quietly away from her real task of washing up, so she could be the first to relay the news. She knew that Sergeant Ruane was very highly regarded by most of the nuns and in particular the Reverend Mother, whose close friendship with him, she long-suspected was one of an unhealthy nature. Nevertheless, Peggy was on the side of church and state, and only too happy to align herself with the Reverend Mother in her admiration of the notable Sergeant.

She also knew that many of the penitents or what she herself called 'country bitches' hated Sergeant Ruane with a vengeance, just because he gave them a good lathering if they tried to escape from the Magdalene.

When Peggy reached the long tables in the centre of the dining hall she called out, "Anyone for more stew?"

Immediately, there was a chorus of requests. Bridie Rodgers called out, and asked, "Have you any more bread? I'd love another cut, because there's nothing in this stew but peas," she said, trying to rise Peggy.

"Peggy, ignored the jibe and instead shouted back into the kitchen, "Another slice of bread for Bridie Rodgers. No! Make that three. No! Four. Four more slices for tables seven and nine."

Then, making her way over to Bridie, she lowered her head and whispered, "Did you hear about Sergeant Ruane?"

For a brief moment Bridie was perplexed, as she tried to recollect anyone having escaped or gone missing. Then the awful thought struck her.

"Oh God, don't say it's Noreen. She hasn't been caught has she?"

"Arrah, what's wrong with you?" said Peggy, giving Bridie a playful dig of her elbow. "Noreen's long gone, and well you know it. It's Sergeant Ruane. He's dead. He was killed yesterday. Run over by a bus. The poor man's as dead as a maggot."

"What?" asked Bridie in total shock as the other penitents at the table began to crane their long necks to see, if they were hearing things.

"'Tis true. One of the drivers just told me. The Reverend Mother's beside herself. I couldn't make out what was wrong with her all morning. Promise me you'll not say a word, because some of them bitches over there," she whispered, nodding her head to indicate the people at the back of the room, "would dance on his grave and the poor man not buried yet."

"But are you sure?" asked Bridie, still recovering from the shock, and half afraid it was just a wild rumour. To Bridie it seemed too good to be true. Though she never liked to hear a bad word about anyone, she had to admit to herself that Ruane, was an evil thug and that perhaps 'twas good enough for him.

"Here's your bread."

"Thanks Berni," said Peggy, taking a slice of bread off the plate and handing it to Bridie. "Amn't I after telling you he was knocked down. Killed stone dead," said Peggy. Remember, blessed are those who have not seen, but have believed. I have to go. I'll see you later. We'll go to Church together and offer up a decade of the rosary."

"If...if I have time," answered Bridie hesitantly, as she didn't want to be seen associating with Peggy, who was widely regarded as a trouble-maker and a gossip, while at the same time she didn't like to refuse.

"I'll ask Julie and Lilly, maybe they'd like to come too," added Bridie shrewdly, without batting an eyelid, knowing Peggy didn't really care for her friends company and wouldn't want to be seen dead in the same pew, never mind in their company.

Peggy half-turned and gave Bridie a cutting glance as she dished out the last of the stew to a hungry penitent, saying, "I don't mind your friend Julie, but that other toe-rag! Forget it."

Then turning around, she headed straight for the kitchen, peeved that Bridie had rejected her reasonable request, and asking herself why she had even bothered to try and make friends with her. She's always the same: neither for you nor against you. Yet, she seems to have loads of friends, I just don't know how she does it.

Bridie sat finishing her dinner, mopping up the soggy stew with relish, while those around her asked if what they had heard was true. Bridie simply smiled and said, "I don't know. If I was you, I'd take it like your dinner, with a good dose of salt."

It was late that evening before Bridie, Julie and her friends had confirmation via one of the Sisters that Sergeant Ruane had indeed been killed. At least Peggy was right in saying one thing, thought Bridie. Some of the penitents were already dancing on his grave, and the poor man not yet buried.

* * * * *

For some weeks now, Josephine Finn appeared to be sliding slowly but surely into the deep, dark throes of despair. This change in Josephine's personality went largely unnoticed amongst her friends and colleagues. They were always too preoccupied with thoughts and problems of their own to notice anyone else. Nobody knew that Josephine had been crying herself to sleep in the loneliness of the warm summer nights at the thought of a love lost. The shock of seeing Bridie's son coming into the Home after twelve long years was almost too much to bear. It had awakened something deep inside of her. She felt as if someone had plunged a dagger through her heart because it brought home to her the awfulness of her own wasted years spent dreaming of a life outside the high, stone walls of her imprisonment. Her lifelong dream of going to London and Broadway, to meet her hero Judy Garland: of seeing her name in big red lights was seemingly so far away; so far away she thought, it was almost out of sight.

Unknown to herself, she had long ago eased the painful memories of her cruel parents and 'Cathal' out of her head, concentrating instead all her energy on that foolish dream of becoming a major star. Expecting all the time that the door to freedom would somehow magically open: or that a knight in shining armour, in the form of Mr. Fincock, from Dublin, would come to her rescue. She began to realise for the first time that it was all a myth, a pipe dream she had created herself to mask her own show of vanity. When all the time what she should really have been doing was plotting and planning her road to freedom, which in turn might have led to stardom. She realised she should have been planning and plotting her escape like Noreen, or at the very least like Bridie Rodgers who continuously hounded and harried people with her begging letters.

Instead, she had resigned herself to her present fate forever, by giving up the fight. Look at Bridie, she thought. If I heard her say it once, I heard her say it a thousand times, how one day she'd be reunited with her son. And all I could think of was 'yeah, good for you', if you can settle for that, then so be it. But one day, I'm going to be a Star. Oh God! I've been such a fool: dreaming my life away. Even my own mother used to say, 'Josephine, you'll never come to anything, 'cause you're only a dreamer'.

Oh why, oh why did John Paschal have to come to her? I can't believe, he was just a baby, the day the three of us came here. And he's near thirteen or fourteen now. And Bridie is worried that in a year or two he'll leave home and she'll never see him again. But at least she had the pleasure of seeing him. To think, if only I'd ran off with Cathal, when we met in Tuam. We could have gone to England. We should have gone, I suppose; what harm, but the thought ran through my head that very day. I should. I should have ran away from home. What's more I should have made a run for it the day I was brought in here, because in the end nobody cares. Look at Julie Murray, at least she tried, twice. She'll surely get out yet. And look at Noreen, got away scot-free. Straight out the gate. I'll have to go too. I'll go straight out like that, because I can't stick this place another minute. Scrubbing floors and shirt collars, day in day out, not to mention all the polishing and praying. And watching people fight over stupid things like rosary beads, and food, and money, and clothes, and cigarettes; even friends: but nobody fights over me, no one, because no one cares.

And as she lay awake in the early dawn thinking these horrible thoughts, she swung her bare white legs over the edge of the frail iron bed, and sighed wearily because she hadn't slept a wink all night. She knew dawn was already breaking and that soon they'd all be getting up and going down to the Laundry to start another long day. Struck by the brightness of the early morning she lifted her bedside chair and placed it quietly beside the tall window and climbed up on to the well-worn ledge, so that she could peep out through the scratched spy-holes of the painted glass. She could clearly see across the city rooftops the distant haze of an azure sky and clearly hear the heart-warming chorus of songbirds nearby. For a long time she stood peering at the emerging blue sky of dawn and the drifting dark clouds rolling gently by. She began recalling the mythical words of her favourite song, which she had sung so many times for the penitents, especially at Christmas. Now she'd give almost anything, anything – even her own body – for some handsome fella to sing it to her. Then and only then could she ever believe in the lines of Judy Garland's song,

Somewhere over the rainbow,
Way on high.
There's a land that I heard of,
Once in a lullaby.
Somewhere over the rainbow,
Skies are blue,
And dreams that you dared to dream,
Really do come true.

She turned abruptly away from the vision and stepped down from the window-ledge. She'd had enough of dreams and rainbows, she told herself. She never ever wanted to hear that blasted song again. She decided, that's it, I'm leaving, before this place kills me. God! Wouldn't it be a good one to climb over the wall, and not say a word to any one. No one knew Julie or Noreen were planning to escape, until they were gone. And now that Sergeant Ruane is dead, that's exactly what I'll do. I'll just vanish. Over the wall and I'm gone. It's as simple as that. I'll not say a word to anyone. I'll go to Dublin and find Mr Fincock and soon I'll be a Star: a real star. I'm a good singer I know, but in Dublin, I'll be a real, real star. I'll ask Bridie and Julie for the loan of some money to buy perfume and cigarettes. They'll never deck it until it's too late, and by then I'll be gone. I'll be Free. God! Why didn't I do this, ages ago? Of course I thought about it a lot, but somehow I never had the courage until now. So, that's it. I'm off out today,

Josephine sighed happily, as she climbed back into bed and dragged the ancient blankets up around her body. If only she could get some sleep now, she thought, before the excitement of this new day, then I'd really be elected.

"...Girls that reminds me, I was wondering if I could get the loan of a few bob off one of ye. I want to get some nice perfume and make-up for the dance on Sunday. I've decided to treat myself to a good night out," said Josephine to her friends, after she'd slipped away from the stifling heat and suds of the washroom. While Julie and Bridie were only too glad to take a breather in the ironing room, the perspiration beginning to make the clothes stick to their bodies, as they stood, ironing garment after garment.

Julie and Bridie looked questioningly at Josephine. She never asked for money as a rule, and certainly never off Bridie because she knew all of her savings went on her son, John Paschal.

"What dance? You mean…?"

"Yeah! You know Sunday night! In the oul' hall, Lee O'…what's his name…Lee O' Byrne is playing. I heard it announced on the wireless."

"Sure I've only a shillin', if that's any good? You might get a man for that," said Julie trying to inject a little humour into the conversation.

She didn't want to think about the money at all. She was fed up with people coming to her for the loan of fags, sweets, money, make-up and ever'thin'. You name it and they were after it, she thought. *F*what harm, but half of them wastrels never give it back.

"And I'm saving for Paschal's Christmas things. But I have two shillings. I'll lend that to you, if you promise me I can have it back soon…."

"Oh I will! I will!" Said Josephine eagerly.

"….Besides, I think that perfume you're buying is awfully dear. Maybe the van-drivers keep some of the money for themselves. Why don't you ask Sister Philomena, to get it for you this time. You might get it cheaper?" said Bridie, reaching into the top of her blouse for the elusive purse, before handing Josephine the two shillings.

Josephine took the money and went back quickly to the washroom, ecstatic that everything was going according to plan. It was an ideal time to make a run for it, she thought, as she now had three shillings to her name.

As it was Tuesday, and last week's dirty washing was in full swing, young penitent girls were staggering to and fro up and down the long corridors under the weight of their trolleys, transporting the soggy masses of hotel linen to the big calenders in the drying room. Others were busy folding and stacking the freshly laundered curtains and drapes, ready to be sent over to dispatch for delivery. There, two of the nuns were overseeing the parcelling and speedy distribution of the city's laundry in time for the Galway Races, where multitudes appeared overnight, eager to enjoy themselves and to seek accommodation in the city's hotels, guest-houses, and private dwellings. The nuns knew they were being stretched to the pin of their collar to have everything washed and dried and delivered on schedule.

But that did not deter Josephine Finn. She slipped quietly away from her post by the sink; saying she was going to the lavatory and disappeared instead out the rear exit and along by the side of the main building, towards the Grotto of 'Our Lady.' There she adopted a crouched position until she reached the nearest point to the high perimeter wall. Then she scurried across at an acute angle, before reaching the far corner of the floral garden, adjacent to the nuns' cemetery, where a large sycamore tree grew close to the wall.

She felt unbelievably calm as she stood for a moment to look around and see if anyone was watching. Perfect. It was just as she had planned. There wasn't a sinner to be seen anywhere as they were all too busy inside. The first city delivery having already gone out from dispatch, there was no prospect of any drivers or nuns approaching the main door, she thought.

All of a sudden she felt clumsy, as she surveyed the most advantageous point from which to climb up onto the wall. As previously anticipated, she decided that one good toehold in the ancient stonework and she'd reach the top of the wall. And as she gathered her long white gown and skirts around her, she wished she hadn't put on so many clothes.

Before going out to work that morning, Josephine had put on an extra-large pair of knickers, an extra brassiere and two light jumpers; as well as her skirt and long, white gown. She planned to remove the gown and cap the minute she was over the wall, and the extra clothing would come in handy when she was in Dublin, she figured.

Now she wasn't so sure if it was such a good idea. All morning she'd felt most uncomfortable working in all that extra clobber, but now she thought she'd suffocate and she hadn't even started to climb the wall yet. Placing one hand on the side of the tree and one hand high up on the wall, she levered herself upwards and spread her sore-infested legs to gain extra leverage. Then she wheeled her body round and with a fierce struggle she managed to get a firm grip on the top of the wall and began to pull herself up until her body lay resting across the top of it. She already knew the wall was very high from the outside. But when she looked down onto College Road and the sidewalk beneath her, she thought it was terrifying. The wall looked as if it was about to topple onto the sidewalk, as a result of being uprooted by the giant tree. She glanced instead across at the neat row of houses, which was 'Mary Magdalene Terrace' and saw a little old lady who was cleaning her window stop, and gawk at her. She just stood there staring as if frozen in time, holding up the lace curtain with her left hand, while her cleaning hand rested on the window. For a brief moment the two stared in bewilderment at each other, before Josephine realised she had to make up her mind quickly: turn round and go back or go ahead now and jump.

She looked to her left and saw that the wall appeared to take a slight turn left around a corner, not more than five yards away. If she jumped now, she thought, she'd better run off in that direction, rather than go the other way where she might run into one of the 'Sisters of Mercy' nuns, collecting for charity.

She made up her mind. She'd have to jump now or face the prospect of a humiliating defeat, without having even tried to escape.

She manoeuvred her body sideways and adopted a sitting position ready to jump, aware that her every, embarrassing move was being carefully watched by the little old lady. She could already feel her cheeks flaming with embarrassment, especially with her having to swing her legs up and over the wall..

When she looked down she soon realised there was no way she could jump. It was too dangerous. She'd surely kill herself. But she was too far advanced now to turn back Glancing quickly down she couldn't even see the base of the wall, such was the angle. The only thing to do, she decided was to turn around and somehow lower her body gradually, seeking out a toe-hold before jumping the last few feet to freedom.

When at last she succeeded in turning herself round on the top of the wall, she got the land of her life. For in the twinkling of an eye she lost her grip and her body began to slither down the coarse stonework, which pushed her brassieres up off her breasts as she plummeted painfully to the ground. And because she landed so heavily on her feet, she fell backward landing smack on her arse as her beautiful splayed legs flew into the air exposing all her finery.

As if all that weren't bad enough, who should happen to be coming round the corner, but two Guards on their way to give evidence in the Galway Circuit Court. They immediately ran to her aid as a stunned Josephine looked up and moaned in agony. They immediately began lifting her up, helping her to her feet as she cried out in pain,

"Oh my feet! My feet!"

The two Guards were well aware of who she was and what her intentions were carried her bodily to the main entrance of the Magdalene, despite her protests. They would like to have helped her escape, but they were duty bound to do the right thing and return her to the Magdalene Laundry. The Guards knew from experience that many of the inmates tried to escape by climbing over the wall. This was just another attempt. And the little old lady who started out cleaning her windows continued to stare as if lost in something of a time warp as the heavy oak door opened in response to the doorbell and one of the Reverend Sisters invited Josephine and the Guards to go right in.

The two Guards escorted Josephine down to the infirmary ward where the nuns took care of her while the officers returned to their duty.

Soon Mother Superior appeared in the doorway and glowered for a moment at Josephine Finn lying on the bed.

"Well! Well! If it isn't 'Judy Garland' herself! The latest escapee or did you just pop out to the Galway Races?" she said sarcastically, going to the foot of Josephine's bed. "Aw, you poor thing. I suppose we'll have to get you a doctor."

The Reverend Mother examined Josephine by grabbing hold of each leg and giving it a sharp twist to the left and right, much to Josephine's distress.

"If it's any consolation nothing appears to be broken, Miss; more's the pity. It might have put manners on you, or better still, you might have landed on your head. That would surely have knocked a bit of sense into you and given you a bit of inspiration: something to think about, 'cause God knows, you're badly in need of it."

Later the doctor was called. He confirmed that she had no serious injuries. He said her hips and legs were severely bruised, and that together with her festered sores would take a long time to heal.

The Reverend Mother's immediate response was to order Josephine's hair to be cut and her food rationed. She remained in bed for several days constantly moaning about her fate.

Julie and Bridie and a host of her friends came to visit her every day in an effort to cheer her up because they themselves were deeply affected by her sudden fall from grace, not to mention the loss of their regular songbird.

After a week she was back standing at her sink in the washroom, but had little or no interest in scrubbing clothes. Instead she continued to moan about her misfortune and was then assigned to carry out menial tasks, by the Reverend Mother. But Josephine point blank refused to co-operate with anyone. After several rows with the Sisters; they decided, she should see a doctor and he confirmed she was suffering from manic-depression. He prescribed a course of medication and ordered her to take a complete rest. Occasionally Sister Philomena, would visit the Infirmary Ward, to see how Josephine was, but each time Sister quickly turned away because of her own internal suffering. Not a day went by that she didn't recall the Health Inspector's visit and his desire to take Josephine to Dublin and to the theatre. But between listening to the Reverend Mother's lofty attitude and the priests' weekly sermon on man's wanton desire to consume the female flesh, she had done nothing for fear of doing the wrong thing. She knew now without a shadow of a doubt that she had done the wrong thing anyway, and it pained her even more.

Meanwhile, Bridie who had lent Josephine her two shillings the day she attempted to escape was desperate to have her money back. She worried that she would never see it again. She did not want to ask Josephine to repay what she owed, but felt sure that she must still have the money, because she couldn't have spent it. She decided, she'd merely hint at it by saying she was looking forward to buying a few presents for John Paschal. If she got her money back it would make life so much easier, she thought. But the very minute she mentioned Paschal's name, Josephine flew into a rage.

"Ah Bridie will you shut up! I don't ever want to hear your boy's name again. Every time you open your mouth, it's John Paschal this, John Paschal that. You know you'd sicken anyone… "

"I'm sorry love, I didn't mean to hurt your feelings…" began Bridie.

"Ah you'd think no one in the world had a child but yourself. Cathal Swanick and I could have had half a dozen …and…."

"Ah, Josephine."

"'Ah Josephine me arse! 'Tis true. You'd think no one else in the wide earthly world had a child but yourself. There are scores of women here, who've had children and they never open their mouths about them."

Bridie was disturbed and surprised at Josephine's onslaught She was hurt by her suggestion that she spent too much time talking about him, but she felt even more hurt by the realisation that her friend was still deeply disturbed in mind and spirit. Perhaps it was the medication, she thought. Nevertheless she would not let anyone talk to her like that.

"That may be so, but I'm different. I'll not…" she started to reply but was again cut off in mid-sentence by Josephine, who looked as if she was going to have a fit, as froth began to appear at the corners of her mouth.

"How're you different? You think the sun shines out of your arse or something?"

"No dear, I don't. And anyway I'm not like that," replied Bridie calmly, as she studied Josephine's contorted features. She knew her friend must be very down to talk like that to her. She'd have to try and help her. Support her in her hour of need.

"Well then shut up and leave me alone!" suggested Josephine.

But Bridie extended her hand and placed it tentatively on Josephine's, saying,

"I don't like to hear you talking like that. It's not like you at all to get upset. And believe me, I know. You're feeling down Josephine after all you've been through. But we love you dearly. Many was the time when we were down, you cheered us up. If only you knew how much we've missed you at work. No other person in the laundry can cheer us up like you do: no one. I don't care what you say to me; you can call me all the names under the sun. You can tell me to buzz off because maybe I do go on a bit about John Paschal …too much for my own good." Then giving her friend's hand a gentle squeeze she continued, "But now, it's you I'm thinking of. I want nothing more than to see you back on your feet and making us all happy again. Then we can plan for the future. I promised you once, if you remember, that I'd run away from here and that I'd bring two of my friends with me. And I intend to keep that promise," she whispered.

"Oh Bridie!" lamented Josephine, shaking her head. "I…I have no future here. I fear God has deserted me in my hour of need and that I'll never know a day's freedom." Taking a deep breath, she seized Bridie's hand in a vice-like grip, before looking at her despairingly " Bridie I don't want to die here. And if I do it will be, because of a broken heart. 'Cathal Swanick and that other eejit from Dublin" she started to babble, "even my own mother...they all...deserted me"

"Stop talking like that!" suggested Bridie because this visit, this whole conversation was too depressing. Soon she'd start to feel just as bad herself, she thought. And seeing Josephine's blotched tear stained face and red-rimmed eyes she leaned over and kissed her lightly on the forehead, adding, "Listen love, you'll have to learn to pull yourself together and stop your raving. And the only one who can do it, is you. I'll help you to start by going down to the kitchen and making you a nice cup of tea, with a thick cut of bread and lots of jam. Wouldn't you like that?"

The Reverend Mother came quickly into the ward, and saw Bridie huddled over Josephine's bed; the two of them in deep conversation.

"Bridie Rodgers, have you nothing better to do, than going around disturbing my patients?"

"Sorry Sister," said Bridie as she bid Josephine goodbye and the Reverend Mother continued on her rounds, visiting the sick and healing the afflicted. But Bridie had made up her mind. She'd be back with the tea and bread, however she'd manage it. As far as she was concerned, friends came first, and apart from Julie, she had no better friend than Josephine. No better friend.

Chapter Sixteen

Julie Murray woke from her slumber and slowly began to rummage through her bedside locker for her toiletries. She could not find her towel. It wasn't there. She stood for a moment to try and think, as the rest of the inmates too began to ease their aching limbs from the creaking wire-sprung mattresses in response to the Ward Sister's call. Julie's memory appeared to have gone blank, and for a brief moment her heart gave a frightening lurch at the thought that she could be losing her mind. She knew for certain that she had a towel of her own. But where was it? It wasn't in her locker or hanging on the bed-rail where it should be. But what really began to bother her was the fact that she couldn't remember if she had a wash at all this past week.

Of late she'd begun to take liberties with her personal hygiene and refused to wash along with everyone else whenever the mood struck her. She didn't dare tell anyone that this rare act of defiance gave her a thrill beyond her wildest imagination. It's the stupidity of it all she was fond of saying to Bridie.

"Sure aren't we doin' the same thing day in day out? Washin' our faces and cleaning our arses, and no one takes a blind bit-a-notice."

But try as she might, she could not now recall whether or not she had had a wash at all yesterday. And as she began to dig deep into the dark recesses of her mind, she knew she was having some kind of a mental block; a block that subconsciously disturbed her. Finally it came to her as a sort of a hazy image. Was it somethin' to do with a stolen coat or broken window below in Kilmaine? No, she sighed, but 'twas something like that: something very close. She had had some sort of a dream, she thought; something to do with home. That was it, she'd dreamed about home; about her mother. Her mother! Then she began to remember how she'd woken up during the night and promised herself she'd recollect all the glorious details first thing in the morning. Only now she couldn't remember a thing. Pity. It seemed such a peaceful, tranquil kind of dream, where birds sang and horsemen rode leisurely by, through winding country lanes that were festooned on all sides with wild flowers and acres and acres of green fields and golden corn. It seemed as if she had been to some sort of a party. But that was all.

The dream, she told herself, was like all the ones she'd ever had before, lost forever in the mists of time. In desperation she turned to ask Lilly if she'd seen her towel or if she might have it. But Lilly was already gone to the washroom.

The oul' fecker, she thought. Do you know *f*what it is, that lady hardly gives herself time to piss: runnin' an' racin', tryin' to keep in with the nuns. Nuns me arse! Sure she'll soon have that Bridie Rodgers as bad as herself. Turning round she saw Bridie coming toward her.

"Bridie, did I have a wash at all yesterday? For the life of me I can't remember a thing and I can't find me towel any *f*where."

"Here! Isn't this it!" said Bridie, reaching forward to pick the crumpled towel mixed in with the bedclothes.

"Sure I knew I left it some*f*where. Do you know *f*what it is I must be losing me memory," she tittered before adding wryly, "I can't understand *f*why them nuns don't give us an extra towel, bad cess to them, instead of goin' round the country collecting money for the black babies. Sure *f*what good's a nice clean towel to that lot? Won't they still be as black as a pot?"

"You know 'tis true," laughed Bridie, as they both went out the door. "If the Reverend Mother hear you talking like that… you'll be the one as black as a pot."

But the Reverend Mother like everyone else had a lot on her mind that morning. For some time she'd been suffering from aches and pains, which she'd put down to a form of creeping arthritis. But when she began to feel faint on more than one occasion she had to succumb and go to the Doctor. The Doctor gave her a stark warning.

"Sister, I don't wish to alarm you, but unless you step down from your position of authority, then I fear you'll fall down."

'Mother Superior' didn't respond too well to that analysis as the reality that she was no longer able to cope with life's everyday woes, slowly began to dawn on her. But what bothered her most was who was going to replace her – if and when she retired. Who would she recommend or appoint as the new Mother Superior. Sister Stanislaus was the obvious choice. But there were times when she felt she was too lenient with some of the penitents. And besides, the new generation of nuns coming through the convent seemed inferior in religious matters and far too casual in their approach to their elders. She herself had already caught two of the young novices talking in the refectory; about crossroads dances of all things, and God knows what else. And the way they go around the convent with their heads in the clouds, you'd swear they were going to a fancy-dress ball. Lord between us and all harm, religion is not what it used to be, she sighed.

Today she faced a heavy work schedule; something she did not relish at this time of the morning. But as she had set aside today for tackling some of the more thorny issues, she had no choice but to meet them head on. Sitting in front of her were her two main advisors, Sister Stanislaus and Sister Philomena. But first things first she thought, I'll go through the mail. Who knows, there might be something to cheer me up while Sisters are sorting out their plan. Sister Stanislaus and Sister Philomena had spent the best part of the week conducting a major survey as to the entire running of the Laundry as requested by the Reverend Mother. She informed them that His Grace, the Bishop was looking for ways to help increase productivity in the Laundry, in an effort to make it more profitable. He also wanted to find a way of making more money to help pay off the huge debt being incurred on the construction of the city's new Cathedral and had turned to the 'Mercy Sisters' in the Magdalene Laundry seeking their advice.

The Mother Superior held the sharply pointed letter opener in her right hand as she studied each letter of correspondence carefully, before deciding to slice it open. She was extremely proud of her ability to identify the source of each letter by its hand-written address and postmark. The letter she held at present seemed puzzling. The handwriting was indeed familiar, but for the life of her she could not put a name to the sender. And the postmark, New York, irritated her even more. Accepting defeat she slit the envelope open with one clean thrust of her letter opener.

Dear Reverend Mother,
Thank you so much for your kind letter, which I received some time ago. If only you knew how relieved and happy I was to learn of my sister, Julie's, continued good health and recovery.
As you are well aware, for some time I've been deeply

concerned for her welfare. Therefore, on receiving your written confirmation as to her overall good health I considered it an appropriate time to request her permanent removal from your care. In order to help speed up the process I further took it upon myself to telephone His Grace the Bishop, at his residence in Galway. He said he would be more than willing to accede to my request; on the understanding that I sign the necessary release documents when removing her from the Magdalene and that I, as her next of kin take full responsibility as to her future well being.

Furthermore I would like to take this wonderful opportunity to thank you, Reverend Mother, most sincerely, together with all of your kind ' Sisters of Mercy' staff in Galway, for the care, dedication and devotion you have shown to my sister Julie over a long number of years.

I've arranged to be in Galway city on Thursday 2nd May, where I shall remove her from your care at midday. I shall of course speak to you by telephone prior to calling, to see that everything is in order.

I do hope this will not inconvenience you in any way...

What in the name of God! Thought the Reverend Mother, as she glanced up quickly at the religious calendar hanging on the back of her office door, as if she didn't already know the date. She felt her intestines heave, her stomach churn at the thought that the date was practically upon her, and that Sister Rosario had gone right over her head by corresponding directly with the Bishop. Not just any Bishop but her Bishop!

Picking up the envelope again she studied the postmarked date in disbelief. She should have known. Three weeks in the post. Airmail how are you, she said beneath her breath; three lousy weeks.

Suddenly, everything was up in a heap. She'd have to cancel this morning's meeting right away and talk instead to Julie Murray and have her fitted out with new clothes, more expense, she thought.

No! First she'd phone His Grace right now, and demand to know why she wasn't informed about Sister Rosario's request to have her sister removed. Then she realised His Grace was probably out in Connemara somewhere, Confirming school children, as his housekeeper had informed her earlier in the week that he had a very busy week ahead of him with Confirmations and First Communions. She'd have to leave it and try later. Visibly shaken the Reverend Mother buried her head in her large purple hands for a second in full view of St. Stanislaus and Sister Philomena, who gave each other a sideways glance before asking politely,

"Reverend Mother, is everything alright?"

The Mother Superior sprang to attention, before snapping,

"If you must know! It's not! Some people are so inconsiderate. I'm sorry Sisters. Something very urgent has come about. I have no choice other than to leave this morning's business over for another day?"

As they began to leave the office, the Reverend Mother wished with all her heart they'd do so more quickly, as she did not want them to see her in her present state of anxiety.

When they had left, she again buried her head in her hands as she pleaded with God.

Please, please don't let anybody disturb me for a few minutes. Slowly gathering her thoughts she sighed wearily. The doctor was right. I'm not able for this anymore. Besides, I can't believe what's happening. Julie Murray about to walk free. That's surely the last straw. I never thought I'd see the day when my most able worker would be free to walk out on me. Never thought I'd see the Bishop accede to such an ill-considered request without first consulting with me. Undoubtedly Julie was the best worker I ever had and now she's being spirited away, she sighed, as she struggled emotionally to pull herself together. She leant back in her favourite armchair because she knew it wouldn't be long before somebody disturbed her. They always did.

Picking up Sister Rosario's letter once more, she skipped through it. '...*Thursday 2nd of May...from your care at twelve noon...*'

The cold-blooded cheek of that woman, she sighed. How could anybody be so inconsiderate as to go over my head like that? Flouting my authority. For all Sister Rosario knew I could have been in South Africa. Then what would she do? Wait 'til I came back? Huh! Oh dear, oh dear. I don't know what the world is coming to. I must be getting old: I really must; when somebody can do that to me. What I need now is a strong cup of tea, laced with a shot of whiskey. I'll ring down. I should have a drop left, she said to herself, as she pulled out the bottom drawer of her desk to reveal a small bottle of Powers whiskey hidden beneath the paperwork. For what seemed like the hundredth time in her life, she trotted out the same excuse to justify her actions. I know it's against my teaching, but if it was good enough for my father in times of stress, then it's certainly good enough for me.

Julie Murray dropped everything and went straight to the office at the Reverend Mother's request. She knocked on the glass panelled door and went in knowing full well that she was going to be asked to repair some gilt-edged garment, belonging to some priest or bishop. Sure I've performed more miracles than Our Lord, she was fond of saying to Bridie after the completion of yet another delicate task for the Reverend Mother. You know I'd love to go and tell her, kiss me arse. And Bridie would say, and why don't you, instead of you getting down on your knees every time and kissing hers?' And Peggy Neary, quietly listening nearby would start preaching the same old mantra. Girls Please! Will ye stop using such foul language! Ye know well it all for the good of the Catholic Church. Ye'll all go straight to hell if ye continue talking like that. But Julie Murray loved to have the last word. Sure! An' if we do it sell, can't we sit on the hob-a-hell warmin' our fannies fwhile we're waiting for you. Then everyone within earshot would break into peals of laughter as Peggy Neary fled the scene hurriedly making the sign of the Cross.

Now that Julie was sitting facing her boss she wasn't so sure if she was called in to do a special job after all. Her ladyship had a sour look, she thought. God have I been reported for usin' bad language again, or playin' tricks? That's the only other reason her ladyship sends for me. But then Sister Antonia's sombre face broke into a faint smile.

"Well Julie, how are you today?"

"I'm fine Sister," answered Julie nonchalantly, not knowing whether she was really good or bad.

"Well, well my dear! You've been with us a long time!" said the Reverend Mother, lowering her eyes and asking, "How long has it been?"

Julie's first reaction was to wonder what all this fancy 'Dear' business was about. Sure that lady hardly ever says that. Then her mind moved swiftly to catch up with what the Reverend Mother was saying, but instead, her mind was telling her that the Reverend Mother looked wrecked. Sure fwhat sort a question is that? Gimme a minute until I think; how long has it been?

Julie, caught completely by surprise hesitated for a long time. She had to struggle strenuously to try and think. She knew every year, month, week and day of her imprisonment off by heart, but still she couldn't bring herself to just spit it out. It didn't seem right. She couldn't be there that long, she thought. It was as if she were afraid to tot up the total. But then she knew that she always added up her age and years in the Magdalene Laundry with important events that happened in her life. Things one could never forget. Mentally she began counting. I was fifteen years of age *f*when the priest put me here. I was eleven years here *f*when I escaped the first time. It was seven years after that *f*when I ran away again, that's eighteen, and that was seven years ago. Twenty-five, that's right.

"Twenty-five," answered Julie, who was now coming to the conclusion, having deciphered the Reverend Mother's body language, that something good was about to happen. She was going to give her some money, or maybe make her an Honorary Consecrated penitent. Only a handful of people were ever known to have received that honour. She began to push the latter from her head, deeming it too good to be true.

"Twenty-five years," repeated Sister Antonia. "Almost as long as myself. This is my thirtieth year here in Galway with the Mercy Sisters," she added proudly.

"Congratulations," muttered Julie. She didn't know *f*what you were supposed to say to a nun who had spent that long on her knees, prayin' an' shoutin' at them, an' the devil knows *f*what.

"Well…Needless to say my dear, you've thought of freedom many, many times over the last twenty-five years," said the Reverend Mother solemnly as she looked deeply into Julie's sea-green eyes, while thinking to herself what a loss she's going to be. What a brave and loyal servant she has proven to be.

Julie sat staring at Sister Antonia. She was left speechless, wondering what she was supposed to say. If she agreed, she might be accused of tryin' to escape all the time, but on the other hand, *f*what sort of a statement was that? Is she a biteen gone in the head I wonder, or has she taken a supeen-a-the-bottle. They say she does.

"Haven't you?" urged Sister Antonia.

"Yes," croaked Julie in reply.

She was now positively afraid of what she might hear from the

Reverend Mother. Maybe they were going to put her into a mental hospital. There was no knowing what this lady might do if she took it into her head. Then she saw the Reverend Mother's lips move again, as she said, " Well so have I! So have I!"

"Christ she must be leavin," thought Julie. Sure as there's a grey rib on my head, she's leavin' and good riddance to her. And I beginnin' to think that maybe I'd get a few bob or somethin'.

Then Julie thought she detected a deepening sadness in the Reverend Mother's voice, as her eyes began to slowly drown in a vale of glistening tears. Don't say she's going to cry? She is. Glory bit-a-God Almighty she's cryin'. Wait 'til the girls hear about this, thought Julie nervously as she watched the Reverend Mother's lower lip begin to quiver. And as these mad thoughts went churning through her head, she saw the Reverend Mother reach out to her and say,

"Give me your hands dear."

Julie raised her hands tentatively, desperately afraid that something awful was about to happen. For a mere fraction of a second, she thought about getting up and running away, because what ever was wrong with the Reverend Mother, it wasn't good.

"You're leaving the Magdalene," she whispered, as she took Julie's large white hands in her own great purple paws: holding them tightly as she struggled to control her emotions.

But in spite of her best efforts a tiny tear began to cascade down her cheek, washing away her shame; her years of guilt at having treated this penitent woman so appallingly. Continuing to look deep into Julie's eyes she began to realise for the very first time that this woman was made of iron. No other human being could have taken the punishment and work I meted out to her. She shook Julie vigorously by the hands to jolt her back to a sense of reality.

"I said you're leaving us dear. You've been granted your freedom. Your sister Kay – Sister Rosario – is taking you out of here tomorrow. Isn't that wonderful?" she whispered emotionally, trying to sound cheerful, but spiritually her soul was wracked with pain and guilt.

During this time, Julie sat staring at the Rev. Mother, in total shock and disbelief. She could not absorb or understand what the Reverend Mother had just said. When first she heard the words 'You've been granted your freedom', a powerful surge of emotion seemed to go rushing straight through her body. It started with her heart. It gave such a frightful lurch, it was almost like an electric shock: so powerful, it jumped violently in her chest almost taking her breath away.

'You're being granted your freedom.'

'You're being granted your freedom.'

'Your sister Kay is taking you out.'

'Your sister Kay is taking you out.'

'Tomorrow.'

'Tomorrow.'

'Tomorrow.'

The words kept repeating themselves over and over again in her head. Julie had to fight hard with her conscience to bring the alarming words under control. Then she suddenly realised she had been in this situation so many times before. The mere thought that she was about to go free was both exhilarating and sickening all at the same time. What if this was just another pipedream, she thought. Her stomach began to heave nauseously at the thought that it might be an illusion. She knew she had dreamt of a moment like this so many times, she had long since given up all hope. She had given up all hope of ever being free, because she'd had so many dreams, so many false dawns, so many endless nightmares, she could not bear the thought of another failure. Recalling vividly for a fleeting moment her worst nightmare. 'Twas over in the Magdalene Chapel late one evening when she fell asleep and dreamed of a wicked priest belting her with his heavy, blackthorn stick.

She banished the thought quickly from her head and tried instead to think of what was happening to her now. Looking at the Reverend Mother's pained expression she felt as if she could feel her spiritual body, with its long angelically draped face, desperately reaching out to lay her mind at ease. At that precise moment Julie felt such a warm glow of satisfaction run through her body it was beyond comprehension. It was a feeling of such utter contentment and unbridled joy; so overpowering that Julie was afraid to take away her eyes, lest the spell be broken.

It disturbed the Rev. Mother to see Julie's unchanging face, despite having given her such extraordinarily good news. Perhaps she is just overwhelmed, thought Sister. But then a tumultuous tremor came over her. What if Julie refused to leave? What if she was unable to accept that there was a *free* world out there, where people did as they pleased? Suddenly the realisation struck her like an arrow, that she herself was guilty of moulding this penitent woman into something resembling a zombie, a robotic figure only now capable of doing what it was programmed to do. Scrub and wash. Wash and scrub, and pray. Pray and scrub and wash. She knew from her long years in the Magdalene Laundry and from her vast experience of human nature; that some penitent women once regarded as the finest examples of womanhood, coming from the finest stock, were sooner or later, reduced to pale shadows of their former selves. For the first time in her life, Sister clearly saw the enormity of her own sins. She now deeply regretted not having dealt with Julie in a more compassionate and humane way when she tried to run away. Perhaps, it's not too late yet, she thought. She would try to make it up to her now, help to ease Julie's mind, before she left to go away, forever.

Standing up and coming out from behind her desk she saw that Julie's bulging eyes followed her every move. Extending her arms again she said in a faltering voice,

"Julie, you're free. From tomorrow morning, you'll be as free as the wind…as free as the birds in the air."

The Reverend Mother stood facing Julie, an agonised look upon her face, her arms still outstretched, waiting for Julie, who rose ever so slowly from her chair: never for one moment taking her eyes off the Reverend Mother until they were both firmly united in a warm, touching embrace. Sister Antonia patted Julie gently on the shoulder and said,

"I want you to know Julie, that you've been a wonderful servant to God…and to me. I know that over the years I've been a hard taskmaster…at times. But you'll always be in my prayers."

Then easing Julie away from her shoulder, she looked at her solemnly and pleaded, "Julie, please forgive my faults and failings. I want you to pray for me. Pray to God for my forgiveness. Right now there's nothing more I want than God's forgiveness, because we're all sinners in the eyes of the Lord."

After what seemed an eternity, Julie glanced briefly around the room, as if uncertain of her surroundings, before she turned once more to look at Sister's care worn pleading expression, and then in a barely audible whisper she said,

"I forgive."

These two little words were more, much more than the Reverend Mother could ever have prayed for. She clasped Julie tightly to her bosom once more, and said, "Thank you dear! I hope and pray that

God in his infinite wisdom will grant you a special place in heaven."

Recovering her composure, she sat Julie Murray down and added joyously and with sincerity,

"Now that we have that little matter out of the way, we'll have ourselves a nice cup of tea. I've asked Sister Philomena to inform all of your friends in the Laundry and tonight we'll have a little party in the Recreational Hall in your honour. Would you like that?"

Julie, still unsure whether or not it was all a dream, felt at that moment so utterly confused, she uttered, "A party? Is it for me?"

"Yes dear! Especially for you!"

The long years of confinement meant that Julie Murray could no longer accept anything said in relation to freedom as fact. The only thing she could accept as reality was the here and now. If she was as free as Sister had just said, why couldn't she go now? What was she waiting for? Tomorrow?

Didn't me father once say 'tomorrow never comes'. Sure if I go to bed tonight an' wake up in the mornin', sure it'll all be forgotten. *F*what will I do if all this oul' *raimésh* of birds and things turns out to be a cod; *f*what will I do then? 'As free as the birds... Your sister Kay...Sister Rosario is taking you out of here tomorrow. Sure that sister-a-mine doesn't give two hoots. An' she in some oul' order her sell over in America, thought Julie, who continued to stare at Mother Superior who was now talking to someone on the phone.

Bridie, thought Julie excitedly, I'll go an' ask Bridie. Bridie and Josephine will know *f*what to do. They'll know *f*whether 'tis true or not...

She rose from her chair and began to go towards the door.

"Where are you going?" asked the Reverend Mother, taken by surprise.

The words 'where are you going' almost stopped Julie's heart. She froze in her tracks and placed her right hand on her chest, as she turned to face Sister Antonia, terrified that she wasn't free after all.

"To see Bridie. I have to see Bridie," she said aloud, more out of fear than excitement. "You said I could go home tomorrow"

"Yes," answered the Reverend Mother, seeing the disbelief still etched on Julie's face. Leaving down the phone, she added reassuringly, "It's true, you're going home tomorrow. But what about your tea, aren't you going to have a cup of tea? Sister Philomena's making it right now."

Julie stood and stared. She didn't know what to do or say: and seeing her dilemma the Reverend Mother thought, perhaps she'd be better off to let Julie go back down to Bridie and her friends, who by now would be well-aware of Julie's imminent release.

Sister Antonia came from behind her desk to escort Julie back down to the laundry, but was met at the door by Sister Philomena bringing in the tea.

"Are you sure you won't have a cup of tea?" asked the Reverend Mother, turning to Julie.

"I'd rather see Bridie."

"Fine! Sister would you ever be kind enough to stay here for a few minutes while I go down with Julie?"

When the Reverend Mother confirmed to Julie's disbelieving friends in the laundry what Sister Philomena had already told them, that Julie Murray was indeed leaving the Laundry tomorrow, word began to spread like wildfire through the entire institution.

In the wash-house and the adjoining rooms, workers stood around in little groups whispering, while ageing penitent women of nervous disposition stood peering questioningly from secure positions behind doors and curtains.

Only the brave and the bold came to congratulate Julie and inquire how such wonderful news had come to pass. But Julie, dazzled by all the attention could hardly speak. She sat on a linen basket, while Bridie, Lilly, Josephine and Margaret Sherry tried to protect her, by explaining to the others what was really happening.

Bridie herself hadn't yet had time to talk privately to Julie and was desperate for a word. Like most of the penitents she couldn't come to terms with the fact that all of this had come about so quickly. If Julie Murray, her good friend, was going to be gone by tomorrow, then she had better try and have a private conversation with her to arrange some secret code of correspondence. She had only ever had three letters from Noreen Donnellan who was now over in England and she felt somewhat cheated by this latest carry on. She secretly thought that Noreen might have offered to help her escape by now. But as yet nothing had happened. Now that Julie was about to leave she might have a better chance of escape through her, she thought. If Julie failed to support her, then she was really in trouble. Of all the girls in the Laundry, Julie Murray was her only true stalwart. They had been through so much together. The mere thought that she was no longer going to be around the place didn't bear thinking about.

Bridie spotted Sister Stanislaus as she crossed the floor of the adjoining room. She ran out to her calling, "Sister! Sister!."

The startled nun turned to see a gasping excited Bridie coming towards her.

"Sister! I was wondering if I could have the rest of the evening off, as it is Julie Murray's last day here?"

"Haven't you two got the evening long to be together? What about your work? Somebody has to do it and from what I see, there's precious little of it being done at the moment."

Bridie hesitated for a second, while she looked at Sister.

"I know, but everyone will be around her this evening, blathering...and I thought if the two of us could be together... to go for a last walk ..."

Sister Stanislaus's eyes widened even more at Bridie's gumption. She looked at her with renewed admiration. If there's one thing you have going for you, she thought to herself, it's fortitude.

"Whatever work you're supposed to be doing for Sister Philomena, will you please finish it, and then as far as I'm concerned you can have the rest of the evening off."

"Oh, thank you Sister. I'll pay you back later by helping out at the altar, or wherever you want," said Bridie cheerfully.

Sister smiled sheepishly, as she went about her business, while Bridie rushed back to finish her tasks and to tidy up, before escorting Julie away from the news-hounds who were still turning up in droves to see her.

But Bridie did not have things her own way. Josephine and Lilly insisted on tagging along too. They felt as much a part of her inner circle of friends as anybody else, despite Bridie's misgivings. They each wanted to know was she going to America to live with her sister.

"Sure I don't know anythin', except that she's comin' tomorrow. The devileen mightn't turn up at all," she tittered nervously. "America! I don't think I'd like America," she added as her three friends fought like spoiled children for the right to link her arms while they walked around the back of Our Lady's Grotto, and round again to the front.

"I think we ought to kneel down and say a prayer to 'Our Lady', for favours received," said Julie.

"Don't forget Julie, 'Our Lady' is probably thanking you now, for all the times you washed off the bird's 'you know what' that landed on her head!" said Lilly, good-humouredly.

"Oh yeah! There used to be loads of birdshite on her head and Julie you always got the job of washing it off," said Josephine bluntly.

"But that was before they cut down that big tree," said Bridie trying not to deviate from the religious fervour she felt for 'Our Lady'.

"And do you remember the time you had to kneel there half the night, saying fifteen decades of the rosary, because you asked the Reverend Mother was 'Our Lady' the first unmarried mother," said Lilly.

"Sure," said Julie, remembering the brazenness of her youth. "Wasn't I awful?"

"Why don't we make a wish now?" urged Bridie trying to change the subject as they all knelt down giddily.

"What are we praying for so?" asked Lilly, "That Julie will get herself a man with pucks of money?"

"And balls as big as a butcher's bag," tittered Josephine, "and... a fella that'll stay on top of her all night, and forget to get off."

"Or better still, forget to take it out," added Lilly, as they all started laughing uncontrollably, and Bridie looked around nervously in case anyone saw them. She looked towards the convent and caught three elderly nuns looking out at them from the upstairs window.

The girls began to wave up at them, as they fell about the place with the dint of laughter. They hadn't had a giggle like it in ages and they were in no mood to end it now.

When they recovered their composure, having watched with glee the elderly nuns continued observation of them, Julie said,

"Now because this is my last day here, I think I'd like to put some flowers round 'Our Lady's statue. Blast ye will ye give me a hand," she urged as she began to pluck some flowers from the side of the garden, while the girls began to laugh once again at their own silliness.

Soon they made a lovely heart-shaped arrangement of scented flowers at the base of the giant gold-leafed statue; thereby adding additional colour and splendour to an already scenic shrine.

Later that evening, Julie, and her friends gathered in the Great Hall, all mingling together and generally having a great time. They drank their tea from the finest bone china cups, as they and the Magdalene nuns chatted away blissfully while devouring an assortment of tinned biscuits and freshly baked scones. Then it was time for music. The ancient grand piano in the corner, though sadly out of tune and with one or two keys missing, was brought into use. Several people played tin whistles and accordions while others sang; but the best rendition of a song came from Josephine Finn. When asked to do something Josephine said that she never wanted to sing again now that her friend was leaving the Magdalene, but rather than be seen as a spoil sport, she'd sing one last song, especially for Julie.

Coming towards the end of the night, Sister Stanislaus gave a few words on behalf of the Reverend Mother, who'd said good night and retired earlier. Then she asked Julie if she'd like to say a few words.

"No, I've nothin'…except to say thanks… to ever'one… for ever'thin'," she said before crumbling emotionally into the arms of her friends and turning her face away. But the round of applause she received from her fellow inmates said more about their love for her than if she had spoken a thousand words.

When Julie and the rest of the penitents were locked in their dormitories for the night, Bridie, Josephine and Lilly stayed on talking and helping her to pack her personal possessions late into the night.

Earlier in the day Julie Murray had very little to her name, but now as she began to pack she had loads of mementoes, given to her by her many friends. A miniature silver-plated picture frame and photograph, several headscarves, earrings and bangles, pieces of crochet material such as place mats and tea-cosies. And yet it all took no more than ten minutes to pack into the medium-sized, brand-new suitcase together with some new clothes given to her by the Sisters of Mercy. Bridie gave Julie her one and only silk scarf that she actually wore to Mass every Sunday and which Julie had always admired. Bridie had bought it a long time ago while shopping in Tuam.

"What'll I do with all this stuff if that lady doesn't turn up?" asked Julie as she stood at the end of her bed, still trying to come to terms with the realism of it all.

"Have no fear love," said Bridie. "If the Reverend Mother says she'll be here, then she'll be here. When John Paschal came to see me the nuns had it all arranged beforehand, so don't worry it'll be the same with your sister."

"Janey, I hope you're right. Wouldn't I look a right amadán entirely…sittin', waitin', an' she not to turn up?" she tittered nervously.

"She'll turn up," said Bridie, reassuringly. "Look! Are you going to write to us, or what? Or when can we expect to hear from you?"

"And in the honour of God, will you try to get us out?" urged Lilly.

"I'll do the best I can. But sure I'm not out mesell yet!" replied Julie

"Well when you do get out! Otherwise we might never see each other again," said Josephine earnestly.

"And when will you write to me so?" asked Bridie, anxious to commit Julie to some sort of an arrangement.

"I'll write to Mr. Hehir, in a week or two. But sure I don't know ƒwhere I'm going mesell! It's hard to do anything when I don't know ƒwhere I'll be," answered Julie.

The four women went on talking in the semi-darkness of the dormitory late into the night. Some of the penitents complained about a lack of sleep due to all their talking, but they were more or less ignored.

Finally, they themselves succumbed to what had been a long day. Bridie having arranged with one of her friends that they swap beds, so that she could sleep near her friend Julie on this her last night in the Home.

But Julie Murray did not sleep. She lay there thinking things while trying to peer across the room at the steel barred painted window, which was straight in front of her bed. She was far too excited, and afraid to go to sleep in case she woke up in the morning and all this turned out to be a dream. Was all this really happening to her, she asked herself over and over; yes it was, she decided. Tomorrow morning, I'll be as free as the birds; after twenty-five years. God! How many nights was that? Sure it must be thousands. An' this is my last one. Then I'll be able to go ƒwhere I want. Buy ƒwhat I want. Imagine, I won't have to run away ƒwhen I see a Guard or anythin'. I can even go home if I want. But sure the neighbours will all be lookin' at me an' ever'thin', an' sayin', that's the wan that stole the coat, long go, don't you remember.' She stole a red coat from the shop. Oh God! I'm not going back there ever, ever again. Arrah hump the lot-a-them. They didn't worry about me...except me sister. At least she'd sent an oul' card at Christmas. Isn't it wonderful, me own sister is takin' me out. I'll be like Bridie then; and John Paschal together again. An' janey mac, I'll be able to go dancin' an' ever'thin', an' get a man and sleep with him an' get married an ever'thin'.

"Bride, Bridie!" hissed Julie, in a low voice. "Bridie, are you ash-sleep?"

But Bridie, who was a poor sleeper at the best of times, had nodded off. She woke with a start and raised her head slightly to ask peevishly,
"What?"

"Bridie, it's me. Do you know *f*what?"

"What?"

"I'll be able to go and see Harry an' ever'thin'. An' I'm not runnin' away this time, if he comes after me," she whispered aloud.

Bridie, who was half asleep tried in vain to understand what Julie was on about.

"Harry…Harry who?"

"Harry! Sure you don't be listenin'. Harry, the fella I was mad after, when we used to meet at the bridgeen in Kilmaine ever'…."

"Oh that Harry! I didn't know what you were on about. Listen love, it's getting late and you have to be up early in the morning. So go to sleep. We'll talk about it in the morning. Goodnight."

"Oh goodnight! Might as well be talkin' to meself!" she sighed.

And as she slumped back on the pillow, and snuggled down once again, she began to dream of that glorious Summer Sunday, long ago, when she'd have done just about anything for Harry's kiss. Just about anything. But didn't.

* * * * *

She stood at the door of St. Teresa's dormitory and tried to interpret the momentary sounds of silence. She thought there was a strange atmosphere about the place. Every thing seemed so quiet. She strained her ear and listened intently. She could just about make out the faint whirring sounds of the huge calender rollers and floor trolleys on the floor below.

She turned once more to pace up and down the dormitory, taking time to count all forty-nine beds that had one sick penitent lying in. All was quiet, except for the occasional moan out of Kitty Mulhare, an elderly penitent who lay there in her sick bed. She'd been ill for days, but it was only in the vast stillness of the room that Julie saw her suffering for what it really was. She herself hadn't been alone like this in her own dormitory for a long time. With so many penitents lying on their beds resting of an evening, very little notice was taken of someone moaning or complaining, because someone was always moaning or complaining of a pain here or an ache there. But the sight of poor Kitty fading away there in bed frightened her like never before.

"Aaaaaah, aaaaaah! Water! Water!" moaned the sick penitent, as she raised a feeble hand.

Julie went to her aid, and held the old tarnished enamel mug, to her parched lips, as she struggled to swallow. The water dribbled down Kitty's sunken chin, and on to her frail chest. Julie tried to stem the flow with the soiled hand towel, and as she did so she felt the awful coldness of Kitty's seemingly lifeless hand, as she clutched hers in desperation.

"Sister! Sister!" she whispered in a barely audible voice, as her head sank back on the pillows and her eyes rolled up to heaven.

"This is Julie… Julie Murray, you remember me don't you? Julie Murray."

When she did not answer, Julie felt really frightened. She thought Kitty should be down in the infirmary, but she also knew that it was usually full and that sick penitents were being moved about all the time. Still, she thought, this was no place for her, and to try and hide her own guilt she decided she'd keep talking to her until Sister Stanislaus came up.

"I'm leavin' today! I'm goin' away Kitty! I told you last night? I'm leavin'."

"Sister, Sister," moaned Kitty as she took hold of Julie's hand, mistaking it for one of the nuns.

When she relaxed her grip Julie turned quickly and went again to the door. In the name of God, will that wan ever come and let me downstairs, she sighed. The hair stood on the back of her neck when she turned once more to look at Kitty. The dormitory had a weird feeling about it, she thought, and for the hundredth time in her life she was convinced she could get the stench of death about the place.

She knew from past experience what death smelled like, and she was convinced that the stench she was getting, meant someone was going to die. She was sorry now that she hadn't agreed to work on this morning. She should have stayed working with her friends until her sister Kay came to collect her. Instead she had been allowed to go back to her dormitory after Mass and breakfast to put on her new clothes and to be ready at eleven-thirty. But when she looked at her new outfit now and felt the crisp twenty-pound note in her pocket, which had been handed to her by the Reverend Mother she felt an awful lot better. Earlier Julie thought she'd like to walk the Magdalene grounds one last time, before leaving. Now she thought she'd seen enough of it. She'd go straight to the chapel, an' the penitent graveyard instead, an' say a prayer.

When at last Sister Stanislaus came upstairs, Julie asked if Bridie and Josephine could join her for a few minutes before she left the 'Home' so that they could pray together; her wish was granted.

Walking down the stairs for the last time she began to feel emotional as Sister Stanislaus carefully locked the intermediary doors behind them. So this was really it she thought, after twenty-five years in the Magdalene Home she was being released.

The three women stood, arms linked together, on the edge of the small penitents graveyard. They stared at the small, black-painted metal crosses, which had the names of the deceased neatly painted in white. Some were of friends they had known, or elderly penitents they once knew. For a brief moment they were afraid to speak, but unknown to each other they were thinking the same thoughts. There but for the grace of God go I. Wondering in their own minds how they had survived at all. But Bridie and Josephine could not bear to dwell on the fleeting thought that somehow flashed through their minds. With Julie being taken out by her sister, they could end up being buried there themselves, who knew?

"You know, this place must be very old," said Bridie trying to lift the heavy gloom she was beginning to feel at her friend's eminent departure. She could see that the first person to be buried there died in 1887.

"I wonder how many people were buried here altogether?" said Josephine, wondering if they were all Catholics, or if there were any Protestants amongst them. She wouldn't really mind being buried here, she thought, if only 'Cathal' was buried beside her. At least we could be together in death.

"Sixty-five," answered Bridie, the figure long-since engraved on her memory, after years and years of walking alone in the same grounds. "I counted them one evening when I saw that young one there in the middle. Do you see where it says '6th November 1937, Mary Flynn, peacefully in her sleep, aged thirty-three'.

"God! Sure the creature was only a young wan," said Julie.

Thirty-three, thought Josephine, almost the same age as me. The thought flashing through her head that she was only a few years younger than Julie: and look at her now; I never noticed it before but her hair is getting very grey, and she has bags under her eyes. It must be the sunlight, because I never saw her looking like that before. Her heartbeat quickened at the thought that she herself would soon be as old and decrepit-looking as her friend Julie. Jesus, am I ever going to get out of here, she thought.

"Come into the chapel in the name of God, and we'll say a prayer. I don't care where I die, but the last thing I want is to be buried here in an unknown grave," said Bridie, suddenly feeling depressed and lonely.

As if reading Bridie's thoughts, Josephine tightened her grip on Julie's arm and rested her head against her ample shoulder, and pleaded solemnly,

"Please Julie! Won't you try and get us out of here! Because if you don't we might all die here."

The mere thought that herself and Bridie would no longer have Julie to console them in their hours of need was almost too much to bear. Julie had been such a tower of strength, such a shining example in her fight for freedom. And now after all these years her prayers were finally being answered. Then a strange notion struck Josephine as the three of them entered the church door: that what Bridie was always saying, was probably true. Every thing that happened in life came in three's. And if Bridie was right, then there was a very real chance that one of them could find themselves walking out the door to freedom in the not too distant future. Noreen Donnellan managed to escape; Julie Murray was as good as gone now; so that meant another of them was probably destined to go free. The thought alone began to warm the cockles of her heart.

The midday Angelus bell was ringing out loud and clear as a small group of penitent women stood waving in the small corridor at the end of the main hall, as Julie, accompanied by Sister Philomena, Sister Concillio and two novice Sisters escorted Julie to the front parlour where her sister, Kay, was waiting to collect her.

"Goodbye! Goodbye Julie! And don't forget to pray for us," they shouted, as they watched her walk ever closer to freedom. Now the penitents poured out of their work rooms in earnest and stood huddled together jamming the doorways, as they waved their white handkerchiefs; frantically jumping up and down as Julie neared the corner. There, just before she disappeared from view, Julie turned one last time and waved to all her friends. But many of them found the emotionally charged moment too much to bear and turned their sad faces away.

Bridie too, who had linked arms with Lilly MacAlastair and Josephine Finn was totally lost for words. She had wanted so desperately to announce to everyone that if ever any penitent in the Magdalene Home deserved her freedom, it was Julie Murray. But somehow the words she had planned as a fond farewell lodged in her throat, and instead she ended up saying nothing. Breaking from her friends she too turned and sighed,

"Ah Well! That's the end of that! I only hope that if the man above had anything at all to do with Julie's good fortune, that we're next on his list."

"Yeah, wouldn't it be great. I hope she doesn't forget to write. Where's Josephine?" asked Lilly, looking round.

She was nowhere to be seen. On entering the workroom they found Josephine sitting dejectedly on one of the huge linen baskets. They said nothing, because like themselves they knew, Josephine Finn had more than enough on her own mind: more than enough.

Chapter Seventeen

It's almost three weeks since Julie Murray took those long steps to freedom, rescued by her sister Kay, the very Reverend Sister Rosario. Would you ever believe it's that long, thought Bridie as she lay in bed resting, after her hard day's work

Ever since Julie went away she didn't feel much like working, particularly at night or in the evening when she was known to help her colleagues with the odd bit of dressmaking, knitting or sewing. But her friends still came, haunting her daily to lend a hand. Instead their half finish dresses and cardigans lay wrapped up in old newspaper and brown paper bags under her bed, because each passing day after work she told herself, she'd do it later, tomorrow maybe. All she really wanted to do now was to be left alone with her thoughts.

One of these days, I'll have to get off me backside for good and try and do something about leaving here. No good depending on Julie Murray. Not a word from her since she left. I can't believe it. Only God knows where she is now. She could be in Dublin, London or America. I'd say America, with her sister. I must be an awful eejit entirely myself, that didn't try and escape years ago. I can't spend the rest of me life in this place. Fourteen years I'm here, could you believe it. I'm thirty-one years of age and as far away as ever from finding out who my mother and father were. As far away as ever from being reunited with my son, and as far away as ever from finding myself a husband. I'm useless, she sighed. Pure useless! I don't think I have the strength or desire to fight anymore. Here I am, year in year out, helping everyone else but doing nothing at all for myself. I'm pure stupid. I really am. If I don't leave here soon John Paschal will have left Williamstown and I won't see him any more. He'll surely stop writing to me, because he'll meet some nice girl and then that will be the end of me.

Ah to hell with this, she thought, as she swung her legs to the floor and sat on the edge of the bed, thinking. It's time I started planning, because I'm going to run away from here one of these days: only I'm not going out on my own. I'll ask Josephine and Lilly to come with me. I always said I'd bring Josephine and Julie with me, but now that Julie has gone… it will have to be Lilly. I'll do like Noreen Donnellan. I'll say nothing and keep quiet until the very last minute. Then the three of us will slip quietly away. I won't even tell the girls because they might tell someone.

Josephine Finn, was returning from her trip down stairs. She'd quietly slipped away to see if the door in the corridor was unlocked so that she could sneak across to the pigs swill barrel at the rear of the laundry to find something to eat. Unfortunately the door was locked. She recalled a night years ago when she went to the barrel on her way back from confessions in the Magdalene chapel. She was determined to raid the barrel that night, despite the darkness and the cold. She'd put her hand into the barrel when a great big cat jumped out. She still felt a shiver every time she thought of it. She let out such a roar that night she thought she'd surely die, and she promised herself then that she'd never do it again.

Yet here she was, prepared to risk life and limp again for the sake of a slice of soggy bread or a half boiled rotten potato, because she was starved with the hunger and sorry now she hadn't put a bit extra in her pocket at tea time that evening.

As she entered 'Our Lady's' dormitory she saw Bridie writing a letter. She was tempted to go and talk to her, but changed her mind. Bridie wasn't herself, she thought, since Julie left. Not near as friendly. I'm not good enough for her now I suppose. Besides, she won't let anyone else share her bed since Julie left; won't even let me cuddle up to her like she used to.

Josephine decided instead to go over and see what the rest of the girls were up to. The atmosphere in 'Our Lady's dormitory all evening, she thought, was a bit like the weather, threatening; as if a storm was about to break. Little groups of penitent women hung around arguing endlessly while playing silly games on the floor. Others were trying to read snippets from old religious magazines. One penitent however, had managed to get her hands on a Mills and Boon paperback. She had to read it quickly, because if the Sisters got their hands on it then it would get the fire; and everyone in the Laundry would get a good grilling on how they came to acquire such filth.

Bridie had just about finished her letter to John Paschal, – the second letter in a week – when one the inmates came and pleaded with her to join their group for a bit of a singsong and to bring over her mouth-organ.

By the time Bridie decided to pull herself together, and join the others; Breedge Courtney and Mary Kelly were reciting a poem they had cobbled together from an old school book.

"...Stitch! Stitch! Stitch!
In hunger, misery and dirt
Stitch! Stitch! Stitch!
In a voice of glorious pitch
We'll sing a song of the shirt
With bodies weary and worn
With scrubbing brush and soap
We women stand in manmade rags
Scrubbing our hearts in hope
Wash! Wash! Wash!
'Till our heads begin to swim
Wash! Wash! Wash!
'Till our brains begin to dim
Oh ye nuns and Sisters dear
While the priest and Bishop strives
It's not church linen you're wearing out
But brave young women's lives.
Stitch! Stitch! Stitch!
In hunger, misery and dirt
Stitch! Stitch! Stitch!
Sowing at once a terrible cloak
A shroud, or is it a shirt.
But why do I talk of death
That image of ageing bone
I sadly fear the terrible shape
It seems so like my..."

"Ah for God's sake! Can we do something else? That thing gives me the creeps," said Lilly, bringing the two entertainers to an embarrassing halt.

"Yeah! do something else! Something different. We're sick listening to that oul' rubbish," added Josephine.

Then one of the young penitent girls in the corner squeaked, "...I'll tell me Ma," and they all laughed and the words were no sooner said than two young penitents grabbed each other and began to twirl wildly on the floor as they sang

"I'll tell me Ma when I go home
The boys won't leave the girls alone.
They pulled their hair
They stole their comb
But that's all right 'til I go home.
She is handsome, she is pretty
She is the pride of Belfast City
She is courting one, two, three
Please will you tell me who is she."

Soon the atmosphere was electric which helped get Josephine Finn into the mood and she made a suggestion.

"Why don't we have a dance and pretend we're at a real carnival. We'll pretend we're all having a big night out in the Seapoint out in Salthill."

"Yeah! Yeah!" replied the girls enthusiastically. "That's a great idea!"

"OK. Half of you go each side of the floor", said Josephine. "Bridie, Mary Kelly and myself will be the band." And don't' forget I want to see all of ye out dancing on the floor.

This proposal, was overwhelmingly supported by the penitents because they knew from past experience that the best night's entertainment was usually of a spontaneous nature; people it seems were less shy about expressing themselves, when there wasn't too much expected of them.

"Bridie, you sit here on the left and Mary you sit on the right with the accordion" said Josephine, eagerly arranging a chair for both of them. "And I'll pull this bedside locker, over to here, so I can stand on it.

Already the penitents were beginning to get excited with eager anticipation, as Josephine continued to make arrangements. Turning to the band members, she whispered

"I think we'll start with *Danny Boy.* Give us the air to *Danny Boy* and we'll see. We'll pretend the place is packed with fellas and we're mad for it; and the music is blaring."

Bridie and Mary began tuning up while at the same time keeping an eye on proceedings. Everyone was beginning to revel in this impromptu form of entertainment. Bridie was particularly pleased that Josephine seemed to have made a full recovery. But Josephine's tendency to go into deep bouts of despair did not go unnoticed. Prior to her escape bid, Josephine was the life and soul of the place. But ever since then she wanted to portray herself as a tart, by dressing up gaudily in weird outfits that did not suit her at all. She would beg the nuns for fancy clothes, which of course they never had, and even if they did, they would never give, because they frowned on anything that vaguely resembled style. Despite that, Josephine always managed to get the loan of somebody's pleated skirt, silk blouse, or horrid lipstick, so she could dress up and go to the recreational hall on Sunday night, and dance the night away listening to 'Ceilí House' on, Radio Éireann making believe she was in some famous dance hall way out in the country. There was one big difference however, one which all of them hated: and that was the sight of three or four nuns sitting at the top end of the hall watching everything and showing them how to dance 'The Siege of Ennis'. And if it wasn't that it was showing them how to behave in a lady-like fashion when invited to dance a jig or a reel, by some imaginary man. It was bad manners to refuse, no matter how much you disliked the man, the nuns told them. And the nuns were always giving out to Josephine lately, because of her gaudy make-up. She'd spend hours in front of the broken mirror below in the lavatory, preening herself. She loved letting her hair down and smothering herself with layers of bright, red lipstick. Bridie got a great kick out of these situations because Josephine was sometimes known to turn on them like a viper by claiming, 'it's none of your business who I'm going out with tonight, or who I shagged last night.

During these innocuous interludes, Bridie's deep concern for her friend's well being would come creeping back. She'd ask herself why Josephine had to always put it on, or was her behaviour for real. Besides, Josephine often accused Bridie of being too plain and stupid, saying that she'd never be able to get a man anyhow because she was too dowdy and not like Josephine herself, who could have any man she wanted. Any man.

On the other hand, Bridie thought to herself, if Josephine was doing this to relieve the boredom and to have a little fun, then maybe she herself should throw off the shackles and join in the fun. Everyone knows Josephine Finn loves nothing more than to be the centre of attention; be it acting the Mick; imitating Judy Garland or dressing up in some fine clothes. God! If only I had her confidence, I'd be elected.

Josephine was now standing, smiling on her new makeshift stage, a facing the audience. She was holding a small statue of the Blessed Virgin in her hand, to use as her microphone.

"Good evening ladies and gentlemen…" she began, but her introduction was interspersed from the floor by yahoo's and wolf whistles. "…It gives me great pleasure here tonight; on this the last step our Irish tour, to entertain you in one of Ireland's foremost venues: the Seapoint Ballroom, here in Salthill. As you're probably aware, this is my final appearance before starting a three-month tour of America. In a few days time, together with my band, I hope to be walking down Broadway…" more clapping and cheering and shouting.

"…So, for that reason I'd like to see you all out dancing, as we begin the night with that beautiful Irish melody, *Danny Boy*."

Oh Danny Boy the pipes the pipes are calling
From glen to glen and down the mountain side,
The summer's gone and all the flowers are dying
'Tis you, 'tis you must go and I will bide.

Almost immediately two girls start dancing as if they were in the great ballroom of romance, followed by several more couples, all of them dancing with the love of their lives. And to add a bit of fun and excitement to the occasion, Breedge Murphy chooses a large pillow from one of the beds as her dancing partner.

And as Josephine begins the second verse of her favourite love song, Bridie begins to realise that any lingering doubts she had about Josephine Finn's welfare were rooted in her own vivid imagination. After all, she thought, when all is said and done, isn't it only a bit of fun? She could clearly see, that by getting up on stage the way she had just done, Josephine was living out her dreams, indulging in her own unique talents in a way she herself never could.

While out on the dance floor, Breedge Murphy was dancing away with her imaginary partner, as if she were taking part in *Swan Lake*. But she soon gets carried away by the tempo of the music and begins to hold the pillow seductively to her bosom before lowering it and squeezing it lustfully between her thighs. And as herself and her imaginary partner begin to gyrate in a deeply sexual way her friends start egging her on, "More! More! More!" they scream in their desire for fun. As if to acknowledge their request, Lilly MacAlastair steps forward and snatches the pillow from Breedge Murphy and throws it away, before wrapping herself lovingly around Breedge, as a visible surge of excitement engulfs the crowd. Soon everyone is out dancing; and amid gasps of amazement, Lilly and Breedge start hugging and kissing each other in a passionate and deeply intimate way.

This real vision of people enjoying themselves sends the blood coursing through Josephine's veins. There's a rush to her head, and she starts to give the performance of her life, by raising the tone of her voice several decibels.

"...And if you come when all the flowers are dying,
And I am dead, as dead I well may be,
You'll come and find the place where I am lying
And kneel and say an 'Ave' there for me.
And I shall hear though soft you tread above me..."

Some of the penitents are so excited by the dancers outlandish behaviour they start to cheer loudly, egging them on. But Peggy Neary can't take any more. She rushes headlong into the crowd, just as Lilly and Breedge are about to start exploring each other's bodies, and grabs Lilly viciously by the hair.

"You feckin' bitch! You leave my friend alone! You disgusting oul' whore!"

And despite being hauled backwards, Lilly manages to turn sideways, hanging on to her opponent for dear life.

"Who, the hell are you calling a whore?" she screams, as she lunges back at Peggy, knocking her to the ground.

They both start flaying into each other, while rolling around on the floor before Lilly manages to get up on her feet. She starts to kick Peggy like a rag doll. *Kick!* "You're nothing but a stupid nun's pet; *Kick!* A bloody weasel!

Suddenly, Breedge Courtney decides to join in the fray and lands like a cat on Lilly's back. Meanwhile, the band has stopped playing. For a few moments they stand there, staring in total shock: Josephine having subconsciously dropped her Blessed Virgin microphone on the floor, where it exploded.

Breedge Courtney tries vainly to save her friend, from Lilly's impending onslaught but its no use. In a matter of seconds 'Our Lady's dormitory has erupted into a full-scale riot.

Skin and hair went flying. Shoes, hairbrushes and pillows were used as missiles: anything that could knock the stuffing out of an opponent or put stars in their eyes was used.

Bridie was terrified she'd get hit by someone or be dragged into the malee, so she decided to escape by going around to the other side, while Josephine and Mary decided to plunge straight into the row. Bridie began jumping from one bed to the next in order to get away; only stopping briefly to pick up a bed pillow that landed on the floor beside her. As Bridie is standing with her back to the wall, holding on to the pillow, the door suddenly bursts open and three nuns, led by Sister Stanislaus enter the room.

For a fleeting moment Sister Stanislaus and Bridie's eyes meet, before the nuns fully observe the wanton scene before them, as small groups of penitent women wrestle half-naked on the floor, some of them bare-breasted, their clothes hanging off their backs as they scream obscenities at each other, while at the same time desperately trying to remove the last vestige of decency covering their bodies.

Sister Stanislaus raised the bell high above her head and gave it such a vigorous, rhythmic jangle 'twould wake the dead. But only when the fighting had ceased and all eyes were on her, did she lower the bronze bell, and hand it to one of the novice Sisters, standing petrified beside her.

"What's…this!" exclaimed Sister Stanislaus in a loud voice, as she hurriedly made the sign of the cross with her large crucifix before letting it jangle once more by her side. "God almighty protect us! And save us from the fires of hell…and the powers of Satan…Look at you! You're like a pack of wild animals! Have you all gone mad?"

There was complete silence as everyone diverted their gaze, and tried discreetly to hide their shame. Everyone, that is except Bridie and a few others who had not been caught up in the rumpus.

Seeing Bridie holding the pillow, and assuming she was up to no good, Sister Stanislaus asked,

"Bridie Rodgers, what have you got to say for yourself?"

"Nothing…Sister."

"Nothing! That's just what I'd expect to hear coming from the likes of you. Why are you holding that pillow? Ready to throw at somebody, I have no doubt."

" No Sister 'twas on the floor…."

"On the floor! Whose idea was this? Whose? I'm not leaving here tonight until I get to the bottom of this. Now whose idea was it?" demanded Sister Stanislaus, as she turned her attention to the unruly mob before her.

Bridie did not answer. Her blushes were saved however when one or two of the penitent women started tittering behind their hands at the mention of the word bottom. They thought it was hilariously funny that Sister Stanislaus wanted to get to the bottom. In a way they thought, that's what they were all trying to do: get to the bottom of someone's drawers.

Sister Stanislaus realised instantly that she had said the wrong thing; used the wrong word. She knew that if she pursued with this line of questioning they would make a laughing stock of her in front of her novice Sisters. She knew very well how it had all started. Jealousy. That was the venomous poison rampant among all of the penitents. If someone was over-friendly with the nuns, their friends were jealous. If some girl was very good at ironing church linen, her friends were jealous. If one was good at sewing or cooking, their friends were jealous. But most of all, if like Josephine Finn, one was good at singing or switched their allegiance from one penitent to another, then everyone was jealous and despised you for what you were.

And that is why, we must stamp out this terrible evil in our midst, she had told her novice Sisters earlier: and the only way to do that effectively was to get rid of the ringleaders. Ringleaders like Josephine Finn, Lilly MacAlastair and perhaps one or two others, who held sway and led by bad example. Some of them are certainly over-due a long holiday in Ballinasloe mental hospital, she told her novice Sisters and I won't be half as slow in sending them there, as the Reverend Mother was.

Sister Stanislaus ignored the tittering at the back of the crowd by pretending she hadn't heard. Instead she decided she would expose the chief suspect, to show she knew who was behind it. Then she'd leave well enough alone, until she got each one of them on their own in the morning. She'd already made a mental note of the chief culprits from their demeanour when she came into the dormitory.

"Miss Finn, was this your idea?"

All eyes turned to Josephine, but she too pretended not to hear by remaining silent and instead began looking around. But when Sister raised her voice and repeated the question, she knew she could no longer ignore it.

"Miss Finn! Yes. You. Was this your idea of entertainment, or whose was it?"

"No Sister."

"'No' it wasn't your idea, or 'no' you don't know who started it?"

"I don't know who started it."

"Were you engaged in singing lewd songs earlier?"

"No," answered Josephine hesitantly. "...I mean..."

"How dare you tell me such bare-faced lies, I distinctly heard you myself! As a matter of fact you could be heard abroad in Eyre Square."

Then turning to her two novice Sisters she said, "I want you to lead these heathens into five decades of the Rosary, and see that everyone of them retires for the night in a decent manner."

Turning to the penitents again, she declared, "Tomorrow morning, I shall carry out a thorough investigation into tonight's unseemly behaviour. I'll take whatever steps I deem necessary, and I shall have no hesitation in calling the Gardaí tonight if I hear another sound. Have I made myself clear?"

The response was muted, but not for long, as the novice Sisters led them into a night of fervent prayer, because for some, judgement day was but around the corner.

* * * * *

The early morning scream was terrifying. It was the most blood-curdling scream she had ever heard. All at once it did three things to her. It woke her with a start. It made her heart beat viciously in her chest and it transported her back to her childhood years in the orphanage out in Clifden. Where often in the dead of night, she'd been woken by screams of somebody having a nightmare or of a child being punished in a remote corner of the building.

Instinctively Bridie looked to the far end of the dormitory and saw Lilly MacAlastair holding her chest. She seemed to recoil in horror at the sight of something or other. As friends went quickly to her aid, Lilly appeared to be talking gibberish as she pointed to the bed.

"Where's...Bridie! Where's Bridie? Bridieeee!" she screamed, as she pointed to the bed. "She won't move."

"What's wrong?" Bridie heard the girls say to Lilly, as heads sprang up all over the dormitory to look down at the source of the disturbance; terrified that something serious was amiss.

With a great deal of fear and trepidation Bridie leapt out of bed and ran quickly towards Lilly, trying desperately to expel the shocking thoughts already accruing in her head; that Lilly had suddenly gone mental or that by the looks of it Josephine was…

The women stood clutching each other beside Josephine's bed; unable to move as Bridie arrived. They were calling out to the crumpled heap, which lay motionless.

"Josephine! Josephine, wake up!" Lilly, barely able to speak whispered imploringly, "Josephine! Ah Josephine! Judy! Judy! Judy! Wake up." Looking at Bridie with a terrified expression on her face, Lilly cried, "she won't move! Bridie, she won't move!"

For a brief moment, Bridie herself thought she was going to faint, but somehow she willed herself to stand next to Josephine and look down at her. She saw immediately that she had that deathly pallor that seemed to indicate there was something seriously wrong with her. She reached out to touch her friend's haggard features, praying fervently that she could feel some warmth there. But she already knew in her heart what the result would be. Dead.

"Jesus, Mary and Holy St. Joseph… she's dead! She's dead!" whispered Bridie, in a barely audible tone.

Bridie's best friend was dead. The best singer in the whole world was dead. The lark in the morning was dead. Judy Garland herself, the one and only Judy, was lying there. Dead.

Again she reached down, this time to clasp Josephine's cold hand, and as she did so she suddenly felt as if they were all dead. Yet somewhere within her, she recalled her religious teaching, which specified that who ever finds the body of a departed soul should at once kneel down, and administer a good Act of Contrition into that persons ear, thereby absolving that person of all the sins of their past life.

Kneeling beside the bed she removed Josephine's decorative rosary beads from her bedpost and commenced her prayer.

"Oh my God, I am heartily sorry for having offended thee. I detest all my sins, because I dread the loss of heaven, and the pains of hell. But most of all because I have displeased thee, who art so good and kind and so deserving of all my love. I firmly resolve with the help of they Holy Grace never more to offend thee and to amend my life. Amen."

Slowly rising to her feet, she continued to look at the lifeless body of her friend Josephine; becoming more surprised each passing moment at how composed and calm she herself had become. Seeing her friend lying there like that, stone cold, made her realise how frail human life could be. She recalled something the two of them had discussed only two weeks ago, on the morning of Julie Murray's departure as the three of them stood at the foot of the penitents' graveyard.

Their conversation springing to mind, she reflected all too clearly on the frightening significance of their spoken words.' Come into the chapel in the name of God, and we'll say a prayer. I don't care where I die, but the last thing I want is to be buried here in an unknown graveyard,' she herself had said to Josephine.

And later that same morning they had discussed Julie's good fortune in being rescued from the home. And Bridie remembered confiding in Josephine that she firmly believed that everything that happened in life came in threes. Noreen Donnellan was free, Julie Murray was free, so that meant that another one of them was destined to go free.

Bridie tried to push the awful recollection from her head. She began to feel guilty as sin for having some strange power, which enabled her to foresee or foretell certain things. She wished with all her heart that she hadn't convinced Josephine that one or other of them was soon destined to go free. She had probably caused Josephine to build up some false hope in her heart that one day soon, she would be free. Free to roam the world, free to meet her Cathal. Free, free, free. As Josephine herself used to say, free to walk the streets of Galway, or free to go and sing her heart out on Broadway.

Unable to speak to anyone and with a heavy heart Bridie turned away as a tidal wave of shock swept through the entire institution. Hardened penitents wept openly as concerned nuns suddenly appeared from nowhere, flitting in and out of the room whispering discreetly as they hurriedly arranged to escort Josephine's body down to the infirmary ward. And as they did so another recollection came into Bridie's head at something Julie Murphy once said. 'Sure it makes no earthly difference Bridie; once you're gone, you're gone'.

There's poor Josephine, only thirty-five years of age and now she's gone. I just can't believe it; lying there like that, stone dead.

* * * * *

They were about to go haymaking when the telegram arrived. They didn't like telegrams because it usually only ever meant one thing, that someone was dead. Their minds raced, doing a quick count of ageing relatives, aunts and uncles. Come to think of it, they had very few left they thought, so who could it possibly be?

Josephine's mother tore open the telegram and flew through the contents.

"Mother of the Divine... It's Josephine, she's dead!" she said as she reached out to a chair for support.

"What?" exclaimed her husband in disbelief, as she handed him the telegram.

They'd not set eyes on their daughter since the day they'd put her away, and had long since resigned themselves to her loss; only ever briefly referring to her as *that one*.

This was because *that one* had brought nothing but ruination on the good name of the Finns, by aligning herself with them Protestant land-grabbers, the Swanicks. Now, after years of doubt, they felt justified in their actions, as Cathal Swanick had turned out to be nothing more than a drunkard. And, rumour had it, he frequently pledged his undying love for Josephine all over town, while wallowing in crates of Guinness and self-pity. It was also rumoured that he had fathered a child to some unfortunate girl in Tuam, and had point blank refused to marry her.

Josephine's mother, had at times felt a tinge of regret at not having made some attempt at a reconciliation with her daughter, but then the idea would balance itself out with the realisation that it could only ever lead to the re-opening of old wounds. Josephine was sure to inquire about Cathal, and would make every effort to see him again. The very notion of their reconciliation repelled her father even more. In his eyes the Swanick's were nothing more than a thieving band of land-grabbers who had robbed generations of tenant farmers of their rightful inheritance. Nothing could change that, and they were damned forever if they'd let one of their ilk – Cathal, the womanising drunkard and all that he was – take their one and only daughter to breed a new generation of land-grabbing Swanicks. No. Never. This frightening prospect had been trotted out time and again by John Finn to his meek down trodden wife, whenever she attempted to broach the subject. Now it didn't matter. It was all too late. Josephine was dead. The only thing for them to consider was would they go to *that one's* funeral or not. And, after a great deal of soul-searching and debate, they finally decided that no useful purpose would be served by attending the funeral. They'd had no contact with her since they put her in, so where was the use in recognising her now? Further more, they had a niggling suspicion that their attendance at their daughter's funeral might mean they would be expected to carry the costs of her burial. Then they thought, what if the neighbours got wind of the word and decided to go along to the funeral: that would show the Finn's in a very bad light, or would it? No, they decided; no one in the village would know because telegram boys don't read telegrams; they only deliver them. The only thing to do was sit tight and say nothing; only make sure that it didn't appear in the death column of the newspapers or local press. Instead they'd send a Mass card. No one in the locality would know anything until it was all over and Josephine was safely underground. In a week or two it wouldn't matter. They could simply claim, it had been a private funeral: family members only.

* * * * *

The procession, was led by a large group of priests, dressed in white, followed by the Sisters of Mercy order of nuns dressed in black: their long flowing habits swishing gently as they slowly swept down the centre aisle of the Mary Magdalene church.

The priests already occupied their positions round the main altar as the nuns, their heads bowed, filed into the front pews either side of Josephine's body, which had lain in state in front of the altar, overnight.

A strong smell of incense filled the air, as Mass candles, began to dance and flicker on the tall, brass candelabras, which stood either side of the marble altar.

Soon the large congregation rose to its feet for the introductory hymn, led by Sister Concillio, which signalled the beginning of high Mass. Bridie and Lilly found it hard to control their emotion as they too sang from the same sheet, during the opening Hymn.

Unknown to either of them, Cathal Swanick was standing just inside the heavy oak door; an unknown lonely figure. He took in a deep breath as he surveyed the scene. Women. God Almighty, I've never seen so many women together in all my life. Where did they all come from, he wondered. So this is a refuge for women. Don't they have some quare places in Galway all the same, row after row after row of head-scarved women. You'd almost swear they were all nuns; except for the coloured scarves, and the fact that the real nuns are all in black, up at the head of the congregation.

Glancing nervously to his right, Cathal spotted two men kneeling by the tall church window. He wondered who they were. Did they live here with all these women? Were they married men, or what was their association with the deceased, Josephine? Unknown to Him, they were two of the Magdalene's most loyal servants, Mr. Hehir and Mr. Tyrrell, both van drivers, who had each completed almost forty years service with the Magdalene Home Laundry..

Mass was only beginning and already Cathal's throat felt dry, despite the fact that he'd had two quick ones at home in Lavally, whilst waiting for the taxi, as well as two more pints when he arrived in the city, just to give him courage to face the day. But it wasn't enough. He'd give anything right now to have another just to calm his fears.

He'd got such a shock yesterday when the Post-Mistress waylaid him outside the Post Office to ask him if he'd heard the news. He'd told her he hadn't. She brought him in to the office so she could show him the rough copy of the telegram as written on her blotted note pad.

'*Regret to inform you, Josephine Finn passed away last night. Stop. Peacefully in her sleep. Stop. Burial tomorrow after11.30 a.m. Mass, in the Magdalene Grounds: unless other wise requested. Signed Sister Stanislaus,(acting Mother Superior)*

'*Unless otherwise requested.*' Nervously, Cathal put his hand to his hip pocket, to make sure the flask was still there, and to reassure himself that if the worst came to the worst he could always slip outside for a quick slug. But he knew it was a last resort. A pint, that was what he wanted. It was your only man for the thirst. But where were the 'Finns,' he asked himself, as he scanned the congregation again. They're not here yet: hypocritical bastards, he thought. They thought that much of their daughter they wouldn't allow her to marry a Protestant, and yet they don't think enough of her to come to her funeral. You'd think they'd bring the poor girl home and give her a proper burial, and not have her buried here in a pauper's grave. I'm half-tempted to arrange it myself, but sure there'd be ructions and blue murder if I said anything; I know there would. They'd gang up on me. It'd give them the perfect opportunity to slate me. Big oul' John with his viper's tongue would rant and rave: look here Swanick: we don't need your Protestant charity around here. Is it what you want to bury our only daughter? A decent 'grave' my arse: you buried poor Josephine fifteen years ago when you destroyed her life; as sure as they nailed Jesus to the Cross. So don't talk to me 'Swanick' about charity, forgiveness or respect. You've no respect for yourself, so how could you have it for others?

Cathal, moved restlessly from one foot to the other. He was tempted to go outside so he could wet his lips. But one of the priests he felt was looking straight down at him. It made him feel uncomfortable.

Cathal meant only to hand in a Mass card to the convent but the nuns were so nice they persuaded him that he should partake fully in Josephine's funeral service. It all seemed so strange to him, this Catholic Church business. He wished now that he'd stayed away altogether because all this singing and lamenting – keening, he thought they called it – was so mournful. And yet, in a weird sort of a way, he found it enchanting.

He continued to stand at the rear of the little chapel listening intently as the notes of the 'Ky-ri-e' reverberated throughout the church as friends of the deceased dropped their heads to mourn softly into their tightly held handkerchiefs. He was even more mesmerised by all the religious fervour, when at that precise moment, a beautiful ray of sunlight began to filter in through one of the tall church windows, casting a spotlight on the chief celebrant and cantor as though he were the epicentre of some famous theatre production, to which his co-celebrants responded,

Chri – ste – e – e – e – e – e – e – e – e – e – e – e -e- l – son.
Ky – ri – e – e – e – e – e – e -e – e – e – e – e – e -e – l – son.
Chri -ste – e – e – e – e – e – e – e – e – e – e – e – l – son.
Ky – ri – e – e – e- e – e – e -e – e – e – e – e – e – e – I – son.

It was only when they had finished singing that the deep sense of shock and loss of his raving beauty assailed him. He wished that he could just see her angelic face once more; dead and all as she was lying there in a coffin as the congregation began to file past her body on their way up to the Altar to receive Holy Communion.

He watched the long lines of penitent women return to their seats where they again knelt down before burying their faces in their pale white hands. Why, He did not know: probably some religious rite or other; and to atone for their awful sins. He thought, perhaps he too should try and make up for the sins of his past life. Yes, 'twas a good idea; only, not today: some other time: maybe. He started to feel restless and pleaded silently; in the honour of God, will the priest get on with it till I get outside for a breath of fresh air, and with any bit of luck, a pint of porter.

There was a brief lull, while everyone was seated after the Communion ceremony and Cathal realised to his horror that the chief celebrant was looking straight down at him, about to say something.

"My dear people, we are gathered here today to pray for the soul of Josephine Finn, who departed this life and who is now seated at the right hand of God. Today, I have chosen my words very carefully; because while most of us sinners can expect – at best – to spend a considerable amount of time in purgatory before being allowed into Heaven, Josephine Finn will have had no such burden placed on her shoulders. Josephine was by all accounts an exceptional human being. That we are all sinners in the eyes of God is without question. And yet, Josephine – from what I knew of her as a member of the Mary Magdalene Choir, and from accounts I have received only this morning from her friends and colleagues, and the Sisters of Mercy, whom she served so loyally and faithfully down the years – was a walking Saint. A Saint who may never be canonised, probably never will be canonised. But a Saint nonetheless in the eyes of God, because of the great love and compassion she has always shown to her fellow human beings. She is at this very moment seated at the right hand of God, because he has ordained that Josephine should be one of his flock. In many ways it could be said that Josephine was one of his 'Lost Sheep', who has now been found and returned to the fold.

My dear people, in creating Josephine Finn, God bestowed on her one of his greatest gifts to mankind, that of a Golden voice. She was and always will be remembered as a beautiful singer, who also had that rare ability to entertain. For as a great many of her friends and Sisters in the choir said to me, 'Truly, she had the voice of an angel.' Alas, it's a voice we shall hear no more.

But I did not have to hear those words today. Many, many years I had the pleasure, or should I say the privilege of hearing and seeing Josephine sing during a rare Christmas concert right her in the Magdalene laundry, and when I think back to the lines and the words – how could any of us forget – "…*Some day I wish upon a star, where*

269

clouds are far behind me."

My dear people, I have to ask myself, could Josephine have asked for a greater wish than to wish upon a star? Could she have asked for anything more beautiful, more majestic more radiant? Yet for all a star's beauty and radiance, we the people of this earth could never feel its touch or sense its rays, except through the voice of an angel. Josephine's voice if you like, was the vital link between God's people on this earth and the stars in heaven.

"Some day I wish upon a star,
Where clouds are far behind me,
Where troubles melt like lemon drops,
Way above the chimney tops."

Wasn't it somehow appropriate that she should always sing that song, which was first made famous by her heroine, Judy Garland in the 'Wizard of Oz'.

And wasn't it somehow appropriate too, that in doing so she should connect us all to our secret dreams; to one day be free of all our cares, through her singing, her kindness and through her great love for us.

Her visit on this earth was but a short one. Today my dear people, may she rest…in peace…Amen."

Cathal could not hide the tears. In spite of his best efforts his head sank onto his chest out of a deep sense of shame, that anyone would see a grown man cry. But somehow, the tears brought a strange sense of relief, as they washed away the awful pain in his heart. The guilt of never having had the guts or the courage to come here to see her while she was still alive. He was amazed at how easy it had been to gain access to the convent this morning, and the nun's insistence that he have a nice cup of tea after his long journey. He had half-expected to be turned away from the 'Magdalene' as an unfit person to pay his last respects to a girl like Josephine.

But the priest…his words…his eulogy…. had flowed so eloquently that it had somehow exposed Cathal's own short-comings like never before. He now saw at first hand, the errors of his ways, the futility of his life.

True, he had never heard his beautiful Josephine sing, but he knew the words of that famous song almost off by heart. It brought him back to their last meeting on that glorious summers day long ago in the Mall, Tuam. He remembered her oh so clearly, standing there in the laneway holding her bicycle, as her lovely floral dress swayed ever so gently in the breeze. He pictured her singing an enchanting love song to him, her face radiant with delight at having just bumped into him. He remembered too, how their so-called love had been nothing more than a few brief encounters, smothered to death by their families' fierce hatred of each other. He remembered how he had allowed his love of her to grow, when what he should have done long, long ago when he had first lost her, was, let it go. Let it go.

He knew he'd always been too weak; too lily-livered to ever stand up to the Finns. Even his own friends, had said so. Afraid too to stand up to his own parents, who while they never actually stood in his way, always frowned on him whenever he cast his eye on anyone other than a girl of his own religious denomination.

At long last, the Mass was over. He turned quickly and slipped outside the door of the little chapel and stood for a moment, surveying the scene. Everything was so quiet and peaceful, he thought, as a little group of men stood waiting beside an open grave a short distance away. Suddenly the thought struck him that his great love affair with Josephine was finally over. Maybe it was time to make a new beginning. After what he'd just witnessed, he decided he'd change his life; his faith, and become a Catholic. He'd go back to Tuam this very day and offer to make a decent woman of Mary Burke, who bore his child. He'd already destroyed one life. He couldn't bear to ruin another. Reaching into his pocket he took out the flask, unscrewed the cap, went across to the grass verge and watched the bane of his life drain away. He shook the last drop of poisonous liquid away with a vengeance. Time for a new beginning, he sighed as the congregation began to emerge from the church. Soon their overflowing tears fell to the echoing sound of the booming church bell as the congregation prepared to escort one of the Magdalene Home's best-loved penitent, Josephine Finn, to her final resting place.

Bridie stood at the graveside without showing a single trace of emotion, while all around her, young and old wept openly. Her only friends, Lilly and Margaret clung either side of her, as the priest said the final prayers. She raised her eyes to heaven so she would not hear or see her two comrades' pitiful cries of lamentation. Suddenly, the two women broke free of her grasp and threw themselves on the coffin, as the gravediggers were about to lower the coffin into the ground and the nuns rushed forward to drag the screaming women away.

But something made Bridie turn away from the mourners and their cries of madness. She had had enough. She could take no more. She began to walk back towards the laundry. She felt like she was past caring anymore, because there was nothing to live for. Yet she hadn't gone more than a few yards when she raised her eyes and pleaded with Our Lord for the right to retain her sanity. Suddenly the very thought of the word sanity terrified her. It was too closely connected to the word insanity. She had a morbid fear of that word ever since her stay in Tuam, where she had listened to Mad Madge's belief that fallen women were put away for life. She could not remember ever being so frightened before. Why, she began to wonder, was life so hard, so difficult, so seemingly complicated for each and every one of them?

Was this some sort of alien, hostile world in which they were all living? Or was it instead some sort of mental institution where they were sent to atone for their sins?

As if to expel those morbid thoughts and to seek some reassurance she stopped for a second, to look back. The nuns and penitent women were still jostling each other as the gravediggers began to fill in the grave. She turned again and began to make her way back into the laundry.

No, they were all in here, she decided, because they were unfortunate enough to have caused a bit of trouble in their youth. Not a single girl she knew had ever killed or injured anyone. Julie Murray was sent here because she stole a coat she was only fifteen years of age. Look at Lilly MacAlastair; she was sent here because she was a bit of a tomboy. Look at Noreen Donnellan; she shouldn't even have been in here at all. She was put away because her foster parents used to beat her. And look at poor Josephine Finn, she wept openly, she was here because she fell in love with someone her father didn't like. And as for myself, I was sent here because I had a baby, she sighed.

Making her way back into the kitchen so she could have a nice cup of tea before the mourners came back, she mumbled aloud to herself in her heart-felt grief; look at me now! I've no one! No Paschal. No Noreen! No Julie, No Josephine; No nothing. But I swear to you Almighty God, I'm leaving this place before the year is out. I swear on the Holy Bible, because if I don't, I know that I'd be better off dead.

Chapter Eighteen

It was while helping Sister Perpetuo – one of the new nuns – to sort out the Co. Clare parcels for distribution that Bridie was slipped an envelope by Mr. Hehir, the van driver. Bridie in turn slipped the folded white envelope into her pocket, much to the relief of Mr Hehir. He'd kept the letter in his pocket for almost a week, awaiting his chance to see Bridie. It was not easy. He knew that she generally worked in the ironing room, well away from dispatch. He was loath to pass on the letter to anyone else. Several times during the week he'd been tempted to give it to one of her friends, but was terrified that she might not get it at all. Many years ago, he'd passed on a message for another penitent, only to be caught red-handed, when one of the nuns intercepted the letter, as a penitent read its contents aloud to her friends. As a result of that Mr. Hehir was reprimanded by the Reverend Mother, and threatened with instant dismissal if caught doing so again. Thereafter, he refused point blank to carry any messages either in or out of the laundry for anyone. But as time went by he felt more and more sympathy for the inmates and began to pass on the occasional message again.

When Mr Hehir and his lorry pulled out into the yard, Bridie asked permission to be excused, saying she wanted to go to the Lavatory. When she reached the cubicle she tore open the letter.

Nurses Home
Merlin Park

Dear Bridie,
I'm after hearing about Josephine's death, and I'm not worth tuppence. The girls here in Merlin said that a girl had died in the Magdalene. They said she was supposed to be a great singer. When I heard that, Bridie I nearly died. I walked all the way to Mr Tyrrell's house to ask him if it was her. I brought one of the

girls here with me because I was afraid the nuns might see me. When he told me it was Josephine, I cried and cried. She was such a good friend, and so good to me, even though we often had our rows. I only hope that God will forgive me for all the horrid things I used to say to her. Sure 'tis hard to be good all the time. I fell out with me sister Kay because I wouldn't do what she wanted and go to America. I said hump America, I want to stay near Bridie. She got me into the Merlin Park Hospital in the end. A girl who ran away from the Magdalene, worked here for a while years ago, but left when she heard the nuns were looking for her. I live in the nurses' home because one of the doctors said I should stay here. I cry ever night, Bridie when I think of our dear friend Josephine, and you still in there. Maybe you should write to that nice man you used to work for. Sure where's the harm? He might come and take you out. I asked the van driver if I wrote a letter would he give it to you. He promised he would. I've stuck in five pounds in case you get out. I hope you don't lose it. Write a letter quick, and give it to Mr.Tyrrell and tell me what's happening or how Josephine died. Goodbye for now, from Julie.

p.s. I pray ever day that you'll soon get out and we'll go to the Seapoint. I've been to a nurses' dance and met a fella. But he kept dancing, I mean standing on me feet and everthin'. The nurses call him 'Johnny Two Shoes'.

After receiving the five pounds, Bridie's faith in human nature was greatly restored. She thought long and hard about what Julie had said, about writing to Mr. O'Malley in 'Conly House' in Tuam. She'd already thought about it herself a dozen times, but had ruled it out. She thought she could never see him getting in touch with the Magdalene Laundry to take her out, especially after all these years. He probably had enough problems of his own. And anyway, if she did write and he came to take her out, he'd probably want her to live and work in Conly House forever, looking after the farm hands, and she didn't want that. Besides, the O'Malley children would be grown up and gone. So they wouldn't want her then? No. From now on she'd make her own way in the world, she decided. First she'd write to Julie and thank her for the money.

Dear Julie,

Thank you very much for the gift. It was so thoughtful of you. I was killed wondering where you were and if you knew about Josephine. Wasn't it awful? I don't think I'll ever be the same again. It was bad enough when you went away but Josephine's death really put the tin hat on it. Everything's the same since you left. Work! Work! Work! I don't know in the name of God how we stick it. Half the girls got the 'flu and I had a touch of it myself for a few days. I pray every day for a miracle like yours. If anything happens I'll let you know straight away.

Goodbye for now, and thanks again for your gift. I'm sure I'll make good use of it.

Love Bridie.

After weeks of careful consideration, Bridie decided it was time to commence her own plan of action. Now was as good a time as any she thought, particularly as several new inmates and nuns had arrived. One of the new nuns Sr. Kieran was appointed Ward Sister, in place of Sister Philomena. Sister Philomena was supposed to have gone to Dublin, because she disappeared without warning and no one knew for sure what happened to her. Some inmates claimed she had left the order altogether. Bridie was at a loss to know how or why she had disappeared so quickly. She had great respect for Sister Philomena because she'd gone out of her way to help her. Especially helping to keep herself and John Paschal in touch when no one else cared.

Bridie's only close allies now, were Lily MacAlastair and Margaret Sherry. She decided she'd try to make a pact with them; to swear them to secrecy about her plans for the three of them to escape. It was always her intention to flee with Julie Murray and Josephine Finn, but all that had changed. She remembered Julie Murray's oft quoted words from her father, 'Time waits for no man.' They were about the only words Julie ever remembered of her father, and now they were engraved in Bridie's memory too. And if ever there was a time to escape it was surely now, she thought, before it's too late.

Having heard nothing from Noreen Donnellan for a long time, she was delighted to receive a secret letter from her via Mr. Hehir. To her astonishment Noreen encouraged her to run out the gate and enclosed five pounds to help her on her way. Bridie immediately tore off the address and hid it with John Paschal's lock of hair before flushing the torn letter down the lavatory. But of one thing she was sure, if she escaped, she would not go to England. She'd stay in Ireland so she could be near John Paschal. But she'd keep hold of Noreen's address just in case she needed it.

The three penitents were sitting on the grass as the sun slowly slid down the broad evening sky, supposedly planning their escape. But Lilly and Margaret were very sceptical. True, they claimed they wanted their freedom more than anything else, but Bridie sensed that like the majority of the women in the Laundry they were being slowly conditioned into accepting their lot and becoming institutionalised. She could almost empathise with their fear of the unknown and their reluctance to come on board. She knew if she failed to convince them she'd end up questioning her own ability to launch such a daring plan.

"But what if the O'Brien's won't let us stay? They might call the Guards," suggested Margaret.

"They won't! I know they won't. I can tell by the letters," replied Bridie as she nervously plucked a few sun-drenched blades of grass and tossed them over her right shoulder. "They're nice people. I know I can trust them. Besides, they've looked after John Paschal for years, so why wouldn't they let us stay with them."

"I don't care what you say Bridie, I think we'd be a lot safer: that's if we ever get out; to go straight to Julie Murray in Merlin Park. I know where it is; it's not far at all from here. Sure Williamstown is supposed to be miles and miles, according to Noreen Donnellan," countered Lilly.

"No! NO! You're not listening to me!" said Bridie, raising her voice somewhat to denote her annoyance.

"I've already told you, it's not safe. That's the last place we should go. I know 'twould be lovely to be with Julie and everything, but the nuns and the Guards would go straight there, because they know we're good friends. And even if we managed to hide there for a day or two, and then they saw us, they could have us brought back anytime because we escaped. Julie told me in one of her letters that a girl who had escaped from here and was working in the Hospital, left there, because the nuns were trying to bring her back. You see it's different for Julie. Her sister signed her papers and took her out. And only a family relative can get you out."

They continued to argue, going over and over the same old ritual for almost a week. But Bridie was adamant that together they could make a run for it, while Lilly and Margaret were of the opinion that the whole thing was too risky. Three of them, together! Who ever heard of it? One, maybe two, but three! No.

"Besides, we're not ready," objected Margaret.

"Look!" said Bridie desperately pleading with them to see a bit of sense. "If we stick together we have a great chance. But If I have to go out on my own then I will. I'll not say anything to anybody and then the two of ye will be sorry. I won't even bother me backside writing to ye or anything," she added as a levering ploy.

"But if we do get out, how will we get to Williamstown?" asked Margaret.

"I don't know! And I don't care! All I know is we'll get there somehow. The thing is to concentrate on getting out of here. If we can do that the rest will follow. I don't want to spend the rest of my life in here. I've sacrificed everything for the last fifteen years for the sake of John Paschal. And I've only ever seen him once. He'll be going to work somewhere soon, Maybe Galway or Dublin or England. And if he goes while I'm still in here, I might never see him again. Please! Do it for me!"

"Maybe you're right. What have we to lose? There was a time when I wouldn't think twice about it," said Lilly as she began to extract a cigarette butt from her secret hiding place in the hem of her dress. "Arrah, to hell with it! We'll take a chance! We could talk about it 'til the cows come home and not do anything about it."

"I don't care. It's up to ye," said Margaret with a shrug of resignation.

"It's not up to us. Why is it up to us? We can't go and leave you on your own," retorted Lilly. "You might tell on us, where would we be then?"

"Will you stop talking stupid! Why would I tell anyone? I'll go too if it makes ye happy. I don't want to be left on my own. Only thing is, if we get caught, we'll get a fierce hiding from the Guards; and the nuns will leather us and cut our hair: that Sister Stanislaus can be right vicious you know. She'd give us a good hammering because she loves showing her authority and then the whole place would be laughing at us."

"No! No! The first thing to do is stop thinking like that. We're going out of here the first chance we get. Are we agreed on that?" asked Bridie, quickly in case they changed their minds.

"Yes." "O.K. What ever you say."

"And if I hear one word about it from anyone I'll say nothing but go out on my own. So, don't breathe a word to anyone," whispered Bridie. "I'll pick the time and the place, and because it was my idea, I'll go out first."

Once Bridie had her friends' support and agreement, she came to the conclusion that it was better to move quickly. The longer they waited the greater the risk that one of the girls might open their mouths. She could already see how excited they were getting, as they would sometimes jokingly ask, "Anything happenin'?" whenever they met in the corridors.

As there was no suitable time in which to strike for freedom Bridie had to figure it all out and make a decision, soon. Saturday, to her seemed to be the best day, particularly as the Galway races were over and the Laundry was returning to an air of normality after the busy summer season. Saturday afternoon, when all the scrubbing and choir practice had taken place was an ideal time to escape, she thought.

It was Friday evening when Bridie took out the goatskin purse from her blouse. It contained the lock of her son's hair she'd kept for all of fifteen years. She sat on the edge of her bed for a moment. She wanted to feel its soft texture and to study the tiny photograph, whispering to herself, Son, some day soon this will be yours. I have sacrificed so much for you Paschal, you are the nearest thing to my heart. She kissed the delicate strands of hair, which still retained a glint of gold, despite the passing years. She checked to make sure she still had Noreen Donnellan's address and the five pound note together with Julie's fiver and put them all back together again. Looking round she saw some of the elderly penitents, polishing the brass doorknobs that had never once grown cold from the dint of polishing over the years. She knew these silent robotic-like creatures spent hours every day wiping away imaginary dust and dirt from their doors and bedside lockers. And they spent hours rummaging under their beds for old clothes, knitting needles or misplaced balls of wool.

Bridie slipped discreetly out of the room and went down the stairs and across the grounds to say a quiet prayer at the penitents' graveyard. She wanted to say a special one for her deceased friend Josephine, asking for her support in her hour of need, and thanking her for making her life in the Laundry more bearable with her humorous songs and ditties.

Bridie circled the Magdalene grounds to admire everything for the last time; her favourite tree; the huge cherry blossom that flowered so beautifully in the spring and that always attracted the birds and the bees. She had a fierce passion for nature and couldn't wait to see what life was like in the outside world. Then she climbed the stone steps to Our Lady's Grotto to ask for her guidance and forgiveness. She reached up to touch Our Lady's strong yet delicate hand before leaning forward to kiss her well-worn feet. Accepting that she'd done all she could, she returned to her dormitory in silence, thinking only that tomorrow was Saturday. The day she had planned to climb over the wall and away to freedom.

* * * * *

She had one eye on the wall clock and was nervously counting down the hours and minutes. Then the unmentionable happened. The new Reverend Mother, Sister Stanislaus, whom none of the penitents had seen all morning suddenly appeared out of nowhere accompanied by a young penitent half-wit, known as 'Hang on Mary' who usually went round with one of the nuns ringing a small bronze bell, to announce their presence. 'Hang on Mary' was like a child with a new toy who loved showing off and flaunting her role as assistant to the Reverend Mother.

When the bell ceased ringing the Reverend Mother came forward, her firmly starched white coif and veil looking as if it might strangle the very lifeblood from her face. All eyes in the ironing room were on her, as her long black habit made a slight rustling noise and her heavy crystal rosary beads clinked as she slid her hands tightly into the deep dark folds of her sleeves and spoke with an authoritarian air. "Girls, what day, it is tomorrow?"

Bridie felt her heart palpitating and wondered if the Reverend Mother knew something. Was the Reverend Mother going to put a spanner in the works, she thought. Please, not now, when we have everything planned. Some of the penitents glanced nervously from one to the other and raised their eyes to Heaven as if to say 'here we go again'. Most of the girls in the ironing room were caught unawares and were unsure what the Reverend Mother meant.

"Sunday," squawked one of the penitents in a bird like voice. It did not go down too well with the new Reverend Mother, Sister Stanislaus.

"I know it's Sunday dear. I know that well, but it's also a very important Sunday. Now, what date is it, and whose birthday is it?" asked the Reverend Mother as 'Hang on Mary' stood behind her, gesturing wildly to Bridie.

A chorus of voices rang out, "It's Our Lady's Birthday!"

"How right you are. It's the 8th of September and Our Lady's Birthday, and what did Our Lady do on the 15th of August, 1879?"

"She appeared in Knock."

"Correct…" Alarm bells began to ring in Bridie's head and her heart began to thump in her chest. She lowered her eyes, so the Rev Mother wouldn't particularly notice her because she knew what was about to happen. She glanced sideways at her two friends as the Reverend Mother continued,

"…at least you've learned something and managed to retain it in your heads. Which is why I'm looking for volunteers for this afternoon to help erect a special Altar to 'Our Lady' for tomorrow morning's Mass. I would like you to put some nice flowers on the Altar, and lots more around the Statue, as we have a lot of Sisters of Mercy nuns from the schools coming in to visit us in the afternoon."

Several penitents put up their hands straight away while crying out, "Me! Me! Me!"

"And Bridie," suggested 'Hang on Mary' brazenly while still gesturing with her hand and indicating that she wanted Bridie to assist her in her task.

Normally this was a job Bridie did without fail. She loved 'Our Lady' with a passion and was devoted to her: but not today of all days. Yet how could she refuse? There seemed no way out. She'd be expected to be the main devotee among the penitents tomorrow. She soon began to feel a fierce sense of resentment towards 'Hang on Mary' and in particular the Reverend Mother: that they should always consider her freely available when ever they chose.

She was always being asked – especially since Julie Murray left – to carry out some intricate needle work and repairs to priests vestments and rare pieces of church linen; not to mention the cleaning and polishing of the church in preparation for a feast or holy day of obligation. Before Bridie had time to realise what course of action to take, she could hear herself talking, and began to turn crimson at the sound of her own voice.

"Reverend Mother, maybe I could be excused today…I'm not feeling that well…besides, I think it's only fair that others get a chance with the altar, as I'm always doing it."

The Reverend Mother's eyebrows shot up in surprise as she turned swiftly to look at Bridie.

"Certainly there's nothing wrong with your tongue," retorted the Reverend Mother, and they all laughed. "What way are you not feeling well?"

"I…I feel kind-a-sick… a bit dizzy at times…" lied Bridie.

"Dizzy! When did you first notice it?"

"Yesterday, Sister."

"And pray tell me, why didn't you inform one of the other Sisters or myself?"

"I didn't want to trouble you…I thought it might go away."

"Would you like to go to bed for a few hours?"

"I think I would," replied Bridie, not knowing what she was going to do, as her plans for today's attempted escape were blown to smithereens..

She could have kicked herself for opening her gob too soon. Why couldn't she have kept her mouth shut, carried out her task, and then tried running away as she'd planned? How could she possibly escape now. And what about Lilly and Margaret?

As Bridie was immersed in these thoughts, the Reverend Mother turned to Lilly MacAlastair and said,

"Lilly, would you like to take Bridie's place?"

"Yes," Reverend Mother." replied Lilly, enthusiastically, not knowing that Bridie had other plans for that afternoon.

"So would I," said Margaret Sherry quickly, not wanting to be seen to be the odd one out.

"Very well! So, we have Mary, Christine, Josephine Rabbitte, Bernadette Comer, Lilly MacAlastair and Margaret Sherry. You're to meet with Sister Aloysius and Sister Consillio over in the church right after you've had your dinner. The rest of you can carry on scrubbing the floors. Bridie will you come with me and I'll walk you to your dormitory."

While Bridie was being led back to her dormitory she could not believe how stupid she'd been to refuse to erect an Altar to ' Our

Lady'. She felt a deep sense of guilt as she watched the Reverend Mother unlock the intermediary doors before leading her upstairs to her dormitory

"I'll get you an aspirin and a hot drink," the Reverend Mother was saying, as she prepared to lock the door behind her. "One of the Sisters will bring it over to you, and if the dizziness gets any worse be sure and let me know right away."

"Thanks Reverend Mother," said Bridie trying desperately not to look Sister in the eye in case she detected her deceit.

There's nothing for it, but to go to bed and sit it out until Lilly and Margaret have finished work, thought Bridie. Nothing much has changed because my big mouth still gets me into trouble every time.

After Sister Aloysius, brought Bridie the glass of warm water and an aspirin, she lay in bed thinking long and hard about what she had done: and she came to the firm conclusion she didn't even know her own mind. She was teetering on the edge of darkness because for weeks the voices in her head had been telling her to Go, Go, Go: but she was terrified of the consequences. What if she failed and let down her two friends. After all it was her idea. What if she ran away and was captured? What if she fell off the wall – like poor Josephine – and landed on her arse? Would she too go mad and like her friend end up being buried in the black-clad graveyard of the Magdalene grounds. The thought sickened her beyond belief. If she was going at all, she'd have to go now, she told herself. She jumped out of bed because she could no longer control the thoughts going through her mind. She felt such pressure within her chest she thought she'd pass out at any moment. Yet another day, another opportunity had presented itself and she hadn't the courage to take it. Today's chance was gone or was it? She'd have to wait and try again next Saturday, she thought.

After pacing the dormitory for a long time, Bridie was relieved to hear Lilly and Margaret returning with the other inmates. They couldn't understand why Bridie claimed to be unwell when clearly she hadn't said anything to them before the Rev. Mother arrived. They were ready to demand an explanation on entering the room, half afraid that Bridie might not even be in the dormitory; that she had pulled some stunt, in order to get away herself. And they were mighty relieved to see her sitting waiting for them.

"No! No! I had nothing planned. But I was fed up with being taken for granted," she replied to their many questions. "Listen, It's a lovely day outside, why don't we go for a walk."

"A walk! Are you mad! It's too warm; and besides I'm too tired. Later on maybe."

But Bridie insisted. She almost had to drag them with her; such was her overwhelming desire to flee the Magdalene Home once and for all. She equated the awful stress and pressure she was feeling as that which had engulfed her body, years earlier when the nuns were about to remove John Paschal from her. At that moment she felt she was about as close to madness as it was possible to be. The time had come for her to make a stand and scale the Magdalene wall to freedom. She'd waited far too long, wasted almost a lifetime. Living every single day of her life in fear: fear of failure, fear of the unknown, fear of the nuns and fear of being betrayed by one of her fellow inmates. Yet some overpowering force was urging her to go: to go now, to climb over the wall and away to freedom.

The three women went out the rear door of the building and stood for a second in the wavering heat. The sunlight seemed to dazzle Bridie for an instant. When she looked up she thought she saw a clear figure of a smiling sun as a child looking down on her, its warm rays spreading out across the broad expanse of infinity. She could feel its glorious energy entering her body. She turned to her friends and half heartedly said,

"I think we'll go now."

"Go where?" asked Lilly and Margaret as they saw Bridie turn to walk in the opposite direction to the one they normally took when going for a stroll. Suddenly the realization struck them that perhaps Bridie was about to make a run for it. That this was the moment they were all waiting for. But at the same time it couldn't possibly be happening now. Not now, of all times and places.

"Where do you think!" answered Bridie, nervously. "Come on, quick!"

"But we can't Bridie, we can't. Look; they're watching us."

"And look at all the people!" added Margaret, who for a moment thought Bridie must be mad to even suggest such a thing.

"I don't care so long as there are no nuns about. I can't stick this place another minute. I'm going, whether ye like it or not."

"Bridie do you realise what you're saying… we're bound to get caught! We've no clothes or anything. You couldn't have picked a worse time as far as I'm concerned. Why don't we wait till the morning: It'll be grand and quiet then," suggested Lilly.

"I thought we agreed we'd go together. If ye don't come now, I'll go on my own," insisted Bridie. "We've wasted enough time. I'm here fifteen years, and every time I walk down by Josephine's grave I get sick. I know if I don't get away from here this minute, then I'm going to die."

The words, 'Josephine's grave' was too much for Bridie's friends. They began to walk hesitantly behind her as if strolling about, towards the farthest corner of the enclosed grounds.

"Listen!" said Bridie. Ye two lift me up on the wall and then I'll try and pull ye two up. If we can manage that, then ye can hold on to me while I try to slide down the other side. Once I get over I'll help ye."

Acting as a human chain, they pushed and pulled and dragged each other until they were halfway over the wall. Looking back they noticed two or three penitents standing watching them from the far side of 'Our Lady's' grotto. They just stood there staring in bewilderment, wondering what they were trying to do. Minutes later all three of them had disappeared completely from view and the penitent witnesses began to wonder if what they had seen was real or imagined; as girls sometimes climbed up on to the wall to steal a glance out on the road, only to receive a severe reprimand from the nuns when caught in the act. Men, and only men, should ever be seen, climbing a wall the nuns said.

* * * * *

The first thing to hit the three escapees when they were safely over the wall was elation, followed quickly by panic. They could not believe that they were actually free. They each wanted to shout for joy as they fled breathless like thieves in the night, along College Road. They wondered if they were going the right way as they quickly removed their white caps and gowns and stuffed them under a hedge. When they caught up with an elderly lady returning home with her shopping bags, Bridie asked her if was the way to Tuam. It was. Then they decided it was better not to be seen to be in too much of a hurry, and to act as normal as possible in case they were reported.

To them the outside world was a frighteningly new place; inhabited by strange sights and sounds. And were it not for the fact that they'd seen lorries and buses at close quarters from the Magdalene Laundry they would have been terrified for their lives. Even the sudden sound of a motorbike and sidecar tearing along behind them, left them terrified..

"What was that?" gasped Margaret as she stood looking.

"A motorbike, I think!" answered Lilly "But that noise! I used to think it was the buses."

"Buses me arse! Come on! We'll have to move faster and see if we can get a lift or something. Me shoes are killing me," said Bridie.

Hitching a lift was something they'd never done before and it was the last thing any of them wanted to do. But some how they had to do it.

When they saw a car coming down the hill behind them, they decided to jump out in front of it and wave the driver down.

"Are you going to Williamstown? We missed the bus," said Bridie brazenly."

"Williamstown? Where's that?" inquired the young driver.

"I don't know," said Bridie. "I think it's near Tuam."

"Tuam! I know where Tuam is, but you're on the wrong road. What bus were you supposed to catch?"

The women looked at each other in a confused state before Bridie blurted out the first thing that came into her head.

"It was a green one."

"Sorry, I can't help you, and like I said, you're on the wrong road. Just take the next 'left' and then turn 'right' and you're on the Tuam road," said the driver before pulling away hurriedly as he was holding up traffic behind him.

After a heated debate about which was left and which was right the escapees made further inquiries regarding Williamstown and Tuam. Soon they found themselves getting a lift in a huge lorry. The driver thinking all his birthdays had come at once when he saw three damsels in distress. Giving them a lift was no problem he said. But despite that they were packed in like sardines in the front of the lorry.

"Where do ye work?"

"We work in a factory," answered Lilly in response to the driver's query.

"It's our first day," added Bridie, conjuring up enough lies and stories to see them safely all the way to Williamstown. The driver having informed them that he was going via Tuam and Castlerea all the way to Donegal and that if they wanted a lift with him, then they were more than welcome.

It wasn't until they had jumped down from the lorry in the small village square of Williamstown that they began to realise, it had probably been the most audacious escape attempt ever made from the Magdalene Home. Making their way on foot, up the winding by-road to O'Brien's house, they soon realised was one thing: keeping ahead of the law was quite another.

* * * * *

When John Paschal came home in the evening having spent a long hard day in the bog, he got one hell of a surprise. Instead of seeing his place set at the table, he found three strange visitors at the table stuffing themselves with lovely home-cooked ham and tomatoes. He wondered would there be anything at all left for him. He was filled with rage and wanted to shout, Stop! And when he saw Mrs. O'Brien offer the visitors yet more ham, saying 'Eat up now let ye, 'cause there's no knowing when ye'll get the next bite,' he was rightly disgusted.

He was half way across the floor when Bridie said,

"Glory be to God Almighty; is this him? Paschal love! How are you?" she asked, as she stood up and gave him a fierce hug. "God, But I wouldn't know you! You got so tall!" And seeing the shock on John Paschal's, face she asked, "Do you not know me? I'm your mother!"

Paschal feigned acknowledgment before she again hugged and kissed him.

After Lilly and Margaret shook his hand, he stood there embarrassed, not knowing what to do; while Mrs. O'Brien pampered them with yet more tea and sweet-cake and biscuits.

"We'll have ours later," she announced, looking at John Paschal's questioning gaze, as Edward O'Brien leant forward every so often with a little piece of paper towards the fire in an effort to keep his pipe lit.

But I want it now! Paschal's stomach screamed. He'd made short work of the tea and sandwiches in the bog and deeply regretted having scoffed half of them before he got there, that morning. The trouble was he loved the blackcurrant jam sandwiches and would eat them until they came out his ears. God knows when I'll get a bite now, or how long they're staying he thought. How come they've no car. I wonder how they got here.

"I believe you're a great worker altogether. Why don't you come and sit down here beside me?" said Bridie, making room for John Paschal.

Instead he looked at his mother and father for guidance and to see if they had any objections, but they just looked at him and smiled. And when he made no move to sit down, Mrs. O'Brien said,

"Why don't you sit down and join them? You must be near kilt working, cause you're as black as a pot. On second thoughts why don't you go out and wash the muck off your face so Bridie and her friends can see what you look like."

The visitors laughed and John Paschal's ears turned a bright red as he made his way into the back kitchen. Cocking his ear, he listened to their every word, as Edward in between blasts of smoke, spat into the open fire and said,

"I think the best thing ye can do now is get the train and go to Dublin. Ye can get the boat from there to Holyhead. Ye'll have no trouble at all gettin' work over there."

Unknown to the visitors, Edward had a particular reason for suggesting this course of action. Ever since John Paschal and his real mother began to communicate with each other, Mrs. O'Brien lived in dread that one day John Paschal's mother would turn up on her door step and claim him as her own: and she after rearing him since he was knee-high to a grasshopper. 'It would be a devil entirely' she had said to him, 'if Bridie were ever let out of the Magdalene Laundry, and she to come down here and try to claim him, after all I've done for him.'

I know Catherine is cranky an' everything, and a devil an' hell to live with, but she's clever enough. She could see this happening and I couldn't, he thought. So I best use me influence and persuasive powers to divert Bridie as far away as possible from here, otherwise there'll be hell to pay.

"Oh God! I don't think I'd like to go to England. Maybe we could get a job here in Williamstown. But I'd be afraid we'd get caught and sent back to the Magdalene again," said Bridie.

"I don't think I'd like to go to England either. Maybe if we went back, we might get a job in Galway, said Lilly anxiously.

"Can't we stay here a while and maybe get some kind of a job in

Williamstown?" suggested Margaret, trying to come up with a solution that would suit everyone.

"Is it what ye want to be arrested and sent back to Galway? If ye are reported to the Gardaí in Galway, this is the first place they'll come looking for ye. So if I was ye, I'd hop it fairly lively, because the people round here seem to know everything," said Edward, an air of deep concern creeping into his voice.

"And believe me they already know who ye are, and where ye came from," intervened Mrs. O'Brien, appalled at the prospect that John's mother would have access to him now: and that herself and Edward would become the laughing stock of the whole parish if that scenario, ever came to pass.

"I'll tell ye want we'll do," suggested Edward, assuming full authority on the issue once more. "I'll give ye a few pounds and arrange a lift to the station in Castlerea' later on this evening. The train will bring ye as far as the boat in Dub-land, where ye can catch the night sailing. That will bring ye to Holyhead and ye can get whatever train ye want: and go to London, Liverpool, Birmingham or Coventry. Ye know ye'll always be welcome to come here anytime ye want, and we'll not say a word to anyone. No one will know where ye are. And besides, when John's a biteen older, he'll be going to England because there's nothing for him around here. What do ye say to that?"

The three escapees looked at each other, the same thoughts going through their heads. Jesus, they're going to give us money and a boat to England: We'll be miles and miles away from the Magdalene and no one will ever find us. Besides Noreen Donnellan is in Northampton and we can go straight to her.

"You know, I think it's a great idea. I think we should go," said Bridie to her friends, before turning to Edward.

"That's very good of you Mr. O'Brien. And we promise to pay you back when we get work and thanks very much to the two of ye for looking after John Paschal so well."

"Ah, thanks yourself," said Mrs. O'Brien.

"I know if it was me, and I was a biteen younger, I'd go in the morning," said Edward, recalling his days down in the coalmines and a good week's wages when he was miles away from Catherine and her mithering ways.

John Paschal took his time washing his face in the back kitchen because he didn't want to go back into where the women were eating;

and where he'd be expected to sit beside his mother: like a sissy. Instead he stood quietly, listening attentively to every single word.

'The Gardaí.... is it what ye want to be arrested...if ye're reported to the Gardaí...'

What the hell is going on, he wondered. They must be criminals. And Mrs. O'Brien wants me to wash myself and sit beside three criminals. And if the Guards happen to come looking here, I'll be caught as well. What the hell is going on? I don't understand it at all. They must have escaped and run away. They've no car or anything. I wonder how they managed to get here because the Galway bus doesn't come until seven o'clock. It's only half past five yet. And they've no money for a bus or train. God! I've heard of many a thing, but this is a mystery: and to make matters worse, they're eating my dinner, he thought.

Mrs. O'Brien, jokingly nudged Bridie and called aloud,

"John, what, in the name of God are you doing out there? If it took me that long to wash me face, you know I'd think I'd drown mesell."

John Paschal re-appeared, sheepishly and red-faced, and stood in the middle of the room watching them all tittering and laughing at him. It was the most mortifying moment of his entire life. He'd have to sit with these people now who were obviously some sort of convicts, who'd escaped and were wanted by the Gardaí and were about to flee to England. And to complicate things further the nicest one of them was supposed to be his mother. His mother! That couldn't be right. Wasn't Mrs. O'Brien his mother? Everyone in the world knew that. So why are people saying that Bridie is my mother. Oh I wish to God I'd stayed in the bog another hour or two. I could have come home then this evening and with any bit of luck they'd have all gone to England and I could have had a right good feed. If I have to sit down beside Bridie now I'll be squashed. And if any of my friends happens to call for me to go playing football they'll see me sitting beside her and tell everyone in school how I was sitting on some woman's lap. And I'll say, that was my mother who lives in Galway. She was down to see me. No, no, I can't say that. Nobody has two mothers. Mrs. O'Brien is my mother, or is she? How come I've no brothers or sisters? If only I could ask someone, but who can I ask? Who could I possibly ask? I can't pretend to my friends that I'm that dumb that I don't even know me own mother. It sounds ridiculous.

He went and sat down beside Bridie, but only because he had to. Immediately she put her arms around him and gave him a gentle squeeze, as Edward rose from his chair, spat into the fire and said,

"I'll go as far as the town and see if I can get 'Kirrane' to run ye as far as the station, in an hour or so. Ye could go in the morning of course, but I think it's better for ye to go this evening. You'd never know the Gardaí might come looking for ye, and 'twould be a devil entirely if ye got caught and ye after travelling all the way from Galway."

With that, Edward jumped on his bicycle and headed straight into town to make the necessary arrangements, so that little more than an hour later 'Kirrane's' hackney stood ticking over in the street, waiting to take the three women to the boat train.

"Paschal love," said Bridie, clasping her son tightly, "I'm sorry I have to go. Won't you promise me faithfully that you'll write to me and that when you're old enough to go to England, that you'll come and see me?"

" I will."

Gently holding him at arms length and caressing his sunburned cheek she pleaded,

"That's all I'll ever ask, is that you write to me," as a deepening sadness crept into her eyes. "You're all I have in this world. You know I could never live without you," she whispered before quietly slipping a half crown into his hand, together with a small harmonica.

Then Bridie and her friends got into the hackney, and waved goodbye as John Paschal watched the gleaming black car disappear down the narrow winding laneway that wound it way out by the lake.

In little more than half an hour, the three escapees would be seated on a boat train bound for England and a strange new world.

Chapter Nineteen

It was early in the morning when the slowing rumbling locomotive ground to a halt. And a fierce cloud of vapour began to sizzle beneath the train's grimy chassis, as carriage doors sprang open and weary passengers spilled out onto the platform. This was Northampton, their final destination.

And it was here amid the welter of excitement that youthful passengers met their Mums and Dads, Brothers and Sisters, before helping each other to carry their luggage to a waiting taxi. When all of the arrivals had all but disappeared, three lonely looking women stood in bewilderment on the platform.

"What will we do now?" asked Lilly. "Where will we go?"

"I don't know. We'll have to get a bus I suppose."

"A bus! A Bus! Don't say we have to catch a bus or I'll die. Can we not get a hackney?" asked Margaret, sheepishly

"Is this Northampton?" asked Lilly in obvious distress, as a small dapper looking man came sidling up to them.

"Excuse me," said Bridie, "Do you know how we can get to Barrack Road?"

"Yes my love, it's just round the corner; five minutes and you're there. You want a taxi?"

"Oh yes please!" replied the girls eagerly, as Lilly picked up the small brown suitcase that Mrs O'Brien had given them and which contained all their worldly possessions.

"OK! Let's be having yous. Follow me." ordered the taxi driver, as he escorted them out of the station and into his taxi.

When they reached Barrack Road, they knocked at number forty-nine but there was no reply. After several more tentative knocks the taxi driver urged them to knock louder and when that didn't seem to work he stepped forward and gave the doorknocker an almighty clatter, which brought immediate results. The three escapees could scarcely believe their luck when their lifelong friend Noreen Donnellan opened the heavy hall door in her dressing gown and hair curlers. In a fit of unbridled joy they hugged and kissed before offering to pay the taxi driver. And as they sat in the cold of a downstairs living room they told Noreen of their daring flight of freedom and how they hoped to start a new life for themselves in England.

Despite, a few minor hiccups, Bridie and her friends soon found themselves a new job. They were taken on as packers in a large shoe factory. But they were not happy. One by one they managed to find alternative employment working alongside Noreen Donnellan. They were now working in the kitchen of St. Andrew's Hospital, and for a while it was almost like old times. Life, they thought, was really wonderful, except for the one thing: the superior attitude of the English, who seemed to detest the Irish. Describing them as thick and ignorant, and a pure nuisance for coming over to England in the first place to steal their jobs. Regrettably the allegations as far as Bridie and her friends were concerned, were not without foundation. They knew they were downright stupid in relation to everyday affairs in Ireland – never mind England: and all because of their long years in the Magdalene Home. They didn't know the value of money, or how to count it. They were unable to use a telephone, and had never even seen a television set let alone a television programme. They didn't know what a pressure cooker was, and when asked to cook something special in one of these new fangled cooking pots it usually turned out to be a disaster. And although they could bake the finest bread and make a decent pot of 'Irish stew', they were looked down upon because they were unable to make 'Cornish Pasties', 'Shepherd's Pie', 'Yorkshire Pudding', 'Hot Pot' or 'Spotted Dick'. The management sometimes showed a degree of latitude to a young girl coming into the job for the first time. But they couldn't accept such stupidity and ignorance in middle-aged Irish women such as Bridie and her friends. Their co-workers expected them to already have large families of their own, and when the local girls found out that the Irish girls hadn't a husband or a single boyfriend between them, they looked on them with a jaundiced eye. And as time went on this attitude forced Bridie and her friends to retreat more and more into themselves.

Even in the house, which they shared with several English girls, they kept very much to themselves; because a discussion on an Irish political figure, or a famous theatre figure left them completely tongue-tied. They didn't know who the 'Moors Murderers' were: they didn't know who 'Mary Quant' was and they didn't know what it was to vote.

Shortly after arriving in Northampton Bridie and her friends had to admit to themselves they didn't know anything. But as Noreen Donnellan said to them 'Ye'll soon learn, yet, so ye will.' So, they stuck together as a family unit: prepared to hide behind their past and to dream about the future: a future that would include men; hopefully lots of men. Only finding the right one was one hell of a problem, thought Noreen.

"I keep telling you, Bridie, them fellas you're after in the Irish Centre are no good, yet. They're only interested in porter, gallons of it. They only smile when they're looking at you over a big pint, don't you know?"

Bridie did not answer, because she was too ashamed and embarrassed by the fact that again she had been conned by an Irish charmer whose spiel flowed as smoothly out of his mouth as the creamy pints of Guinness flowed into it. And before that she had fallen head over heels for another Irish man, only to discover that he was already married. And she had lent money to a man whose mother was supposed to be dying in Ireland.

"I'm telling ye girls," continued Noreen in her motherly fashion. "We'd be better off in Ireland, somewhere: maybe in Dublin or Galway or Limerick. All a man over here wants, is for someone to wash his shirt don't you know, the lazy oul' feckers."

Bridie was relaxing on her knees in front of the fire – taking it all in – because she was perished with the cold, despite her mug of hot tea and packet of fags. She continued to stare into the fire, taking Noreen's criticism with a pinch of salt. Although she knew that Noreen was speaking the truth and that the truth hurts, she wondered what would happen if she herself turned the tables on Noreen. Bridie knew that Noreen herself had stayed out several nights with some fella, but she decided to say nothing. She was a lot happier, however, when the girls changed the subject slightly and started talking about going back to live in Ireland.

"You know, I think we really would be better off at home. God, just think of it! Wouldn't it be lovely to be dancing away in the 'Seapoint', or 'Hanger', and not have to be listening to some old crooner below in St. Brendan's, crying like a Banshee, *"If we only had old Ireland over here,"* sang Lilly with enthusiasm.

"Oh, I hate that song!" said Margaret. "Over here, me arse!"

"So do I," added Bridie quickly. "Every time I hear it I get so lonesome I want to go back home to Ireland. But sure we can't. You'd think they'd play something decent. And if it's not that it's '*I'll take you home again Kathleen*', or '*The Siege of Ennis*'"

"Oh, I like 'The Siege of Ennis', yet," said Noreen cheerfully.

"Did you tell Noreen about your new man and the drink you got the other night?" asked Lilly, out of the blue.

"No," answered Bridie, slightly embarrassed.

"Tell Noreen. Noreen, are you listening?" insisted Lilly.

"I am, yet. Go on."

"Lilly, I'll kill you," said Bridie. "Why did you have to open your big mouth?"

"Ah, go on! Isn't it only a bit of fun, a bit of oul' codology; it could happen to any of us, yet."

"Let me think, yes 'twas last Saturday night, I had a date with Tomás. We were in the Irish club and he was after buying me two Babychams; and as he had brought me home the night before, I thought I'd like to treat him. He was drinking pints of beer but I wasn't too sure what they were, so I said to him, 'What'll you have, I'll treat you to this one.' And he looked at me, a bit surprised like, that I was treating him at all. Then he said, 'I'll have a *Bush*. Of course, I thought I was hearing things, or that he was pulling my leg, because I didn't know you could get such a drink. I said, *A Bush*? And he said, 'Yeah, *a Black Bush*', and I thought, that must be what he was drinking. Anyway, when I went up to the bar I asked the barman for a Babycham, first – to give me a bit of courage – even though I didn't want another drink myself. Then I asked for a pint of *Black Bush*. Well, I nearly died", said Bridie, laughing. "You should have seen his two eyes. He said, 'A pint of *Black Bush*? We don't sell pints of *Black Bush*. You can have a small one or a large bottle; which is it?' Lucky enough, I said a small one. But if you saw the little drop he put in the glass: it would hardly wet your finger. And I was thinking about changing it for a bottle when the barman asked if I wanted to add some water to it. So I told him to fill it up, because I didn't want to go back down to the table with the little drop that was in the glass or Tomás would think I was mean. I never knew that *Black Bush* was a whiskey until Tomás told me…"

"And what did Tomás say to you? I'll have another, yet," suggested

Noreen humorously, trying to egg Bridie on.

"Oh. He wasn't a bit pleased," laughed Bridie, lighting another Park Drive cigarette. "He told me that I had killed a good whiskey and that it tasted like mare's piss; and that I was stupid to have put any water at all in it. He said he liked his whiskey the same way as he liked his women, nice, neat, and naked".

"Now there's gratitude for you," laughed Noreen, heartily. "What did I tell ye, yet? We'd be better off in Ireland, so we would."

"Well then, why don't we go, and stop talking about it?" suggested Lilly.

"Tis true," agreed Margaret Sherry. "We'd be able to meet Julie Murray in 'Merlin Park'. She might get us fixed up with a job. Who knows, we might end up having to dress some good looking doctor."

"You mean undressing him! Sure you're not able to dress yourself," suggested Lilly, mischievously.

"Oh shut up you. You've men on the brain," retorted Margaret Sherry

"But what about me? I can't go," said Bridie in a distressed tone of voice. The very mention of Julie's name sent a wave of emotion searing through her, as she feared that her friends might desert her and enjoy Julie's great company at her expense.

"Why not?" asked the girls in unison,

"Because of John Paschal, he's in Manchester now: remember I told ye I had a letter from him last week and he said he might be coming down to see me."

"Oh that's right. You did, you did, yet."

The three girls looked at each other in silence before Margaret plucked up the courage to say,

"But can't you come home with us for now, and maybe come back here again for a holiday?"

"No!" replied Bridie, disappointed that Margaret could come out with such a mouthful. "I'll stay here because I want to be near Paschal. I promised myself in the Magdalene, a long time ago that I'd follow him to the ends of the earth; if I ever got out of there. I only agreed to leave Ireland and come to England because the O'Brien's said he'd surely come here when he was old enough. Besides, I've never seen him properly, even though he's near seventeen now."

Again there was a strained silence, as each of the girls considered their lot. Deep down, none of them liked the idea of leaving Bridie alone. They had been together so long and been through so much it was almost unthinkable. But the reality of the situation was that they couldn't wait to get away; away from Northampton's smog and the constant smell of shoe leather, for which the city was noted. As the weeks and months went by, they began to realise that they needed to carve out a life of their own; that they were no longer bound together being dictated to by a group of nuns: and that they were all bound together only by the value of the pounds in their pockets. Bridie was determined to stay in England despite the prospect of not being able to meet Julie Murray, who had continued to write regularly, asking her to come and live in Galway. Even the comings and goings of romantic life in the Seapoint Ballroom, as conveyed by Julie's letters wasn't enough to persuade Bridie to pack her bags.

"I'll tell ye what. Ye go home and I'll stay here. I'll wait until I can meet John Paschal. Then, when I have a few pounds saved up, I can go home for a holiday and meet ye all. You'd never know, John Paschal and myself might end up going back to live in Ireland."

"Right!" said Lilly, "What ever you think yourself."

Noreen and Margaret agreed.

The three girls set sail in the spring of 1964. Their parting was a tearful one; but hopefully they'd all meet again in the not too distant future, they said. And Bridie told them she looked forward to meeting her son John Paschal. And if things went anyways well, she might even find the time to go to Dublin and look for her mother and father.

All she had ever wanted in her entire life, she said, was to be part of a nice family. And now that her friends had returned to Ireland there was nothing to stop her: nothing in the wide earthly world.

* * * * *

John Paschal was in Manchester but a few short months, and was fast learning, that life for a sixteen year old in a strange English city was not an easy one. Up at 6.00 a.m. of a cold frosty winter's morning, ready to leave the Company depot at 7.00 a.m.; he'd sit for an hour in the freezing canopy, on the back of an open lorry with some of the toughest men he was ever to meet. They would be driven to various building sites within a forty-mile-radius of Manchester, Buxton, Liverpool, Leeds, Ellesmere Port or Chester. Forty miles in traffic-jams and freezing fog, while 'Keane' the lorry driver laughed contentedly whilst listening to his cronies in the comfort of the warm cab.

When they arrived on site, the heavy wooden toolbox would soon be opened, to reveal a mangled heap of forks and shovels that were all welded together with frozen muck. And there was usually a mad scramble to get hold of the best and cleanest looking implement as they were considered less painful to begin digging with.

John Paschal invariably always ended up with the meanest looking implement of all. He barely had the strength to lift a dirty shovel out of the box, such was the severity of the cold; having sat motionless on the back of an open lorry for an hour or more: while cold hard chaws stood around, swaggering in their opened necked shirts; awaiting instruction on where to begin. The majority of these men John Paschal soon found out were habitual dossers, who only ever worked enough days each week to pay for booze and rent.

Their breakfast consisted of steak and onions, consumed while standing around a big open fire, which always brought some respite. There were times when the workmen fought over their food, like prairie dogs over a fatted carcass. One breakfast morning John Paschal saw an ageing beer-merchant, knocked to the ground by a young fella, who was holding a knife to the man's throat; and having forcibly removed the juicy steak dangling from the mouth, he began ranting,

"You thieving poxy bastard! You're the cunt that's been taking my steak every fuckin' morning."

"No! No! It wasn't me!"

"Own up to it you miserable poxy bastard! Own up!

"No! 'Twasn't me, I swear!"

The young fella straddling the suspected thief, held him by the hair of the head with his left hand, while his other held aloft a sharply pointed steak knife. He began hopping the man's head off the ground.

"Own up, you whore's melt or... or I swear I'll slit your throat from ear to ear, you dirty dog's knot. You're too mean to shite. Own up!" he roared, banging the man's head off the ground, again

"Maybe 'twas a mish-take," the man pleaded, his eyes two holes of terror.

"Aha! I knew it was you me bucko. Mistake my arse! Let this be the last time you do that to me... because the next time...I swear on my mother's grave, I'll gut you... so I will."

With that the young fella or 'Connemara', as he was more

commonly called, picked up the piece of steak that was lying on the ground and fired it in the general direction of the seagulls. At that moment a huge cheer went up from the rest of the gang due to the entertainment they had derived from it.

"I declare to Jesus, some people would take the bit out of your mouth," quipped a gleeful 'Keane', before one of his cronies, added for good measure,

"Musha 'tis true for you Martin! 'Tis true for you! 'Tis hard times when a dacent man can't get time to feckin' chew, and the land-lady cocking her snoot when a man goes home after a hard day's work; and maybe fourteen-pints-a-stout. Huh?"

After the excitement of a good early morning row, dinner on site was usually a hurried sandwich, quickly followed by four or five pints of Guinness in the nearest pub. Then it was back to the heavy digging; or pulling heavy cables for the rest of the day. All of which meant it was often a tired and broken John Paschal who returned to his digs late into the evening.

During these hard times he wrote long rambling letters to the O'Brien's in Williamstown; slipping in the odd few pounds whenever he could manage it. Correspondence with his mother Bridie however practically ceased, even though she continued to bombard him with letters begging him to stay long enough at the same address so that she could come up to visit him. But of course he never did. He didn't like the idea and wrote back saying he was very busy, what with work and attending night classes and the devil knows what.

But in truth, such was his hatred of digging the roads and the gang he worked with, he set about looking for something more meaningful, and in early Spring he found himself a new job, working on the Buses.

On more that one occasion, he was taken to task by the Depot Bus Inspector and threatened with dismissal, unless he made a marked improvement in his accounting practices

What upset John Paschal most of all was that things seemed to be getting worse in his mathematical returns not better. It didn't make sense to him. He thought he was clever and good at figures but these reports were proving him wrong. Yet when he applied for the job as a Bus Conductor, he was told he had done exceptionally well in his aptitude test, and after his six weeks in school and a further six out on the road with a qualified Instructor, they said he had the potential to work his way right to the top. But at the rate things were going, John

Paschal knew he'd soon be working his way to the bottom.

Obviously, he was doing something wrong. He wasn't counting his money properly. There were occasions when he would count his takings up to three times at the end of a shift, and make mental notes to keep the dates in mind. But then when he'd check the shorts list again the following week he'd discover he was down half a crown on that particular day.

His morale was taking a fierce hammering. He felt like walking away shame-faced, but he couldn't, because all his friends, particularly the girls, knew how much he loved the job. They would definitely think he'd been sacked, if he left the job, when clearly that wasn't the case. But if he stayed much longer without improvement, he'd surely be shown the road.

In desperation he had a quiet word with the Cashier and informed him, that it was the ticket-machine that was at fault. It was the ticket-machine which had stated he was one and six-pence or one and nine-pence or half a crown short. The Cashier disputed this and said it was not possible. Ticket-machines don't lie. The Cashier said he didn't want to argue, but if the machine stated that he was short, then he was short and that was that.

"John, stop worrying! Every bus conductor is short in his takings at some time or other!"

"But I'm not every Bus Conductor. I want to be able to do the job properly."

"Ye bleedin' Oirish, ye're always fighting or arguing," said the Cashier in jest. "John! You know that lovely pair of leather gloves that you handed into lost property; and the camera; and that umbrella: they've not been claimed, and they've been here three months. So you can have them. Here! Take them away with you!" he added, reaching under the hatch and pushing the items towards John Paschal.

"No, I don't want them."

"Here John, don't be stupid! They'll only go to auction!"

"No, I can't take them. It doesn't seem right, and anyway I don't want them."

John Paschal wouldn't take them. Not because he didn't want them, but because it didn't seem right to be taking something that didn't belong to him. If he wanted a thing that badly, he knew he could always go to the auction room where he'd probably pick them up for a song.

For a short while his accounting miraculously improved. He was in heaven. Then he looked at the shorts list again after some wisecrack whispered in his ear, only to discover that he was short nineteen shillings and six-pence. Looking at the figures in bold red lettering for all to see, made him sicker than he ever could have imagined. His name and badge number up there on the board in bold red lettering. The Depot Inspector hauled him into his office, where the friendly cashier witnessed John Paschal getting a right royal telling off. Later that night John Paschal engaged his friend, Nobby Clarke, bus driver and ex conductor to cross check his takings. They were as expected, spot on.

The following afternoon when he went to start his late shift, he again went to the cashier and asked how things had gone the night before.

"Paddy! What are you playin' at? You were down another shillin' last night. You really should be getting the hang of it by now."

Paddy didn't say anything because he had that awful, sinking feeling that he was being done and there wasn't a whole lot he could do about it. Someone was diddling him. In that case, he thought, there was only one thing to do and that was to walk away. Forever.

* * * * *

Bridie's worst fears while being held in the Magdalene Home, were now being realised. John Paschal had all but stopped writing to her. When she wrote to him in Manchester trying to arrange a visit, he ignored it altogether or had moved house yet again.

But dispite his roving nature John Paschal still managed to find himself a new girlfriend and life couldn't be better, he thought: if only they'd stop asking such awkward questions; about his mother; about his father, about his whole family. He knew he had no real mother or father like everyone else, but he didn't care. He knew he had no brothers or sisters, aunts or uncles, nieces or nephews, or another living relative in the whole wide world, but still he didn't care.

Not so his latest girlfriend: she seemed to care about everything. They were standing in the doorway of the nurses' home, in Withington Hospital, where she worked; and with their arms lovingly entwined around each other, she asks how many brothers and sisters he has.

Paschal says the first thing that comes into his head. Twelve; because it sounds so virile, and because there were twelve apostles, and besides most of the married men he knew had twelve children. She wants to know the names of John Paschal's brothers and sisters, their ages and if he's the youngest. He tells her, as far as he can remember he's somewhere in between, right slap bang, in the middle of the lot.

A week later she catches him out, telling lies. An argument ensues and that's the end of a beautiful relationship

Next time he meets a girl, he thinks he won't be so smart. That's until he meets the beautiful red-haired, Sally. She too wants to know the names of his brothers and sisters, their ages, and surely they're not all girls. Well no, not all. How many brothers are in England; and America? John! I don't believe you! Surely they're not all living in Ireland. They can't be. Everyone has at least one brother or sister in America. So he decides to spread his relations all around; until weeks later, he's caught out again.

And it's with a heavy heart he decides it's time to change tact, completely. He meets Teresa Brady and decides it's time to tell the truth. He tells her how he's an only child. But she's not impressed. Not impressed at all.

"You must have brothers and sisters!"

"No. I haven't."

"But you must have! You must! Everyone has at least three or four brothers or sisters."

"No. Honest, I'm the only one."

"And are your mother and father still alive?"

"Yeah."

"They must be real big shots then, if they only wanted a son."

"Well, they're sort of separated: anyway I don't like talking about them."

"Oh! And how come you never told me before?"

"Because you never asked."

"John! I shouldn't have to ask, if you were honest with me. But you're hiding things. You're always hiding things."

"I'm not!"

"You are!"

"I'm not!"

"OK. So where are they now?"

"Theresa, would you ever stop asking questions?"

"No I won't! Where are they now?"

"If you must know my father lives in Galway, and my mother's in Northampton, OK?"

"Why are you getting so upset? Are you ashamed of them or what?"

"No, I'm not! Why would I be ashamed of them?"

"I don't know! They're your parents! Did they get separated in Ireland?"

"Yeah."

"Well that's a lie for a start; you can't get divorced or separated in Ireland; so there! I knew you were telling lies!"

Every day John Paschal feels as thought his past life is coming back to haunt him. He's so ashamed of his family background he wants to run away forever. Each person he meets is a potential friend until it comes down to the awkward questions. And sooner or later they have got to be answered. But how can he answer them when he doesn't know how to answer them? Especially when his newfound friends insist on introducing him to their brothers or sisters. They even invite him to their homes for the weekend. All of a sudden life's wonderful again: great altogether, until they in turn ask if they can come and stay at his place in Galway. They believe Galway's a magical place. Are you sure John your old pair won't mind? No! No! Not at all!

But how does he explain that he's not like them? That he never really had an old pair. Instead, he tells them that his 'Mother' is not that good; that she has taken a turn for the worst: that perhaps it would upset her to have two or three visitors coming into the house on top of her.

But Teresa Brady does not give up that easily. She wants to know why she can't come and visit his divorced parents; so one day he decides to come clean, and he tells her everything.

They're hiding beneath the stairs in Teresa's house, because her landlady is very strict, and says there are no visitors allowed, particularly men. Teresa has her arms around his shoulders and whispers caringly, that it doesn't really matter about him not having any brothers or sisters, aunts or uncles. That it's not really his fault. She says she understands everything because she herself doesn't know who her own mother and father are; where they live or where they came from or anything. Teresa says, she was reared with her two older sisters in County Mayo and now the three of them are over here in England.

Her two sisters are married: one to a Spaniard. They have a lovely son who's a year old now so that makes Teresa an aunt, who has a nephew, which in turn makes her a normal human being like everyone else: whereas John Paschal is still a lost soul, but she forgives him anyway. Her other sister's husband she says is from Cork and he comes home every single night drunk as a skunk and belts the shite out of her: while at the same time she has to cope with their four screaming kids. Despite that, Teresa herself thinks that she'd love to get married and have lots and lots of children.

It's early spring and the birds are singing sweetly; daffodils are in bloom and romance is in the air as John Paschal and Teresa go strolling hand in hand, around Manchester's beautiful Piccadilly Gardens. And because it's Saturday the streets are thronged, and shades of Carnaby Street, Mary Quant, Best's Boutique and beatlemania waft from every store and window. And like everybody else, Teresa and John Paschal go window shopping, admiring the clothes, the shoes, the fancy hats and the jewellery; particularly the Jewellery. Outside the jeweller's Teresa turns to John Paschal and says she'd love to get engaged.

"Engaged! Why would we get engaged?"

"Because John it's time! We're going out six months, we should be engaged."

"But Teresa, people only get engaged if they're going to get married and we're ..."

"You mean ... you don't want to get married?"

" I do! I do! Sometime... but not..."

"Then what are we waiting for? I get the feeling John if I waited for you to ask, I'd be waiting for the rest of me life. Oh Look! Look! Isn't it beautiful? Look at that ring there! Oh, I'd love to get that one! Why don't we go in and buy it ...and get engaged?" she asked, looking at him longingly. "Please John! Please!"

"But Jesus Teresa! Will you look at the price of it! And besides I've no.... Let's wait 'til I save up a few pounds."

"Ah for God's sake I'll buy it myself! You know John, you're pure useless. You've no proper job, no money, no nothing. Well I'm buying the ring whether you like it or not."

So, in they went. Out they came. Half married; because now they were officially engaged. They celebrated by dining on burgers in Wimpey's famous burger bar across the street.

The following week they drove down to Northampton to see John Paschal's mother and to convey the good news. Teresa, wearing her sparkling diamond, and John Paschal wearing his new pin striped suit, which he could ill afford, but he bought it anyway, to keep the *quare one* happy. In Northampton, they both smiled and Bridie's camera rolled. They were treated like the royal family.

And, in a private moment, Bridie whispered, that she'd love to visit him in Manchester; and that whatever he did, he shouldn't get married too soon. You're still young love, and have plenty of time. Bridie says she might go up and live in Manchester, where she could wash his socks and iron his shirts and cook his meals, because Paschal, I love you and nothing in this world matters more. I want to do everything I can to help you. I've waited all these years to be with you; I prayed every single day that sooner or later, you'd come back to me and now my prayers have been answered.

Yes.

John Paschal drove back to Manchester late that Sunday evening in his big Consul motorcar, feeling anything but contented. He was deeply disturbed in both mind and spirit and couldn't figure out what possessed him to go all the way to Northampton to see someone he neither knew nor loved. He was deeply concerned about the hatred he felt for everyone; especially his mother. He thought he was developing some form of mental illness. What was wrong with him at all? Every one, he knew simply adored their mother? Their mother was like a God to them. But he didn't want to see his mother ever again. Never ever, he thought.

He glanced furtively at Teresa as she lay sleeping contentedly on his shoulder. The powerful Ford consul cruising majestically on the motorway as they overtook car after car after lorry. He tried to tell himself, he was now a man of the world and at eighteen years of age officially engaged. But he didn't feel engaged. And he most certainly didn't want to get married. Maybe he should see a doctor. Could a doctor tell him why he never wanted to see his own mother again? Could a doctor tell him whether or not he was ready to get married? And for God's sake could a good doctor tell him what being in love was: because trying to find the answer himself was killing him.

For weeks, John Paschal lived in constant fear that his mother would turn up at his flat in Manchester and ruin his life. He moved out at the earliest opportunity and wrote home urgently, instructing the O'Brien's and their daughter Maureen Keane to inform Bridie that he had now gone to Australia, without leaving any forwarding address.

He starts to drift aimlessly from one building site to another all over the city in search of suitable employment. Only to suddenly walk away again because he hated the bullying foreman, he hated the job or he hated them both. But most of all he hated 'the gimp'.

'The gimp' was an image he was meant to portray when looking for a job in the building industry. Prospective workers would congregate on the corner of a noted street in the city slums at 6.30a.m. surrounded by a vast array of buses and lorries. Dressed in their heavy hob-nailed boots and mucky trousers, they'd hang around and wait for the boss to arrive. Then one by one they'd boldly step forward; their two thumbs hooked into the bottom corner of their trouser pockets. But that wasn't enough. Not near enough. If they wanted to get a job they had to display a sort of a workman's swagger. With their shoulders slightly stooped, they were expected to wear a white dirt stained shirt – from previous exploits – which should be opened all the way down to the waist to denote a touch of class; and if it happened to be six degrees below freezing, so much the better.

There were usually scores of men, all looking for work. And as soon as you spotted your prey you were expected to go forward, and say in a broad west of Ireland accent 'Any-chance-a-the-start' in the hope that you might find a kindred spirit.

Needless to say John Paschal was very backward at going forward and when he did, it was minus 'the gimp'. In a soft gentle tone of voice he would mumble something like,

"Have you got any jobs?"

The West of Ireland Gaffer would stop and blink, look and stare, as if he were an alien. And if he was really desperate for men and he thought you had any bit of a shoulder at all on you, he'd rant,

"You! Take the third wagon on the right. You're going to Ellesmere Port. Come on! Come on men! I haven't all day! What the fuck are ye waiting for?"

On one occasion when John Paschal asked – after being told that he was being hired for the day – how much he was being paid, the Gaffer lost the rag entirely. He began ranting and raving, as if dancing an Irish jig in the middle of the road, which John Paschal enjoyed better than any stage presentation.

"Jesus Christ Almighty! Amn't I given' you a cuntin' start! Jump on that wagon, *there*, before any more of them poxy bastards jump off. Ye're like a fuckin' shower-a-cripples, the-lot-a-ye! Ye're not fit enough to send to Lourdes, never mind to an oil refinery. Hup! There lads. Hup! Come on boys, Hup!"

But John Paschal would think long and hard before jumping on any particular wagon or what kind of a day's slavery it might bring. The general going rate was reckoned to be a fiver a shift, but when he heard some of the men grumbling about having been paid only four pounds and some of them only three ten, then he'd lose all heart and go straight home. Other days he'd stand around in the freezing cold and wait until almost every man was hired and pray silently that when he'd ask for a job he'd be refused: only then to go home to his flat, fully convinced that he had done his level best to find a job.

A lot of these men John Paschal soon noticed, had the appearance of being half-human or ape-like, from years of hard work and heavy drinking. Instead of a nice T-bone steak for dinner they'd consume six, eight or ten pints of Guinness at an alarming rate, followed by an afternoon of ranting and raving, and those who worked with them took their lives into their own hands. These mad men were usually rewarded for their hard work and heavy drinking exploits, by being made a foreman or ganger, which meant they drank even more and worked less. And it seemed to John Paschal, that from London to Glasgow, Manchester to Hull there were mad Micks everywhere. He wondered how he could ever describe them individually. To him no poem could ever do them justice; and in his idle hours, at home he'd happily scribble on the wall.

THE IRISH IN BRITAIN
Cold hard chaws
What romanticism in a name
Instead I found big brutish monsters
Who'd work you like a slave – some dame
Who'd skin you alive for the price of two pints of porter.

THE BEAR
Big bad Jimmy, his legs askew
'He'd shout at you,
'Take that fucking Dumper off that Poxy bastard'.

Standing, his arms agape
I'd ask myself, is he really a Monster, a shite, or a hape.

Then, John Pascal would stand back to admire his handy work and if the mood was on him he'd scribble another line or two making the print smaller and smaller in the hope that the owner of the house wouldn't see it, and he'd dream that perhaps one day he'd become a poet or a writer, because deep down he felt that was all he ever wanted to do. To write, write, write.

But then turning to go out the door and down the road again he realised it was only a foolish dream. That it wouldn't help to put bread and butter on the table. No sir. It would not. Only a decent job could do that. But where would he find one of them? Where?

Chapter Twenty

Around about the same time as John Paschal was contemplating looking for a new job in Manchester, a group of women sat spellbound in the sitting room of their home in number 49 Barrack Road, Northampton. Arms neatly folded they were too deeply engrossed in the unfolding saga of 'Coronation Street' to notice who it was that had entered the front door.

'Coronation Street' however was the last thing on Bridie's mind as she carefully checked the mountain of out-dated bills strewn on the hall table; still, no letter from John Paschal. Glancing into the room she couldn't make up her mind whether to join the girls, or go up stairs to be alone with her thoughts. But then the thought of sitting alone in her room repelled her. Instead, she'd stay downstairs and try and think things through.

It was weeks and weeks since John Paschal and Teresa had come to see her. She remembered being so overcome, so overjoyed at having seen him again. It was as if all her birthdays had come at once. Although she had some misgivings about his intention to get married, she thought it better not to intervene. She would have liked him to wait a while longer, at least until he got to know his real mother again. Nineteen years apart was such a long time. Yet, she had only ever seen him three times in all those years. And even then, for only a few hours

But since that memorable weekend visit, she'd heard nothing. Absolutely nothing. Not a word. Why hadn't he written, she asked herself. Was he ill? Had he been involved in an accident at work? Had *Teresa* whipped him off to Ireland to get married? No, she thought. John Paschal would never do that without letting her know. But then why hadn't he written? He always wrote.

Sitting in the corner, she began to regret not having gone up to Manchester, as she'd planned. It was her intention to surprise John Paschal. But then her boyfriend Tomás would not hear of it. She had to cancel the idea at the very last minute because of him. She couldn't dare tell Tomás that she had an nineteen-year old son out of wedlock. To do so would be akin to going around with a sign round her neck, which read, 'I am a tart.' Even when John Paschal and Teresa came to see her, she had to postpone her date with Tomás and claim she had cousins staying with her. And when she hinted she was going up to Manchester on a return visit he accused her of seeing another man. In the heat of the moment she cancelled the whole idea, feeling it was better to stay with Tomás. Deep down, she knew she needed Tomás as much as he needed her. On the surface he appeared to be the life and soul of every party, yet he suffered fierce bouts of depression and alcoholism. She found it hard to make up her mind whether she liked him enough to stay around. There were times when she convinced herself that she loved him, and others when she knew she could never share the same house with him.

"Bridie? Did you have your tea or would you like a cup? I'm putting the kettle on, said Beryl Foster, as the T.V. commercials came on.

"Oh, I'd love a cup dear, if you're making one."

Going out into the kitchen, Beryl shouted " Bridie! There's a letter here for you. I picked it up off the floor when I came in."

"Oh thanks bit to God!" answered Bridie, excitedly, before going into the kitchen.

Climbing the stairs with her fresh cup of tea she was a bit disappointed to see that the writing was not John Paschal's. But then again a letter from her friend Julie Murray was almost as good any day, she thought.

Dear Bridie,
You're great for writin'. I don't know how you do it. Sure I'm pure useless, but I know you don't mind. Anyhow I had to write quickly and tell you the awful news. Lilly was attacked and raped the other night She was nearly strangled. The Guards were here in the hospital an' ever'thin'. She's in an awful state, black eyes, an' cuts, an' lumps, ever'where, an' she won't talk to anyone.
    I was so upset when I went to see her in the Hospital, I'm not the same since. You're good at writin'. You might write as soon as you can an' cheer her up. Sure she's such a wonderful person, I don't know how any man in his right mind could do such a

thing.

I go to the Seapoint, ever' weekend. Men! Sure you never saw the likes. Packed with them, but awful hard to meet anyone right. They haven't a spark of sense between them. Drink, and a hand up the skirt is all they want. Sure I had to give one of them a clatter last weekend, but I was sorry after, because he was gorgeous. Is that spelled right Bridie, sure I'm hopeless at spellin'.

Why don't you come back to Galway? I'd love if you were here with me. I get lonesome when I think of the times we had in the Magdalene, an' them oul' raps-a-nuns. Sure I can't stand the sight-a-them nuns here in the hospital: they always seem to be whisperin' and prayin' an' ever'thin'.

But the doctors and nurses are wonderful. They're always traytin' me an' ever'thin'. I have no more news. Besides, I have to go to confession now, or I'll be late. Won't you say a prayer for me that we'll all be safe from that mad yoke that attacked poor Lilly. An' think about what I said about comin' back to Galway, or are you still going out with that drunkard. I don't mean that Bridie. Honest, I mean the same fella. Sure you know what I mean. I had to laugh when you said he was gorgeous, but a biteen of a drunkard, and that you hated drunkards. Sure Bridie, they're all the same, except there are a lot of pioneers here in Galway. But they're nearly all snapped up.

It's too late for confessions now I think, so I can't go. But with any bit – a- luck, I'll have somethin' besides impure thoughts to tell the priest the next time. Bridie, I often wonder do they, you know, like other men? There's one- a – them here in Galway an' he's supposed to be at it all the time. I wouldn't like that, would you?

I'm going now. Goodbye. Write to Lilly. Don't forget, because she's always talking about you. Try an' come to Galway; you keep promising'. Goodbye and God Bless,
From your best friend, Julie xxx

p.s. How is Paschal? Tell him I was askin' for him.

Bridie gasped when she read about Lilly. She read it again so she could get a clearer picture. '...*I had to write quickly and tell you the awful news. Lilly was attacked and raped the other night. She was nearly strangled. The Guards were here an' ever'thin'. She's in an awful state, black eyes an' cuts an' lumps ever where...'*

Bridie was devastated that such ill luck could befall her friend. The mere thought that anyone could do such a thing to such a lovely person upset her.

The thought of being attacked by some madman terrified her. She knew she herself harboured a deep-seated fear that it could happen to her. She knew only too well what the result of something like that might be. Even as it was, Tomás was forever trying to get her to go to bed, and she was forever making excuses. She'd say that she didn't really know him well enough yet; and then he'd get into a bad mood and she'd be sorry afterwards.

She'd heard all about contraception and 'Frenchies', but Tomás would never mention them. She often thought, if only he'd offer to use one of them things, then she might take a chance, because God knows she often felt like doing it again. But the fear of getting pregnant and being put into a Home and being made to work for the nuns was always uppermost in her mind. Then again, she thought, if she could meet someone nice, who was interested enough to marry her, things would be different. Maybe she should go back to Galway, to her friend Julie. Again the lines from her friend's letter jumped into her mind. '...I can't stand the sight a-them-nuns, here in the hospital..."

The words echoed her very own thoughts. Nuns and Homes, and priests and babies, and laundries and Galway were all too close to the bone for her to ever think seriously about going back to Ireland. Especially Galway. Who knows, they might even lift her off the street and put her in there again, just because she ran away.

Anyway, I could never leave John Paschal here and go home, she thought. And when she thought of her son again, her heart began to ache. She had that uneasy feeling that something was seriously wrong. Why hasn't he written to me? It's been eight weeks, eight long weeks and not a single word.

* * * * *

In an effort to improve his station and because he hated working nights in Kellogg's corn flakes factory, John Paschal found himself working as a machinist in Dunlop's rubber factory. And at the end of his twelve-hour shift he would flee out the door, thankful to be away from all the racial aggro that seemed to go with the job. Back to the lodging house, where he and his friends would listen to the Beatles, Herman Hermits, Gerry and the Pacemakers and the Monkees. On Saturdays he'd go shopping; buying mod clothes and the latest L.Ps.

But then on Monday morning it was back to the rubber curing department of Dunlop's factory where two Northern Ireland workers passing through his department would have a go at him again.

"What's a fenian bastard like yous doing over here? Och aye, you'll take the Queen's shilling alright."

And every day the same insults keep piling up until they can think up a more disgusting comment. "Yous still here! You papish prick. Why don't yous go back home, back where yous belong, back to the republic?"

There were other times when he just happened to be in the toilet and the two Protestant workers would come along, and if there wasn't anyone else in the toilet they'd try to push him around saying, "Is it true yous fenian bastards wash your mouths out with soap? Have yous heard of Harland & Wolff? No Fenian bastards need apply. Och aye! Good sound Protestant State: part of the British Empire ya know. Och aye! 'Shorts' the biggest aircraft manufacturer in the world. Why don't you fuck off outa here, you scumbag," they'd scream, trying to draw a kick on him as he went out the door.

On and on it went, day in, day out. Week after week, month after month until one day this loyal Protestant Orangeman declared,

"Hey! You papish scum! Don't you ever set foot in Belfast, or we'll cut your Fenian throat. Och aye! There's only one place for yous papish prigs. That's at the bottom of the river Lagan."

Paschal could see the venom in their eyes, but he never once responded to their continual goading. He just stood there and looked them straight in the eye, or if he happened to be working, to carry on as if they never existed. Whenever he saw them coming through his department, he would hide discreetly behind the huge rollers of his machine. But each time they spoke, his pride was deeply wounded. Yet he felt he could hold his head up high and thank God that if nothing else, he'd had a decent up bringing in the South of Ireland; free from all forms of rancour and hatred.

Day after day they still strode arrogantly by, dressed in their pinstriped suits, hair neatly oiled, which only seemed to highlight their sickly-looking, down-turned, Protestant mouths. Instead of him washing his mouth out with soap – as they claimed all papists did – he thought, he'd love to ram a few bars of the horrid carbolic soap down their own throats: and watch them wriggle on the floor as the soap began to destroy the poisonous venom, lying dormant in their swollen gullets.

No such luck, he thought. After working there for almost a year he was offered promotion; only to turn it down flat because he knew he could no longer work alongside such despicable people. Instead he gave in his notice an walked out the gate. And in a matter of weeks he suddenly found himself without a job, without a penny, without a room, without a bed to lie on.

And it was during these semi-turbulent times that Teresa would castigate him for being such a useless oaf. They seemed to have rows about everything. But then they'd make it up again quickly, only to start all over again the next day. He hardly ever drank except on social occasions. He just loved dancing and music and going to the pictures.

He would arrive at the Nurses' Home adjacent to the Hospital to take Teresa out and everything would be grand. He'd arrive back again in a day or two to be attacked for his appearance. If it wasn't his hair, it was his shirt. If it wasn't his shirt, there was something wrong with his trousers.

"John! It looks awful! I'm not going out with you dressed like that. If you had any respect at all for me you wouldn't come dressed like that. Who ever saw a fella wearing a shirt with a belt on it? Is it that you think you're a bit of a pop star or something?"

"If I was a pop star, I suppose that would be all right?"

"Yes! It would, because then you'd be something. As it is you're nothing," she replied.

"That makes two of us."

"Oh, shut up!"

Occasionally the ornaments went flying as he stormed out of the room and went home. But then they'd make it up again the next day.

He's nineteen years old and they're strolling through the park of a summer's evening, where they end up rolling around on the grass with not a care in the world: when straight out of the blue, Teresa asks,

"When are we going to get married?"

Paschal, somewhat taken aback sits up and looks at Teresa.

"I'm not sure."

"But for God's sake, isn't it time we talked about it? You never even mention it. Not a word. You carry on as if it didn't matter."

"But it doesn't matter! Sure you can get married any time. Today. Tomorrow. There's no law saying we have to do it now! We can do it next year," he added with a shrug of his shoulders.

"John! Be serious. I'm talking about us! When are we going to get married?"

"Teresa! I don't know! I have no desire whatsoever to get married...yet, and that's that! OK!"

"But you're nineteen years old for God's sake! I'm nineteen! Do you want me to wait until I'm an old woman or what? You're living here this last three or four years with nothing to show for it..."

When she gets like this, his blood rises. He wants to run away. Instead he sits there trying hard not to listen to her tirade, or see the picture she's trying to paint. It pains him so much because everything she says seems to have a marked grain of truth about it.

"...You've no proper job! No money! No house... and no notion of getting one. You had a good job on the buses and you left! You had a good job in Dunlop's and left! All you do now is go from Billy to Jack. You just don't seem to care about anything. John! Are you listening to me?"

He said nothing because he was incapable of thinking. His mind and body were in turmoil. He didn't know what he wanted. The one thing he didn't want was commitment. He wanted to be free. Yet he wanted more than anything else to love and be loved and to drift wherever tide and time would take him. Deep down he knew he was very unhappy because he had had such high hopes of success when he first came to Manchester.

"I said, are you listening to me?"

"Yeah! Yeah! yeah! You're like a flipping gramophone!"

"And what are you going to do about it?"

"Teresa, would you ever leave me alone, for the love of God?"

"No, I won't. What are you going to do about it?"

At that precise moment, he wanted to grab her by the throat just to shut her up. He doesn't know in God's earth how such a small beautiful looking creature can inflict so much pain? He's terrified he'll reach breaking point, and maybe end up killing her. He doesn't ever want to hit a woman, any woman. It isn't right. He knows in his heart of hearts that it isn't right. He thinks that maybe there is something wrong with him. Why does he feel so terribly lonely at times like this? Scores of fellows would give anything: anything to be like him; young and free, with a beautiful girl hanging on their arm. Yet, he's not happy. Maybe *he* should consider getting married. But how can he get married when he doesn't know anything about the world. He doesn't know if he loves Teresa. He thinks he loves her, but he could never say it to her the way they do at the Apollo cinema. He wants so desperately to be able to say those words to a beautiful girl, but he knows he can't. Not even to Teresa Burke. He craves a million and one things in life but he can't put them in any order. He starts to think to himself how he loved working on the buses. But what can you do when you can't count money? He knows he can count money. Any fool can count money, yet *he* couldn't.

He'd love to work in a shop, or a department store. He was supposed to have been a bit of a scholar in school, but now he can't even add up a few sums. And because of that failing he wouldn't dream of looking for a job like that again. Besides the bus people would probably write back to his employer and say, that fella can do everything under the rising sun, but he can't count money.

Sometimes he thinks he'd like to be a musician, or a pop star, like the Beatles.

He takes a sneaking look at Teresa lying there on the grass, hands under her chin, eyeing him up, probingly, as if reading his mind.

"Look at you! You don't know whether you're coming or going. You know I never met the likes of you, John. Never! What's wrong with you? Is it that you're afraid to commit yourself or what? I know… you're afraid of responsibility, and you want me to do everything. I even had to tell you when it was time to get engaged! And you're waiting for me to arrange the wedding now, I suppose. Well I'm not feckin' doin' it. You can arrange your own wedding."

He looks at her longingly, and pleads,"Teresa! Why are you so hard on *me*! So hard on *yourself*! Aren't we all right the way we are? Haven't we a whole lifetime ahead of us? Can't we wait a while and see what happens? And see how we get on. I'll get a proper job as soon as I can. Something good will turn up, you wait and see."

"No we won't! I'm fed up with the way you carry on! Besides, you've never once said you loved me. And I'm sick listening to you saying, how you'd love to do this; and love to do that. But you've never once said you loved me."

Paschal thinks it sounds horrid when she puts it like that. All he can do is shrug his shoulders and say,

"Well…you know."

"Well what?"

"You know."

"Know what?"

"I like you."

"But do you love me?" she asked.

"Yeah…"

He knows it has a very hollow ring to it.

"Well, say it then."

Choosing his words with care, he finally says,

"I like you."

"Say you love me."

"I won't."

"Please John, just once. Say you love me."

"I won't!"

"John, I'll throw this ring back at you if you don't say it."

"Teresa! Would you ever shut up and leave me alone?" he shouts. "You're turning out just like your feckin' sisters."

She rises quickly to her feet in obvious shock, flicking her mane of raven black hair over her shoulder, which together with her short mini-skirt accentuates her heavenly form.

"My sisters!" she exclaimed. "What have my sisters got to do with it?"

John Paschal hadn't meant to say anything about her sisters. It had just slipped out, and now that he had said it and could see the effect it was having on her, he couldn't resist turning the screw.

"Well one of them married a Spaniard, had a child, then he left her. Your other sister got married, had four children and he has left her. And I'm damned Teresa if I'm going to be a third, no feckin' way."

"John!" she squealed. "That's an awful thing to say. How could you say such a thing?"

Bursting into tears she took off the engagement ring and threw it in his face, saying, "You can keep your lousy ring. I never want to see you again as long as I live," as she stormed off across the park.

John Paschal, sighed deeply, rose to his feet and started walking dejectedly towards the exit gates leaving the diamond ring lying on the grass. He had no desire to pick it up or to say, sorry. Yet he couldn't resist turning round to deliver one parting salvo.

'Teresa! When I buy a ring it's because I really am getting married, and not thinking about it.'

Embarrassingly, he heard the echo of his own voice as it reverberated across the park. Walking towards the exit he saw the Park Keeper waiting patiently by the grass green gates, ever ready to bind the chains around another trying day.

Arriving back in his lodging house he was surprised to see a telegram waiting for him on the table. With a trembling heart he tore it open to learn that Edward O'Brien, the only father he had ever known, had quietly passed away.

* * * * *

Bridie's theory that all things come in threes, came to the fore after she received yet another rotten letter. First, the news about Lilly MacAlastair, then a telegram from the O'Brien's; and now *this*. She feels she can't go on and has decided to take a few days off work in St. Andrew's. The work is energy sapping, and demoralising; scrubbing the same old pots and pans seven days a week, for breakfast, dinner and tea. Things were bad enough before all *this,* she thought, what with breaking up with Tomás and all that; but *this* letter was something else.

Sitting alone in the front parlour room of number of 49 Barrack Road, she tries to make sense of it all. She has each disturbing word and syllable of the letter firmly engraved on her mind. Yet she takes it out of her pocket one more time, in the hope that its contents will somehow dissolve the awful pain she feels in her heart.

> *Dear Bridie,*
> *Just a few lines to inform you, John Paschal has left Manchester and is now living in Australia. He came home from England for my father's funeral a few weeks ago. He asked if I'd write and tell you how sorry he was that he hasn't been in touch with you lately. He thought it best to go away and say nothing. He left no forwarding address, so God knows if I'll ever hear from him again. He says he intends to settle there for good.*

Bridie, I know it won't be easy but you'd really be better off to forget all about him. I don't think he really knows what he wants. He was very close to my father and we thought he's settle on the land, but no. John didn't want to work it, so there was no reason for him to stay. I don't expect I'll ever see him again. Australia is such a terribly long way to go. Perhaps it's for the best. He'll probably meet a nice girl over there and settle down.

I don't particularly like being the one to bring you this news. But he asked if I'd let you know, so I suppose that's that.

I wish both yourself and John Paschal all the best in the future.

Yours sincerely,
Maureen Keane (O'Brien)

It's still the same rotten letter, thought Bridie. Still as bad as ever; no matter how many times I read it. My only son has rejected me.

She had never felt so low in her entire life. How could John Paschal do that to his own mother, his own flesh and blood; cut her out of his life entirely; at nineteen years of age; and all she did for him? Where did she go wrong? '...*You'd really be better off to forget all about him...*' How! How in God's Holy name could anyone say such a thing, she pleaded. She went to the sideboard and opened her jewellery box; took out the goatskin purse, which contained her son's lock of golden hair and held it lovingly between her fingers: feeling the soft silken strands as she recalled that fateful morning long ago when she cut it off, prior to their separation. It would soon be twenty years she thought, as a single tear ran down her cheek. And all for nothing, she cried. Will I ever know a single day's happiness? Will I? She wondered should she just throw the hair into the fire and start anew. No, she sighed. I can't do that. If nothing else I'll keep it in memory. He was a good son; my only son. Gone now forever, she sobbed, as she broke down and wept openly on the rug in front of the fire.

She took out her handkerchief to wipe away the tears. How could any son do that to his own mother? It must be that Teresa, or Maureen, or someone. John Paschal would never do that to me; after all I have done for him, she surmised. All the letters and parcels I sent from the Magdalene. Oh God! How I suffered in that place, because I had you my love; locked away for fifteen long years. Oh, how I begged and borrowed off poor Julie, and now this. There must be a reason, there has to be a reason. Why didn't he just write himself from Manchester? Why?

She slammed the door behind her and went for a walk in the park. She felt so utterly dejected that she didn't really care if she walked out in front of a bus, because at the end of the day no one cared; not even her own son.

She sat there alone in the park, staring into the wide-open expanse of oblivion. There was really nothing to live for anymore. She had gambled that day long ago whether to let the nuns put him up for adoption in Ireland, England or America, or to insist that they foster him out to a good local family. She had gambled with his life that day when he was taken away from her and lost. Nothing, she cried aloud to herself, nothing in this whole wide world could be harder for any mother, than to have to gamble with your son's life: and nothing more painful than to lose. Again she took out her handkerchief. Life would have been so much easier if I'd just given him up there and then, instead of getting to know him like I did: only to lose him in the end.

She thought briefly of her boyfriend, Tomás. He was gone. She thought of her dear, dear friend Josephine Finn; dead and buried. And now her son, John Paschal, lost forever. Even her friend, Lilly MacAlastair attacked and raped. Dear Lord, was there no end to it?

She'd have to pull herself together somehow, she thought, otherwise she'd lose her job. The very thought of having to catch the early-morning bus reviled her. What if she didn't go back to work? What if she went back to Ireland instead, to Galway maybe; because, it seemed there was nothing here for her any more?

Slowly making her way out of the park she tried to control the mounting desolation; trying desperately to make sense of it all. There must be something I can do, she thought, because I swear I will not give in; not now, never. I'll do whatever it takes. But what can I do? It's too late to go to Manchester now, because Paschal's lost, somewhere in Australia. Left no forwarding address. '...*Bridie, I know it won't be easy but you'd really be better off to forget all about him...*'

Suddenly she stopped in her tracks to extract the letter and to read the following line one more time.

'...*I don't think he really knows what he wants...*'

As sure as night follows day, thought Bridie, in sudden heart felt relief; He's confused.

'...*He was very close to my father...*'

That's what happened. The poor lad is totally confused. And as for that bitch Teresa Burke: unless I'm greatly mistaken, she was no help to him at all. Confused, that's it. He's confused. I'll go to Ireland for a few days and see Lilly. Poor Lilly. Maybe I'll stay a while longer and see all my friends; and If I know Paschal at all, despite what anybody else says, he'll write. As sure as night follows day he'll write. The question is, when?

Chapter Twenty One

Bridie sat up and breathed a deep sigh of relief. She was feeling so much better now after her week in hospital. The doctors had told her, she was severely rundown and suffering from physical and mental exhaustion. They had also advised her, to change her job, otherwise it would kill her. Twelve hours a day was too much, they said. And while she was considering their advice, she collapsed at work in St. Andrew's Hospital shortly after her return from Ireland.

Deep down she knew it wasn't the work that was killing her, but the stress and strain of the past few months. She remembered all too clearly the daily strain of waiting for a letter: only to stand-alone again the following morning in the wind and rain, waiting for a bus. She recalled, how there were days when she felt so overwhelmed by the sheer hopelessness of it all. She felt she had lost everything; She remembered, one particularly cold winter's morning, looking up at the fading moon as a vicious black cloud swept over it and thought how every dark cloud was supposed to have a silver lining: and that it was long past time that she herself shared in some of its glitter. All she ever wanted in life was to *know* what it was really like to love someone. To *know* did she ever have a real mother or father; to *know* did she have a brother or sister; to *know* if her own son, her own flesh and blood, ever, ever really loved her. She remembered too, how that particular morning the bus never came as the Heavens opened and she stood there in the rain, mumbling to herself, 'Lord God Almighty will I ever *know* anything'?

But now suddenly everything seemed so bright and beautiful. Beryl, her lovely English friend from work had called to visit her every single day in her hospital bed; promising each time to introduce her to her brother, Gordon, who'd recently divorced.

At last they came, both of them kissing her tenderly on the cheek and she smiled broadly at them as Beryl said,

"Bridie, this is Gordon. You know, when I first told him, about this beautiful Irish friend of mine, he simply insisted on coming along, because he said, he'd like to meet you" smiled Beryl proudly, tipping a wink at Bridie.

"Wha' you been doin' then, heh?" said Gordon cheerfully, his broad smile already putting a gloss on Bridie's pale complexion as he extended his welcoming hand.

"Hello Gordon! It's lovely to see you," she replied, taking his warm hand in hers.

"Gosh Beryl, he's just like you, the same features and everything."

"I know, and he hardly ever drinks. He's just mad about cars and loves to go for long drives in the country."

"How abou' it then? You and I go for a drive when you get better, heh?" suggested Gordon, his white teeth displaying a ring of confidence.

"Oh Gordon," gushed Bridie. "That would be lovely, 'cause I hardly ever go anywhere. And I love the countryside and I love looking at the animals and everything."

"Right then, that's settled," said Gordon, rubbing his hands together in unrestrained glee at having scored so quickly.

And on their first outing, they went for a long drive in the country, where Bridie gave Gordon the gift of a lovely little dog that he placed in the back window of his car. She was so pleased, as she watched him smile mischievously, at the sight the little dog's head bobbing from side to side.

And again the following Sunday they went for another long drive in the country, followed by another the week after until one day they both agreed they were deeply in love. Bridie in particular was so happy to have met someone who loved her for what she was and not *who* she was. And so, so happy when her good friend Beryl helped set her up in a nice flat, and gave her bits and pieces because she didn't have a stick of furniture or anything to her name.

After two years touring the countryside, and whispering sweet nothings over wild flowers and picnic baskets, Gordon proposed to Bridie and asked if she'd like to become Mrs Bridie Foster. Without hesitation she said yes, because Gordon was the kindest most caring man she ever met, and who didn't drink the way the mad Irish did. Then the two of them drove in Gordon's Morris Minor car to the Registry office where they were married with two friends as witnesses: Beryl, as Bridesmaid and Gordon's brother Raymond as best man.

Gordon was Church of England by birth, but Bridie didn't care. But the one thing she did care about was that she hadn't had a church wedding, in spite of her best efforts. Even after they were married, she never gave up hope that one day she would marry in a Catholic church, dressed all in white. It was one of two things she prayed for, last thing at night before going to sleep; To get married in a Catholic church: and to one day be reunited with her son, forever.

"Byedee! It doesn't matter! All weddings are same! They're just a money racket," said Gordon in response to her continuous goading, as he slapped up another length of wallpaper on the living room wall, while Bridie set about tidying up the place so that they could both have a bite to eat.

"I know love, and I'm pleased we got married in a Registry office, but I don't feel that it's right; it's not the same. I'd still like to have a proper church wedding."

"Byedee!" replied Gordon, raising his voice in anger. "I've told you a dozen times! We can't get married in Cat'lic church! I'm not Cat'lic, Byedee!"

"But we could if you weren't so stubborn. You could easily become a convert."

"Aw Byedee! Give over. Pass me that cloth, a minute."

Instead she went into the back-kitchen and pretended she hadn't heard him, and when he saw the disappointment etched on her face, he tamely added,

"Gimme me time to think abou' it; you know it'll cost a packet; an' we barely got enough to get by as it is; wha' with mortgage and everythin'."

After months and months of cajoling, Bridie got her wish. Marching down the aisle in her beautiful white wedding gown, she felt more radiant than at any time in her entire life. She was very happy to have Julie, Noreen and Beryl as her new bridesmaids; while Gordon's friend, John, was best man.

Putting together her wedding album, Bridie feigned contentment, because she couldn't bear to tell Gordon that her heart still ached, in the absence of her son. She knew that no album would ever be complete without a recent photograph of her son. She would have given the whole world just to have him walk her down the aisle to give her away. She didn't care that it would have been strange to have her twenty odd year old son escorting her down the Aisle or that people might whisper behind her back. He was her son and she was proud of him. But sure where was the use in thinking that now when she didn't even know where he was, and besides he didn't seem to care. What could she do when he chose to ignore her; to rule her out of his life? It was years since she had last seen or heard from him. But who knows, perhaps he'll turn up one of these days, she thought.

After they were married Gordon insisted that Bridie give up her job in St. Andrew's, where she had worked for eleven years. There was the offer of an easier job working for the City council, looking after the elderly in their own homes: where the hours were much shorter and you were more or less your own Boss.

Bridie took the job and handed in her notice at her old place of work. She almost cried with relief at the thought she would have no more early mornings. No more dark winter evenings going home in the rain, where if she was lucky Gordon might just be in the door before her and have a nice fire on. Being a onetime chef in the Defence Forces, Gordon could rustle up a tasty morsel in no time at all; particularly his favourite recipe of pork pie and mash with loads of gravy and Yorkshire pudding.

And while Gordon did all the cooking Bridie wrote to her friends Noreen and Julie. Sometimes lamenting the loss of her John Paschal, she would ask them to be on the look out in case he ever returned to Ireland.

On her last working day in St. Andrew's Hospital Bridie strode up to the main office in the administration department to collect her wages.

"Mrs. Foster, you know, you're entitled to a bonus of one pound for every year of service."

"That's right," said Bridie, thinking a pound seemed such a miserly sum when you considered the long hours and years of loyal service she had put in.

"…And as you've been here ten years that means…" he was working it out on the calculator

"Eleven," intervened Bridie, nonchalantly, before the wages clerk looked questioningly at her. "I'm here eleven years!" reiterated Bridie, who'd thought she'd be entitled to a much bigger bonus.

The wages clerk went to the filing cabinet to study her employment record. He consulted his colleague, in whispering tones, and returned with a triumphant look on his face.

CHAPTER TWENTY ONE

"Actually, Mrs. Foster, you've only been with us ten years."

"Eleven! As true as God is my judge, I'm here eleven years, and I think I should know," reiterated Bridie again.

"I'm afraid that not quite so. You're actually one week short of eleven years. Therefore that constitutes a ten years' bonus."

"Well," replied Bridie, feeling very embarrassed at not having got her facts right in the first place. "I hope none of ye ever die with the hunger and all I did for ye. I washed and scrubbed from morning till night seven days a week. And no patient of mine ever went hungry and no doctor ever went to work of a morning, without being offered a nice cup of tea…. and that's the thanks I get. You know when I think about it, my husband was right. He said, killing people ye are with work, not kindness."

"Now, now Mrs. Foster! That's not a nice thing to say," replied the wages clerk feeling somewhat peeved as he came toward the hatch and handed the two pay packets to Bridie.

"I'm sorry Mrs Foster, but these things are completely outside my control. You see it's not up to us. It's Department of Health's regulations and we must apply the rules."

But Bridie was still angry as she clearly saw the small brown envelope, marked 'Bonus' she asked,

"How much is in that?"

"Ten pounds! It's your bonus for length of service and this here is your two weeks wages together with your holiday pay and super annuity."

Pushing back the envelope marked 'Bonus' Bridie said,

"Here, ye can keep it! It looks like the Department of Health needs it a lot more than I do," then turning on her heel she stormed out the door.

A week later she received a cheque in the post from St. 'Andrew's Hospital, It was made out for the sum of ten pounds and eighty-three pence.

* * * * *

After the break up of John Paschal's romance with Teresa Burke, it would have taken an exceptionally able character to have kept tabs on him: once the travelling bug set in. For in truth, he moved around so fast he never knew himself where he was going. And never stayed any where long enough to call it home. He never wrote to his mother Bridie, or had any desire to contact her again. Instead he drifted aimlessly from one part of the country to another before finally deciding to emigrate to Australia; for good.

And while in Australia he was as fleet-footed as ever. Working first in the sprawling gold mining fields of Kalgoorlie in Western Australia, he then went to Albany in South Australia; to Melbourne in the South East where he worked as a conductor and tram driver for a year or more before deciding to pack his bags yet again. This time he headed to the far North, living and working in such diverse places as Sydney, Brisbane, Townsville, Ayr and Cairns. And it was during one of these flights of fancy that he decided he was going nowhere. He had become disillusioned with life in Australia. He made up his mind to return to England, where he soon got himself a good job working on an oil rig in the far north of Scotland. There, he managed to survive the arctic-like winter conditions long enough to save up a few pounds to buy himself a lorry and start a haulage business.

But before making any major decision he decided to take a short holiday in Ireland; only to learn on his immediate arrival that his beloved foster mother, Mrs O'Brien has passed away a few days earlier.

"Why didn't someone contact me?" he ranted.

"We would have and gladly, if only anyone knew where you were," replied Maureen.

A year later, after getting over the shock of Mrs O'Brien's demise, he decided to spend a few days with his long time friend Joe Hennessy down in Kilkenny, where he thought the craíc was always good. And it was on one of those glorious summer evenings as he did the rounds of the town, that Joe introduced him to some of the best watering holes in Urlingford; frequented by many of Joe's cronies. But John Paschal was more interested in a young lady he spotted walking down the other side of the street.

"Jesus Lads! Look at that! Who is she?"

"Oh! That's Julie," laughed Richie Brennan, perched on his high stool. "Keep your shagging eyes off that lady, I'm bringing her to the dance tonight...so you've no chance, JP."

"OK, O.K. I'll tell you what we'll do, just to make the thing fair. We'll go fifty, fifty. One of ye chaps can take Julie to the dance, but I'm taking her home. Isn't that fair enough?" laughed John, to which a loud alcoholic cheer went up in the bar.

"Fair play to you JP. You never lost it. You know it's her eighteenth birthday today, so you'll have to buy her a big box of chocolates" added Richie.

"Yeah, and a massive bunch of flowers, I suppose. Do ye know something lads, ye're the greatest shower of hoors I ever met. I wouldn't like to believe one solitary word that comes out of yeer filthy mouths," replied John Paschal.

This line was followed by yet more jibes and laughter, until Joe said,

"Come on lads! Drink up! Time for the road."

John Paschal and his friends drove straight into Thurles and went to the Anner Hotel, where John Paschal looked eagerly around to see if he could see Julie anywhere. No such luck. Half an hour later he spots her being escorted into the Hotel by a male friend, but she is soon lost in the midst of the huge crowd as the laughter picks up where it left off and the beer flows free. And as the band continues to pound out rock and roll music John Paschal slips quietly away from the bar, in order to have a few dances and maybe with any bit of luck meet somebody nice. But most of all he'd like to meet Julie, to find out if she's committed or not as he couldn't accept the word of his friends who were giving him a fierce slagging altogether, claiming she was well and truly spoken for. She was the finest looking girl, he thought, he's seen in a long time. This in turn made him more determined to speak to her. What was she like to talk to, he wondered. The curiosity was killing him. But Julie was nowhere to be seen, and then he spotted her again, not more than a few feet away as he ordered himself a drink at the small cocktail bar. She had her back turned to him and was leaning across a table talking to her female friends. There they were, blathering on and on; he thought they'd never stop. He was really desperate to talk to her, and knew that if he didn't act quickly the opportunity would be lost, perhaps forever.

But he couldn't just tap her on the shoulder and ask her to dance. To do that would be to give all her friends the chance to laugh and snigger when she refused which she might well do. Jesus, he thought, will she ever stop talking. He knew what he was going to do. It was something he'd never, ever done to a woman before; and which could result in him getting a slap across the face. But, on the other hand he'd be guaranteed a quick response.

Seeing the exposed flesh of her lower back, where her white top had rode up, he reached forward and poured a small drop of his bottled Guinness onto her bare flesh. She sprang to attention immediately, turned and looked him in the eye, while all her colleagues sat there with there vodka's laughing their heads off.

"Hi Julie! Sorry about that, but desperate times call for desperate measures. I had to talk to you?"

"Well Jesus! You'd better start talking fast. You realise you have me drowned. What made you do that?" she smiled, as she tried drying the small of her back.

"Desire! An overwhelming desire to… talk to you…"

"And who are you? Do I know you?"

"You do now! My name is John. I'm a good friend of Joe Hennessy, whom I believe is a neighbour of yours. I saw you walking down the street earlier today, and I thought I'd like to get to know you."

"Well did you now?" she smiled broadly. "Isn't that strange. And I saw you walking down the street yesterday and I thought I'd like to get to know you too."

Placing his drink on the bar counter he turned round and said, "Good! That's what I like to hear. Let's go and have a dance."

They had several dances before returning to the bar. There he treated her to a cocktail as it was indeed, Julie's eighteenth birthday. Then they danced the rest of the night away, before he waltzed her out the door and gave her a lift home in his white vintage motor car with it's chrome wire wheels, which he'd brought home from Manchester.

A week later John Paschal decided, that having met the woman of his dreams he had no desire to return to England: preferring instead to set up his haulage business in Dublin from where he commuted up and down to Kilkenny to see Julie.

Then one sunny afternoon, almost two years later, in the grounds of the Dublin Annual Spring Show, in Ballsbridge, he asked her to marry him.

She said 'yes'.

But her mother said, "Who is he Julie? Who is he? You're going with that fella two years now or more, and you don't even know the first thing about him. And him not having two pennies to rub together and nobody belonging to him. And now you're telling me he has no mother or father: that…that he was reared God knows where … above

… above in county Galway. Faith if I was you Julie, I'd think long and hard before I'd have anything at all to do with a fellow like that: long and hard, so I would."

"Mother! I'm marring him! I don't care whether you like it or not!"

Despite that major hiccup, they got married in Rome and later decided to buy a house in Williamstown. It was of a Friday, the 13th day of April that they moved in to their new home

Time to start a brand new life, thought John Paschal.

* * * * *

The scene was as old as the universe itself. It was that a very old woman, so frail and decrepit looking it was almost beyond belief. It was as if some unseen spirit was enacting the spectre specifically for him. The old woman was going through every dustbin in the bowels of the city trying desperately to uncover something that would reveal the whereabouts of John Paschal. Even as he stood there watching her, she continued with her pain-staking search, going from one rat infested alley to another checking every crumpled letter and piece of paper for news of his whereabouts.

John Paschal sat bolt upright in bed as a cold sweat ran down his forehead. He was more frightened, now, than at any time in his life. What was really terrifying about the whole thing, was, he was seeing the face of his own mother Bridie. Not only that, but it was the image of a woman steeped in poverty, and it was poverty of the mind that was destroying her, not hunger. She was slowly starving to death for news of her son.

In an effort to banish the hideous scene from his memory he got out of bed, dressed quickly and went down stairs to prepare breakfast for his three young children. But Julie knew instinctively that something was amiss, that something was troubling John Paschal. After much coaxing he disclosed that he'd had a terrible dream; and after a detailed discussion they both put it down to being one of those things; a bad dream: things that come and go and pass in the night: things over which people have absolutely no control. And although he never said as much, never admitted it, he felt that it was indeed a stark reminder, a message from the other side.

Fortunately, when he first met Julie he had told her everything about his mother, and how he had walked away from her: disowned her entirely. Not so much because he had to tell her, but because he felt it was the right thing to do. He knew he couldn't go on living a lie all his life. Julie understood this and was happy to go along with whatever he choose to do and the subject was never mentioned again.

But when three weeks later the self same dream occurred again it threatened to put his state of mind in jeopardy. No one, but no one he felt, could fail to be effected by such a dream. He lay there in bed his body swathed in a sea of sweat-soaked rags. He knew instinctively that this was now bordering on paranoia. It could only mean one of two things. He was slowly entering the realms of madness, or else it was a clear sign that his mother was looking for him. He chose to believe the latter. Something, somewhere was clearly amiss, and as he played the image over and over again in his mind, and saw her rummaging through the litterbins – yet again – he equated that scene with the numerous parcels she had sent to him over the years and the countless letters she had written. Thinking about it at all made him feel ill and guilty as sin. He felt he was unworthy of her name. Nobody in their right mind could have been so selfish, so rotten as to ignore their own mother. Yet that was what he had done. He had disowned his own mother, and all she had done for him.

"How long since you've seen her?" asked Julie.

"Oh, too long I fear!" replied John as he paced up and down the kitchen floor. "I have to try and think. This has to be a clear sign, that she's dead or something."

"Oh God! Don't say that!"

"It is! It is! I know it is! It's a clear sign. But what it is I don't know. And what if she *is* dead, how am I going to find out? I have to go and find her. The problem is it's been such a long time. It's fifteen years since I last saw her, in Northampton, and I've had no contact with her since."

"What about her address? Maybe you should write, if it'll make you feel any better."

"No, no! I've got to go to England: besides I don't know where she lives; all I have is a vague memory of her address, but that was… fifteen… sixteen years ago. It seems such a long time. And believe me this is urgent. To dream about her once, is a coincidence: to have the same dream a second time is telepathic. I know it is. She is calling out to me. Perhaps she's in a Home somewhere, with no one to look after her. She may even be homeless or on the streets, or seriously ill in hospital or worst still, maybe dead."

"So what are you going to do?" asked Julie, struggling to feed Síle, the youngest of their three children.

"I'll go straight down to the bank, draw out a few pounds and go over to England on tonight's sailing, and while I'm over there I'll pop down to London and buy a few canvas paintings for framing. That way the trip won't be a total loss."

"Well I don't care what you do, so long as you're happy about it. But I think maybe you should wait a while, think it over and not rush into anything. You must have had some reason for not keeping in touch with her in the first place. And what if you find her and she wants to come here and live with us, how will we manage?"

"No, No! It was my fault. I was in the wrong. I was a bit too young and I couldn't cope with it all." admitted John as he prepared to put a rasher on the pan and to make some sort of a breakfast.

Turning to Julie, he added "As regards her wanting to come and live with us, we'll cross that bridge when we come to it. Besides, fifteen years is a hell of a long time. It might not be that easy to find her. But whatever it takes I know I've got to track her down and that's that."

Julie, having finished feeding Síle said, "Well darling, she's your mother; and whatever you decide to do, I wish you the best of luck," as he hurriedly grabbed a suitcase and began throwing a few things into it.

A few hours later he was on his way to England.

Chapter Twenty Two

They were snuggled up on their brand new couch in number 34 Cloutsham Street, Northampton, having a nice cup of tea while half watching television and discussing their respective family ties. Bridie having decided it might be a good time to disclose to Gordon a little bit more of her past life, a little more of her secret dreams and desires.

"Did I ever tell you how I cut off a lock of my son's hair the day I had to leave him?"

"Your son's 'air!" exclaimed Gordon. "Wha' you on abou' Byedee?"

"I cut off a lock of my son's hair, the morning I had to leave him…. I keep it in my jewellery box upstairs. You see I had a dream the night before he was taken away that if I kept something belonging to him he'd come back to me and that's why I've kept it all these years. I thought I told you about it before?"

"Aw, Byedee! Everybody's got dreams! An' you keep on abou' it: they're just waste-a- time, as far as I'm concerned."

"I know you don't believe in them Gordon. But I'm different. I'll never ever give up on him. Even when I go to bed at night, it's the last thing I think about. I pray every night Gordon that he'll return or write to me: only I wouldn't like to be an old woman when it happens. I wouldn't like to have to wait that long." Slipping her arm lovingly around Gordon's shoulder, she continued. "I know love, it's hard for you to understand: what with your own family; your ex-wife and everything, but sometimes that's all I ever think of. And it upsets me when I hear you giving out to your grand- children. There only young, Gordon; at least you can talk to them every day. If only I could talk to John Paschal, I'd be the happiest woman in Ireland…."

"Island, Island! What you on abou'…" chuckled Gordon, unable to pronounce his Rs.

"Sorry love, I meant England… you know well what I mean. But isn't it funny, I keep trying to figure out where in the world he might be. Sometimes I think it's like standing on top of a tall pillar and looking down onto the streets of London; watching the millions of people go by: trying desperately to pick out the one you're looking for. And it's far worse when you don't even know which country they're in. It makes it so much harder to reach out to them in your prayers."

"Why not go to Island then? Someone must know if he's been abou'."

"Oh, Gordon, that would be lovely. Maybe next year when we go on holidays we could go to Galway and I could make enquiries. But I wouldn't like to meet up with him without first letting him know. It's up to him to find me if he wants. You know he could be in Ireland, England or Australia at this very moment. The last I heard of him, he was supposed to be in Australia. But somehow, I feel he'd never stay there. He might be back living in Ireland now or maybe Manchester," said Bridie as she leaned over the side of the couch, to pick her cigarettes off the floor. And as she lit up another 'Park Drive' for herself, and Gordon, she continued.

"All I know Gordon is, that I shall never stop praying. I know that my prayers will be answered, but that the time has to be right for the two of us. The last time we met I think I may have frightened him away because he was young and didn't know me. Did I ever tell you I was psychic and had the power to know certain things at certain times?"

"Wha'? You-a-medium?" laughed Gordon. "Cor blimey! That's a good un. I'll have to take you to the market on Saturday; we'd make a packet…". !"

"'Tis true Gordon. Did I ever tell you…and please don't laugh, that I met a man when I was what… about seventeen or eighteen, who was very good to me? I remember his words to this very day. He said, 'I can tell you Bridie that you'll never be rich, but then again you'll never be poor. But someday perhaps years from now when you'll least expect it and need it most you are going to win'. And isn't it a funny thing, I don't think he meant money – although I keep doing the pools and every free competition, just in case. I think he was talking about Paschal even though he wasn't even born then. But it was the way he looked at me, I know he meant every word of it."

"Must be a gypsy or some thing?"

"It's a strange thing he wasn't. He was a gentleman farmer I used to work for. He had a wife and three lovely children. But I'll never ever forget how kind he was to me. Somehow I always feel that his words will come true and that John Paschal will come back to me. I'm sorry Gordon to keep going on about it, but I just know that if I could reach out to him, he'd come running."

"I doubt it," sighed Gordon, wearily. "But you never know, do ya?"

He was tired listening to Bridie. He had enough problems of his own, he thought; without dwelling on hers any longer. "That's it! Move your backside, Byedee, I got to be in Abbington St. in morning at eight o'clock. You go on up; I'll put things away."

But Bridie stayed there, lying on the couch. She was in no mood to get up as she savoured one last puff of her cigarette, while trying to imagine what it would be like if her son were to ever walk in the door of her living room. It would be absolute heaven, she thought. Absolute heaven

* * * * *

The Holyhead boat train swooshed its way past unsuspecting hamlets, as it sped across the English countryside, bound for London. Its dimly lit carriages were packed to capacity; with mounds of cumbersome luggage strewn here there and everywhere. Trying to make sense of it all while studying the toothless gaping features of his fellow passengers was John Paschal. He wished at that moment he were an artist; for truly the late night scene was a cartoonist's dream. Yet, despite the enormous pleasure he derived from looking at the human form, he could not rid the image of that awful dream from his head. The very thought that he had deserted his own mother and was now going to England to try and right a wrong made him feel ill again. He had an uneasy feeling that his past might be coming back to haunt him. No, no, that wasn't a fair assumption he thought. His mother would never haunt him like that; and it all happened such a long time ago. But what was it that made him feel so bad, he wondered. It was as if he had committed some heinous crime. A crime he couldn't explain. And the very thought that he wanted to be reunited again with his mother brought back memories of a word he hated more than any other in the English language. Illegitimate. He'd heard so many crude interpretations of the word as a youngster and had it's meaning up-casted to him so many times he never ever forgot it meaning. It was the legal term for a bastard; a child born out of wedlock. And here he was himself, a bastard, going to England aboard the night train to look for his mother. He wondered were there any more bastards on the train: sure the world is full of bastards; and mother-fuckers; and sons-of-bitches, who wouldn't even write to their own mother never mind their Granny. So in a sense, he was a bastard: a real, real bastard: who would always be a bastard and a bastard until the day he died, even though he hadn't ever raised a hand to any man woman or child. At least he could be proud of that if nothing else, he thought.

But would he be proud of his mother when he saw her? If she was going to be anything like the image portrayed in his dream he wasn't so sure. He prayed with all his heart that the dream was no more than a secret sign; a sign that he must save her. But save her from what; from sickness, from death; or the twilight zone? The twilight zone like death was one of those subjects people were loath to talk about. But that horrid dream he had somehow made him recollect a frightening memory from his own past, which had occurred years ago when he lived in Manchester.

He remembered, how he was returning home from work one evening when he saw a bowed elderly figure pushing a rickety old pram laden with rags down the cobble stoned alley, at the back of the house where he lived.

The old man was calling out in a clear, distinct voice, 'Rag-bone… Rag- bone… Rag-bone…!' The very sight of that man, whom he never saw before, frightened the life out of him. For some strange reason, he thought the piercing tone of that man's voice was synonymous with death. Later that same night, on his return home from an enjoyable night out, he suddenly developed an uneasy feeling as he neared his house. There was something eerie about the deserted, dimly lit street that made him break into a run, as the hair stood on the back of his neck. Something or someone was following him; of that he was sure: not a human form but a form nonetheless. He reached the house safely and was never as glad to go to bed. He'd only been in bed a short time when he heard the most awful cry of lamentation coming from the front of the house. He thought it was the most terrifying wail he had ever heard. It made both himself and the man he was sharing a room with, rear up in their beds with sheer fright. He could clearly see the silhouette of his roommate in the bed beside the window, as he exclaimed in a loud voice, 'Jesus Christ, John! What was that'?

'I don't know, it sounds horrid, replied John Paschal, in fearful dread. 'Ah! It must be some old drunkard.'

'But I can't hear or see any fucker. There's no one around', said his roommate looking out the window. For a few moments they both sat there, terror-stricken as the neon city lights cast hypnotic shadows across the room. Then they quickly buried their heads beneath the blankets to hide the ghostly shadows dancing on the walls of their abode. But when John woke in the morning, his roommate was lying there, dead.

And that dream he had had of his own mother, was the nearest he had ever come, to reliving that horrible moment. He didn't want to relive that dream, ever, ever again: and prayed that it wasn't a premonition of his mother's death.

If so, he didn't know how he would ever cope with the knowledge that he had denied his own mother. And the reason he now felt so bad, he knew, was because of this stain on his character, this sin on his soul. There was only one way he could redeem himself, and that was by finding her. He would have to find her at any cost, before it was too late. Maybe in God, just maybe it wasn't too late, and she might still be alive, and living in Barrack Road. But what did he know about her, he asked himself. Damn all. And apart from a few old photographs, he had nothing to show that his mother ever existed. No letters, rhymes or poems and certainly no mouth organ. Absolutely nothing. And all the letters she had written. She must have written hundreds, no thousands of letters; because she was forever writing. And after all that, 'twas sad to think he still didn't have one solitary letter of hers to his name. But I'll find her, I promise you that, he told himself, as the train slowly ground to a halt and a pleasant voice came over the public address system, announcing,

"All passengers bound for Northampton change at Rugby. All passengers bound for Northampton change at Rugby; Rugby next stop."

It was around seven thirty a.m. when he arrived in Northampton, so he decided to go to the Cafeteria and have a full breakfast to help him gather his thoughts. There was only so much he could do at that hour, but first and foremost he'd try to find some suitable accommodation in some cheap hotel or guesthouse. Regardless of how things were going to go for him during the day, he'd be stopping in Northampton for the night, so that would take care of his luggage for a start. Then he'd hire a taxi and go straight over to Barrack Road and see what sort of a response he'd get from No.49. Knowing his luck, he thought, the place would probably be demolished, pulled down – like when he went to see a former girlfriend at an old address in London years ago, only to be left standing there like a fool, because there was no house, no former girlfriend: nothing, but a pile of rubble.

Oh God, he pleaded, don't do that to me. I don't think my ailing heart could take it. At least if the street still exists, somebody somewhere might know of her whereabouts. This was his first real opportunity to prove how good a detective he was. Secretly he almost wished she wouldn't be there so that he'd have some detective work to do and the thought of the challenge ahead filled him with excitement. Now, approaching his thirty-fifth year, he knew that solving this great dilemma was destined to be the most critical moment in his entire life. Not only was he endeavouring to find a blood relative, he was also trying to turn the clock back, and to make amends for lost time.

Three hours later, John Paschal turned a key in his hotel bedroom door, happy to have got rid of his luggage. Then he ran down stairs again and jumped into a waiting taxi. "Barrack Road, please."

" Very well Sir. Which end would you like?"

"I'm not sure, No.49, where ever that is."

No. 49 was a neat, red-bricked house, situated about half way down the road. It was part of a continuous block, which stretched to one hundred houses or more either side of the road. The houses were fronted by rows of cars and vans.

The newly painted green door of 49 had a ships anchor doorknocker as well a doorbell. John Paschal weighed the ships anchor for the pleasure that was in it and let it fall heavily on the door. He did it again and again and when no one answered he rang the doorbell. From somewhere a voice said,

"They're at work mate, they'll not be home 'til late."

When John Paschal turned towards the voice he saw a small elderly man standing, outside the house directly across the way.

"Oh! I take it you live around here. I'm trying to find a family relative, who used to live in No. 49. Bridie Rodgers. Do you know if she still lives here?"

"Bridie Rodgers?" The man shook his head. "Never heard of her.

Alec and Winifred live there now… a long while…elderly Jamaican couple. Ain't no Bridie…what's it…?"

"Rodgers."

"Rodgers? Ain't no lady by that name, not that I know of any road, an' I've been here ten year or more."

"Ten years!" exclaimed, John Paschal. "How long have this couple been here then?" he asked, realising too late that it was a stupid question.

"About six…maybe seven year. They won't know 'ought. Nah mate. No woman by that name lived about here any road," said the little man, as he began to move away from the house. "You could ask Jack, lives in number 59," he said, pointing to a house a few doors down the street. "He's lived here all his life, he might know summit?"

"OK mate, thanks."

John Paschal went straight to 'Jack's' house and cursed his luck because there was no one there either. Nothing for it now he thought, but to knock on every door. He tried the doors either side of number 49 and those directly across from it. But he got nowhere, because hardly anybody was at home. He took note of those that weren't; He'd have to call back later. Somebody was bound to remember her.

It was fast approaching dusk and he had tried every house in the street, including the paper-shop on the corner. He felt exhausted, having knocked on so many doors, and having asking so many questions, while at the same time giving away as little information about himself as possible. In desperation he went back to Jack's house for the third or fourth time. Jack appeared to be the key to everything. Finally, he collared him on his way home from work.

"Bridie Rodgers?" queried Jack, thoughtfully, while John Paschal tried to figure out what class of a tradesman Jack really was. A coal man he decided, as the unmistakeable rings of dust, shrouded the man's bright blue eyes.

"I never knowed, what lady's second name were", he said, shaking his head thoughtfully, but I remember a lady what used to live at number 49. A lovely lady she were and all; Irish lass, black 'air: she were a Bridie I think, wha' used to work in St. Andrew's."

"That's her! That's her! Where did she go, or how long is she gone?"

"Aw mate, haven't seen her in years. All moved out of area, see, wha', ten twelve year ago? Been lots a changes since then, lots a changes."

"Well, thanks for your help anyway. I'll probably try St. Andrew's first thing in the morning. They'll surely have some idea."

"Sorry mate."

"No problem. Thanks."

Day two. John Paschal made his way to St. Andrew's Hospital, and hung around the reception area for a long, long time. Nobody seemed interested in his query, because the lady he first spoke with, never came back to him. So he figured she must have gone home or else she was removing somebody's appendix.

And after repeated requests to various members of staff, as to the likely whereabouts of Bridie Rodgers he was at last, approached by a dour looking lady who asked,

"Are you the gentlemen that been inquiring about a Bridie Rodgers?"

"Yes, I am."

"Bridie's Rodgers, left here years ago. She used to work as a domestic. That the lady?"

"Yes, yes! That's her! Do you know where she went?"

"Sorry. I've no idea, and even if I did, I'm not at liberty to give out that sort of information."

"I know, I know. And I appreciate that. But I'm her son, and I'm trying to find out where she has gone. Have you any idea where she might have lived?" pleaded John.

On hearing this, the Matron's eyebrows narrowed and her thin lips curled in distaste, as she raised her ample chin and replied,

"I'm sorry sir, you must be in the wrong place, or else it's somebody else you're after. The Bridie Rodgers what worked here had no family. So how could you be her son? The lady wasn't even married."

"I know that, I know that. But I *am* her son! And all I'm trying to do is find my mother… It very urgent."

"Well, you've come to the wrong place," retorted the Matron quickly, before adding, "Now, if you don't mind, I have to get on with my work."

"OK, I understand. But maybe I could speak with someone else…one of her friends. They might be able to help me," suggested John hopefully, lowering the tone of his voice.

For a moment the Matron's eyes blazed as she studied him. Then she replied forcefully,

"Sir, I've already told you. We do not give out information on any of our staff. Now if you don't go away, I'll call the security men and have you removed from the premises, immediately."

John Paschal turned away devastated. His face, he surmised, like many before him, didn't fit. Now where do I go, he asked himself, as he sat atop a red bus all the way back to town. He went to a café and sat thinking over a refreshing cup of coffee. After some serious deliberation he appointed himself commander-in-chief of this investigation. He began work immediately by drawing up a long list of possible sources of information, beginning with the Deaths' Register: because there wasn't much point in searching for someone if they were already dead. After that he would proceed to check the Marriage Register; with any bit of luck she might have got married, he thought.

Paschal spent the rest of the day going from one records office to another, and in the heavy downpour it wasn't easy. His feet ached like never before. He felt as if he'd walked miles and miles and yet he had nothing to show for it. What if she was still living and married? What if she had married, but had since passed away? She'd then be listed in the deaths under her married name. It would take days to check all the registers. There were so many permutations to deal with it was almost beyond comprehension

That night he went through his list again. Death registers, marriage registers, social welfare, and taxation records and any number of Hospitals where she might be working.

Then over a beer it occurred to him that she might not be in Northampton at all. What if she moved and was now living in maybe London, Leeds, Birmingham or Manchester? If that was the case then there was no hope at all: particularly if she was married and using her married name. Then he had a brain wave; the voting register. They keep very detailed records there: every name under the sun, every street; every last detail of virtually every citizen in every town. He would begin with the list of residents for Barrack Road. That would surely shed some light on the matter.

It didn't. He checked all the names on the voting register going back light years. Nothing. He checked the tax offices, haphazard and all as they were; and again, nothing. And again the problem arose; what if she had married and had given the marriage register a false name; then he might as well be looking for the proverbial needle in a haystack. Someone suggested the Salvation Army as a great source of help. He merely cringed at the idea. He had started this investigation and he would finish it. Again he went back to the deaths and marriage records: a futile exercise.

He had now spent three whole days on the beat, and was absolutely knackered, both mentally and physically. His body ached as he lay flat out on his hotel bed. The thought of defeat did not go down well with him. He was hungry, but the prospect of dining out, knowing he did not deserve it because he hadn't earned it, killed his desire to eat anything. How could one possibly eat anything nice, when one had worked hard for three whole days, and had made no progress what so ever? To do that would be to accept defeat. He decided instead to go out and buy himself a newspaper. He'd read it first to take his mind of things and hopefully starve himself into submission. There was no other way.

Returning to his Hotel room with the 'Evening Echo' tucked under his arm, he again lay down on the bed to ease his aching limbs. He read the Echo from cover to cover, every last sentence. He was about to fold the newspaper and cast it across the room out of sheer boredom and frustration when something caught his eye. It was the Personal Column in the small ads section. He sprang from the bed in sheer excitement. Why hadn't he thought of this before; the stupid bloody idiot. An appeal, an advertisement: that was surely the key, he felt. He would run an advertisement in the Evening Echo. But how would he phrase it? If nobody on Barrack Road could remember Bridie Rodgers or knew of her whereabouts, then who else would bother to answer it? Would she herself be likely to see it? No, but perhaps some of her friends or work colleagues would. But the chances of that happening were astronomical. Pacing up and down the room he knew within his heart that this could be the defining moment. Placing such an advertisement in a newspaper; was an extremely long shot; he would have to sweeten it, because people were always open to the powers of persuasion. What address, he wondered, would he use for a reply: a box number? He didn't like box numbers because he felt there was something secretive about them, so he wouldn't use that. And there was little point in using the Hotel as an address as he'd have to hang around Northampton, waiting days for a reply and he couldn't afford it anyway. Nothing for it but the oul' reliable, he thought.

Next morning John Paschal delayed his trip to London – to buy some canvas paintings – long enough to run the following add:

> **'Reward Offered!** Reward offered to anyone knowing the whereabouts of Ms. Bridie Rodgers, last known address No.49 Barrack Road, Northampton about 1965. Please contact John Rodgers, Main Street, Williamstown, Co. Galway, Éire.'

He paid for the insertion and requested that the Newspaper run it for two days. Everything else, he told himself, was now in the lap of the Gods.

* * * * *

She was relaxing at home with her evening newspaper. It was one of the few pleasures she enjoyed more than any other; to be able to read in the quiet of her own home, particularly when the evening chores were done. For an hour or so each evening, Beryl Foster, always read the daily news, followed by a look at the gossip columns, before considering the merits of a nice cup of tea and tasty biscuit. But as always she delayed putting on the kettle because she was a mite lazy and would much prefer to do the crossword first, but she knew that this could take hours. She was about to put away the newspaper in favour of the kitchen, when something caught her eye. It was the two words, in bold black print, 'Reward Offered' in the Personal Column. She had a special fascination with the Personal column because Solicitors were always looking for claimants to property or wills. And of course someone was always apologising to someone they'd already hurt or offended in some way, while other people preferred giving thanks to St. Jude for favours received.

With utter dismay Beryl Foster, began to read,

'Reward Offered to anyone knowing the whereabouts of Ms. Bridie Rodgers, last known address No. 49 Barrack Road…'

Her eyes did a double take. My God, 'Ms Bridie Rodgers …1965… that's Bridie, that's my sister-in-law. Quickly removing her feet from the small footstool and sitting up with immediate interest she read the article again and again. *'Reward! Reward!* That's my friend Bridie. It has to be! She has a son, John, John Paschal. That must be him, John Paschal Rodgers. God! I wonder if Bridie knows? A reward offered. Gosh, I wonder how much it is. I know Bridie would give anything to see him. I don't think she has heard from him in years, I wonder if that's really him? Bridie and I used to live on Barrack Road. That's where she was living when we first met, herself and a few of her friends: Noreen… what's her name? …Donnelan. Noreen Donnellan used to live with her, and Lilly MacAlastair, before they went back to Ireland. Bridie told me not so long go, that the girls still write to her. Gosh, I can't believe this, in the 'Evening Echo'. She checked the date at the top of the page in case she was making some horrid mistake. But there was no doubting her eyes. It was there in black and white.

She must ring Bridie right away. But then she thought, no. She would drive around to Gordon and Bridie instead, so Bridie would be able to see it for herself. Gosh, I can't wait to see the look on her face, she thought as she put on her shoes. Then she decided to ring first just in case they had visitors, or had gone out visiting.

"Hello! Hello Bridie! I was just checking to see if you were at home."

"Hello Beryl. How are you dear? Is everything all right?"

"Oh yes Bridie! Everything's fine. Do you mind if I pop round to see you. I've something to show you. I'm not a hundred per cent sure but I think it may be good news."

"Oh! Are you sure everything is alright?"

"Oh yes dear. There's nothing wrong: nothing that a nice cup of tea won't put right. I'm on my way over then… see you in ten minutes."

Bridie left down the phone in the hallway and went into Gordon in the living room.

"That was Beryl on the phone. She's on her way over. I must put the kettle on. She said she has some good news. I'll bet, she's won the pools or something."

"Beryl? Not likely" chuckled Gordon. "She hardly ever does 'em. It'll be a new job, I'll bet She's been on abou' it for ages."

"God I hope she has. Wouldn't it be great," agreed Bridie, while secretly convinced it was something more important than that. She could sense it in Beryl's voice, but she didn't want to say anything to Gordon. It wasn't like Beryl to come half way across town to tell them she had a new job. Of course, she could be wrong she thought, as she put three new china cups on the tray, before adding sugar and milk while waiting for the kettle to boil.

When Beryl arrived, she couldn't wait to see Bridie's face. She didn't know which of them would be the more excited. Bridie on reading the good news, or herself as the bearer of warm tidings

"I think, Bridie you'd better sit down," she said breathlessly, "and get your glasses on. Read this," said Beryl, thrusting the newspaper in front of Bridie.

"What's up then?" inquired Gordon, seeing the excitement mounting on his sister's face, as he stood in front of the fireplace. "Won a free holiday or wha'?"

"Gordon! Listen, please."

"Jesus, Mary and Holy St. Joseph! It's John," exclaimed Bridie, looking up from the newspaper. "That's my John," said Bridie looking at Beryl.

"John...?" asked Gordon in bewilderment, as the two women looked at each other starry-eyed for a few moments.

"It's my son! John Paschal! Gordon, I've found him. Oh, Beryl, it's him! It's him! Oh thanks be to God Almighty: how can I ever thank you!" said an emotional Bridie, as she clasped her hands together and raised her eyes to heaven. "'Twas God sent you, the first time we ever met." She stood up and the two of them fell into each other's arms in unbridled joy. Bridie could not hide her emotional excitement any longer as she asked, falteringly "Gosh, Beryl...what will ...what will I do now?" as she began wiping away the tears of joy that had cascaded down her pale cheeks

"Reply.... of course! Reply straight away dear! This is your golden moment. This is what you've been waiting for."

* * * * *

He phoned his wife Julie, from London and told her of his disappointment at having failed to locate his mother. But he was adamant that he could still find her, with more time and resources. Somebody somewhere was bound to know her, he said. It was more a question of time and patience.

"When are you coming home, that's what I want to know? The children miss you terrible. They keep asking, where's Daddy and when is he coming home."

"The day after tomorrow, all going well."

"Oh, I'll look forward to seeing you then. So make the most of it while you're over there, 'cause I don't want you running off on me again. You might get fond of it over there. And don't forget to bring me something nice."

"What! Bring you something nice! You know I can't do that. There's nothing in the whole of London good enough for a lady like you," he laughed.

"Well, you could always try! Surprise me. Make believe you're buying something for yourself."

"What! A pair of frilly knickers! I don't think they'd look good on me."

"Well seeing that you've mentioned knickers, it it's not such a bad idea."

"Listen. I have to go now. My money's running out. I'll see you on Saturday morning, before midday, please God."

"OK, give me a quick call, so I'll know what time to expect you."
"All right! Bye. Have to go."

"Bye, bye, and don't forget, I'm thinking of you."

"Me too, bye."

"Bye."

* * * * *

He was almost there. Another three miles and he'd be home. He wondered would there be any response to his advertisement. Yesterday was Friday, the last day of publication. Perhaps it was too soon to expect anything. Maybe a letter might come over the next few days. That's the problem with not having a phone, he thought, as he rounded the last bend in the road, before home. He was so glad to be getting off the road. He was sick of travelling. Travelling all his life, and where did it get him he wondered, as he pulled up on the footpath, in front of the house. He was early. It was only ten o'clock. He inserted the key into the front door and opened it in silence. Almost immediately the children came running. Within seconds all three of them were around him. Their eager eyes said it all. Roisín, the eldest at five years of age, turned and ran back into the kitchen, calling out excitedly,

"Mammy, Mammy! Daddy is home!"

And not to be outdone, the others said, "Daddy! Mammy said you might bring us presents from London if we did the dishes. Were you

348

really in London?"

He made them wait a second. He had to find out if they were really, really good: did they deserve a present.

"And where's my kiss? Have you forgotten all about me?" teased Julie, coming forward to give him a big hug. "Welcome home. It's great to see you again"

"How could I forget you, *bossy-boots*? Sure I'd never hear the end of it. How are you anyway? Did you miss me at all?

"Well delighted, now that you're here. I've cooked a lovely breakfast or have you eaten or what? I thought you might phone, to let me know what time you'd be here."

"No, I had nothing to eat; besides where would you get a breakfast this hour of the morning coming down from Dublin? And anyway I figured you'd probably have something ready, so where was the point."

Before eating, he dished out the presents to his children and then gave Julie hers.

"Oh, at long last! Chanel No. 5! I never thought you'd get it for me. Well fair play to you. You know I've always wanted a bottle of the real stuff. But it must have cost you a fortune. Thanks very much" she beamed, as she planted another kiss on his cheek.

"What do you mean, you never thought I'd get it!" he joked

What John Paschal didn't say, was, that he'd got it in Bond Street, off some wheeler-dealer con artist, who'd disappeared at the first sight of a policeman and with John Paschal's money safely in his pocket. For all John knew, he might well have purchased a bottle of Lourdes water. Still, there seemed to be a decent enough pong off it: not bad for a tenner and if it keeps the *'quare one'* happy, then who cares, he thought.

"And now, I've a little surprise for you," she said, handing him an envelope. "Danny delivered it yesterday evening. It's addressed to you, so I couldn't open it. I was hoping you'd ring on the way down and you could tell me whether I should open it or not. What is it, I wonder?

"A telegram!" he exclaimed in glorious surprise, as he examined the envelope carefully before attempting to open it.

But there were no tell tale clues, because it had come via the local Post Office. It was a telegram sure enough. His hands began to tremble slightly as he tore the envelope open. He prayed that it wouldn't convey bad news: could it possibly be connected to his mother; so soon? He read it silently.

'Please phone 0604 24772 immediately. Stop. Signed: Bridie Rodgers.'

His raised his eyes to Heaven in thanksgiving, as an overwhelming gulf of emotion gripped his entire being. It was as if a tidal wave was washing itself over him; removing him from all the debris of his past life. He was powerless to control the unbelievable sense of joy flowing into his heart, rising higher and higher until it over-flowed and ran down his sallow cheeks. He felt almost whole again; A normal human being with a real mother.

"Congratulations dear," whispered Julie, leaving down the telegram and putting her arms around him. "You did it! You did it! And that's all that matters!" They held each other as they both wept openly for a long time.

"How does it feel," whispered Julie, handing him a white handkerchief as the children sat around quietly; concern clearly etched on their tiny angelic features

"I think this has to be the greatest single moment of my life," he joyously replied. "It's not every single day that you find your long-lost mother."

"Well, it's certainly one for the family records," said Julie as she reached for the chart hanging on the back of the press door, which contained all the family's notable records such as birthdays; the date they moved into the house; when they had the mumps, the measles, the chicken pox and every other disease under the sun. But this particular bit of good news would go under the heading, memorable events. It would take pride of place all on its own. Julie wrote,

'Saturday 13th June 1983, John found his mother. Amen.'

"The next entry now will be when ye finally meet," she added as she finished admiring her handy-work.

John Paschal sat at the breakfast table and cuddled his three children, as Roisín, worryingly asked,

"What's wrong, Daddy?"

"Nothing love; nothing in the wide earthly world."

"Then why were you and Mammy crying?"

"Well," he replied slowly. "It was because we got some really good news, and now I'm going to share it with you."

"I know, you've brought us another present," ventured Óisin.

"No! No! It's better than that Óisin. You know how ye have a lovely Granny down in Kilkenny?"

"You mean, Nan, Nan?"

"Yes. Well, I've just discovered ye have a brand new Granny over in England. What do ye think of that?"

"And what's her name?" "Can we still keep 'Nan Nan' down in...down in..." "An' will we be able to see our new Granny?"

"As sure as night follows day! We'll all be able to see her...and when we do we'll all have one big party."

"When?" "When?" "When?" they cried. "Can we have it now?"

"No, No! We'll have to wait a while yet. But soon! Real soon!"

The three children stood looking questioningly at their father, before their small, porcelain like features broke into an everlasting smile.

Chapter Twenty Three

Bridie was kneeling on the hearthrug in the small downstairs sitting room, entering yet another free competition. She was happier now than at any time in her entire life and knew that she was having the best of both worlds. She'd already received letters and photographs from John Paschal, his wife Julie and their three children, on an almost weekly basis. And for the past two weeks her old friends Julie Murray and Noreen Donnellan, were staying with her.

On Gordon's days off they'd go for long drives in the country while at weekends they'd go shopping in Abbington Street or to the open-air markets on Kettering Road. The visitors buying loads of toys for their family relatives and friends back home. This gave Bridie a wonderful opportunity to rummage through piles of old bric-a-brac; to look out for miniature bronze figures of dogs, cats, birds and fancy pieces of jewellery. And if she saw an old brass picture frame, or an old picture postcard of a dog or cat, then she had to have that too: so that every inch of space on the sideboard, the mantle piece and window sill in number 34 Cloutsham Street was choc-a-block

Julie and Noreen were upstairs, studying the latest Photographs of Bridie's extended family.

"...She was very lucky, yet" said Noreen. "And Gordon's such a fine man. Look at the way he has the house beautifully painted and everything: and will you look at the ceiling, isn't it beautiful? Like I said, you can't bate a man about the house, so you can't."

"Sure 'tis wonderful entirely. An' Gordon can turn his hand to an'thin'. Fwhere did *we* go wrong, I wonder?" tittered Julie light-heartedly "We were too choosey, that's *f*what was wrong...we were too choosey."

"But where would you find another man like Gordon, yet. They don't make them like they used to." said Noreen.

"Are you comin' down stairs? You know I'd love a cup a tea.... I wonder has she the kittle on."

Bridie was still kneeling; filling in the relevant details in the free competition when Julie and Noreen came into the sitting room, having finished packing, because they were going home tomorrow. Bridie told them what she was doing.

"It's a free competition, I just love doing them. Besides, it passes the time for me, and it doesn't cost me anything."

"God, but you're great." said Julie. "I'm no good at that sort a thing. I've no patience or an'thin'. Sure I can hardly write me own name."

"Did you ever win anything, yet?" asked Noreen, as herself and Julie threw themselves down on the settee.

"No, Not really," replied Bridie. "But I know that someday I'll win something big ... maybe the Pools or something."

"Wha' you on about, Byedee! Wha' about the nags! Tell 'em abou' the nags," suggested Gordon excitedly

"Oh, that's right. I won a few pounds on the horses. Gordon you tell them," she laughed.

"Julie, you should've seen our Byedee, a few months back" said Gordon enthusiastically, turning to the visitors. "There I were one Sat'day, tryin' to paper the kitchen an' Bridie's by the fire, like she does, sticking a pin in an 'orse here, an 'orse there; Wan I Byedee...?

"That's right I remember I was frozen with the cold and all I wanted to do was kneel in front of the fire to try and warm me self, while I picked out a few horses"

"...And there's me up on ladder, covered in bleedin' wallpaper an' paste, wan I Byedee?" laughed Gordon, turning to Bridie for confirmation, before turning back to the visitors. "I said, 'For God's sake Byedee, give us a hand.' But she wouldn't. Ain't that right Bridie?" he pleaded again, laughing at the memory. "...Instead she goes off to the bookies..."

"That's right" confirmed Bridie, laughing heartily at the good of it all. "Honest to God, you won't believe it, but I won two hundred and ten pounds on a Yankee..."

"My ... you should have seen 'er," interrupted Gordon, humorously. "She goes into Bookies with thirty pence, an' comes out with this great big bundle a dosh. I thought, My God, wha' she done? She's gone and robbed the joint! I were expectin' cops to come knockin' on the door any minute, weren't I Byedee?" laughed Gordon, hysterically

"Honest to God, 'tis true. Gordon wouldn't believe me when I came back with the money. You know I love to have a bet, especially of a Saturday: usually ten or twenty pence. But I always think you're better off putting it on a Yankee; you've a far better chance."

"God! Aren't you great? I must think a' that now fwhen I get home. A Yankee," said Julie thoughtfully. "Is that horse from America, or fwhat...?"

"What's wrong with you? You oul' Amadán! You can't be that stupid, yet," intervened Noreen, angrily, while giving her friend Julie a good dig in the ribs to shut her up. "A Yankee's a bet, not a horse."

"...An how's it, you didn't put a bet on it yoursell, if you're so smart?" retorted Julie, annoyed that she'd been up-staged once again by Noreen, whom she thought was a right show-off when ever they were in company.

When they had ceased laughing at her gaffe, Julie quickly turned the subject to something more light-hearted and which she knew would please Bridie greatly.

"There's a new thin' at home now, fwhere you can buy a ticket for a pound, and win a mill'on pounds," said Julie, anxious to prove that she wasn't as stupid as some people thought. "An' you can buy a scratch card in any shop or Post Office an' win an'thin', from two pound to ten-thousand."

"That's right," endorsed Noreen, sorry that she herself hadn't thought of telling the story in the first place. "A friend of mine, Mrs. O'Keeffe won one hundred pounds, don't you know, and she only bought the one ticket, yet. Straight out-a-the-shop, so she did."

"God, it sounds great, and I never even heard tell of it. I must get ye to send me two tickets when ye get home."

"Byedee! Byedee! It's no good! You can't use 'em here! Be a waste of money, because Island's a foreign country," said Gordon, angrily, annoyed that Bridie should waste yet more money on tickets and what not.

"Well I don't care, Gordon. I'd just like to get one or two...out of curiosity."

"You'd never know Gordon," countered Noreen, "It's the winning that counts, don't you know? Maybe in God ye'd be lucky, yet. I'm sure I heard Mrs. O'Keeffe say you can send them all over the world; all over the world so you can."

"Sure there's no harm in havin' a go an'way? If you don't chance your arm, you can't break a leg," tittered Julie

"And if we didn't win, itself, 'twouldn't be the end of the world,"
added Bridie, which reminded her she'd better finish the competition
she was at, before she started making the tea.

"Bridie, before I forget, do you think you could parcel up me oul'
coat and send it home to me? Sure I'll be kilt, murthered entirely if I
have to wear it goin' home, an' the weather so warm. I didn't realise
I'd so many things for the little ones. Sure I could hardly close me
suitcase!"

"Of course I will love. I'd be only happy to do it. When do you
want   It?"
"Arrah! So long as you post it before the frost sets in, that's all I
care," tittered Julie. "An' I'll give you the money now."

"An' why don't you bring it yourself, yet? What'll you do if it
rains?" asked Noreen, who couldn't understand Julie at all, at all.
That lady's always doing things arse-ways, she thought.

"Sure I've no room. Me suitcase is bursting and I've a load of
bags besides. An' how can I go home without little gifts for the
nephews?" said Julie, annoyed that Noreen couldn't understand her
predicament.

Bridie stood up to get the tea ready, and left the two women at it.
It was the visitors last evening, so she wanted to be sure to give them
a good send off. It's not every day that I have my life-long friends
visit me, she thought. And no two people deserve it more. Besides,
won't Gordon and myself be going home to Ireland shortly to meet
John Paschal, and with any bit of luck we'll stay a night or two in
Galway with Noreen and Julie. Oh God, I look forward to that day so
much I don't know how I can stick it, she sighed to herself: to see my
own flesh and blood again, after all these years.

* * * * *

She rose at the crack of dawn and the thoughts going through her
head were ones of contentment. Bridie loved looking after the elderly
on behalf of the City Council. She worked on her own, and could
come and go as she pleased with no one to say a cross word as long as
she carried out her duties. As well as that, the early morning shift
always gave her a chance to do a little bit of shopping on the way
home, with time to marvel at the way her life had evolved over the

last few months. Now she'd done her morning's work, she could enjoy the rest of the day off, she thought to herself as she made her way home, taking a short cut down a narrow little side street.

She had enjoyed her Irish visitors' company so much, but what she was really looking forward to now was a reunion with her son, his wife and in particular her three grandchildren. She'd already received numerous photographs and letters from them, and was expecting another letter from her son this morning. Letters, she thought, made the world go round. She adored letters, both writing and receiving them. Perhaps if things had been different when she was young, she could have made something of herself, instead of being a slave all her life, because she loved books and art and reading and puzzles and everything.

Stopping to draw her breath for a moment, she stood at the front glass panelled door of her house and inserted the key. She gently pushed open the door and closed it behind her. Home at last. Just time to rest and have a nice cup of tea before starting to get the dinner ready. I think I'd like a piece fish today, she thought to herself and then she saw the letters; Two of them, strewn at the back of the front door. Wonderful. She recognised the writing immediately, one from John, and one from Julie Murray. She decided she'd put on the kettle and make herself a cup tea before opening them. Four more weeks now and she'd be going home to Ireland to see her son, for the first time in almost sixteen, seventeen… or was it really eighteen years? Funny how time plays tricks on one, and I thought I could never forget those things. I always thought I could remember everything; especially the years I was separated from John Paschal.

She made herself a mug of tea, and knelt on the rug, which covered the hearth of the fireplace. She opened Julie's letter first and read the contents carefully before admiring the enclosed scratch cards. She had requested them from Julie when she posted home the coat, making sure to enclose the two pounds for them. She was forever scratching cards unknown to Gordon, usually for the blind, the handicapped or some social club, like the British Legion. How could she refuse them, for twenty or thirty pence, when they were for such a good cause? But these new one's cost a pound a piece. She wondered which of them should she scratch first. They were both the same. So acting like a child she reverted to an old rhyme to help solve her dilemma. Separating the two cards on the floor, she began.

'Eenie, meanie, minie, mo;
Jump, on, a, buggie, and, away, we, go.'

"That's Gordon's, this is mine," she said as she picked up her ticket and scratched it with a silver coin. ' Match any three figures or symbols', it said, win that amount. She had two fifties, two five's, a thousand and a hundred. Nothing! Ah well, better luck next time, she thought. She looked at Gordon's ticket, and thought she'd love to scratch it too. I wonder would he mind? Sure where's the harm? If there's nothing in it, it doesn't matter, and if he wins anything it's his and I'll tell him. So she scratched and scratched. God! Was she seeing things? She reached for her glasses, but she couldn't be sure. She got the little magnifying glass out of the drawer. She went over and stood by the window and read the rules again. God! It seemed unthinkable to her. She'd have to wait until Gordon came home, to see what he thought of it.

And when Gordon did come home, worn out and breathless after his busy morning on the beat as a traffic warden he was none too ready for Bridie's outlandish remark.

"Gordon love, I know you won't believe this, but I think you've just won £10,000 on a scratch card."

Gordon, took a wayward glance at Bridie as he hung up his warden's hat, before replying,

"For God's sake Byedee, wha' you on abou'?"

"'Tis true Gordon! Look at this! I've been sick waiting for you to come home. It was your card and I scratched it because I thought there'd be nothing in it."

"Wha's for dinner then? Byedee! Wha'! Wha!" asked Gordon aloud, as he recoiled in horror at some item Bridie was thrusting in front of his nose.

"Just look at it."

"Wha'! Wha' you playin' at Byedee! I hardly have time for me dinner."

Gordon took the ticket reluctantly and examined it very carefully before turning it over to read the rules, as Bridie stood nervously by. Then he turned to her and said,

"Cor blimey! Byedee! Looks like we've just won ten grand! But where'd you get the ticket?"

"Julie Murray. You know how I posted home the coat she left after her: well, I slipped in two pounds and asked her to get me two tickets because she was on about them when she was here."

"Cor!" said Gordon, still studding the ticket. "I can't believe it! Ten thousand quid; just like tha'!"

"But Gordon, do you remember – I'm sure I told you before – I met a man once who told me that I'd win. He said that when I'd least expect it and need it most, I'd win. And I never gave up hope. I have never stopped praying, and now my prayers have been answered."

"But how do we get the money?" asked Gordon, as he sat down in a daze, still holding the ticket and staring at it in disbelief.

"I think I've it all worked out, if you'll agree to it," she said, as she went quickly into the kitchen to fetch two glasses.

"I'll tell you what I think later. Here! Take this," she said handing him a glass of Bailey's Irish Cream. "Cheers!"

"Cheers!" he smiled. "I knew first time I saw you in hospital, you were a good-un. I knew you'd bring me luck. That's why I married you. I could see ten grand etched across your forehead, he laughed heartily.

"I know love! I know. But I could see the money long before you; only I never told anyone," she laughed, as she went and sat down beside him. And as she kissed him on the cheek she added, "I think the dinner might be a bit late, but I'm sure you won't mind, now that we're ten thousand richer."

But Gordon's smile said it all as he slipped his arm around her shoulders and pulled her that bit closer to him.

* * * * *

Bridie was packing her bags in the small upstairs bedroom, getting ready for her trip to Ireland the following day. She stopped momentarily to admire the large framed photograph of her son, his wife and their three children, which took pride of place on her bedside locker. She was trying to decide what she'd say to them when they'd meet and to make it a memorable occasion. But what ever she was going to say to her new family could not be said the first day, because it just wouldn't be right. But later on, if everything went well she'd choose her moment. She could not believe that at last a day was dawning when all of her dreams were about to come true. Seeing her daughter-in-law's kindly image in the photograph and having read her soothing words in many of her letters she felt sure they would understand each other. She put down the photograph and began checking her luggage once more, double-checking to see that all her clothes and gifts were carefully packed. This time tomorrow, she sighed, and I'll be in Ireland.

* * * * *

John Paschal sat at the breakfast table reading the daily newspaper. He was trying to catch the very latest on the sporting scene, particularly in relation to the state of play in Galway football. After only a few minutes he folded the newspaper and threw it aside because his heart wasn't really in it this morning. He was feeling nervous and trying hard not to show it. But despite his best efforts, his wife Julie could sense the uneasiness in his every move.

In a little over an hour, his mother Bridie and her husband Gordon would arrive on their doorstep to spend two whole weeks with them. He'd never met Gordon before. And as for his mother Bridie, he figured he hardly knew her at all, having met her only two or three times in his entire life. He couldn't help but wonder how they'd get on. What if he didn't like her? What if the children were nasty to her? John Paschal could never imagine them doing that, but children were children and might show their displeasure by ignoring her: it was one hell of an 'if' he thought. And what about Gordon? Julie in particular, found it hard to understand a single word he'd said to her on their new house phone.

Time and again he tried to reassure himself that things would work out all right. For God's sake, stop worrying man and grow up, he told himself. Haven't you met all kinds of people before on your travels, and didn't you get on with them? Yes, yes, but this is different. These people are staying with us – for two whole weeks. We've never had that before, and besides, Julie might not like them. They're my people, my family. And sure I mightn't like them myself. Gordon too, might feel awkward being here. How much of my mother's past does he really know? How much do I know? Nothing. Somehow I could never imagine her telling Gordon how she had been institutionalised for years and had only escaped to England by climbing over the wall with Margaret Sherry and Lilly MacAlastair.

John Paschal thought he heard the screech of breaks outside the house and when he looked out the window he saw a red Morris Minor

Traveller parked out side the window; the driver waving in at him, smiling. They'd arrived.

"Jesus! They're here!" he exclaimed. "I thought they weren't supposed to be here for another hour."

"Well, open the door before they start knocking," suggested Julie, as she hurriedly tried to clear away the last residue of dirty dishes from the draining board.

John opened the front door and saw a small, dapper man get out of the car, and begin to stretch himself, to ease his aching limbs, before turning to meet John.

"Morning," he said, beaming from ear to ear as he extended a limp hand, forgetting that he'd left his wife Bridie sitting in the car. "You must be John, then? Wha' a bloomin' drive. You should've seen the roads, great big potholes and the traffic in Dub Linn, Cor blimey!"

"Yes. Gordon, it's wonderful to meet you, you're very welcome. Bridie, is she able to get out of the car?"

Gordon turned quickly and went to the offside door.

"Byedee! Byedee! Wha' you playin' at?" he said, opening the door reluctantly for her.

"I'm sorry Gordon, but I can't get used to that door handle. I'd much prefer our old car."

"Aw Byedee Byedee! Our old car were clapped out, wern' it? Hardly bring us to bottom-a-street. I changed it so you could come on holiday, an' still you're moanin'!"

"I'm not moaning Gordon, far from it," retorted Bridie, stepping gingerly from the tiny estate car. "But you shouldn't leave your wife locked in the car and she supposed to be on holidays," she laughed. But he ignored her by turning to John,

"Nice little motor then? Wha' you think?" But before John had time to reply Gordon added "Two and half hours from Dub Linn; forty-eight miles to the gallon. Not bad goin' then, if it wasn't for those bloomin' potholes. I'm not kiddin' you, it were hardly safe to drive down here in a bleedin' tank never mind a bloomin' car." he beamed.

" Forty eight miles to the gallon…not bad at all." " Bridie, how are you dear?" said John, going forward to welcome his mother. For a split second they both stood to look each other, before giving each other a great hug.

"Oh, Paschal! It's been such a long time! It's wonderful to see you again, and thank you so much for getting in touch. You'll never know what it means to me."

John could not speak when he heard her say those words. Instead he hugged his mother again and kissed her on the cheek. When he heard her say those magic words 'You'll never know what it means to me,' his first thoughts were 'and you'll never know what that telegram meant to me'.

"I thought I'd lost you," he whispered. Recovering his composure he turned and said, "This is Julie."

Julie was already welcoming Gordon and talking to him about the children.

"Bridie, how are you? You look great, all out in your lovely suit, your fancy brooch and everything," said Julie, giving her a hearty hug and handshake. "And this is Roisin," nodding towards the little girl who was edging closer to meet her new Granny, and beaming like the morning sun.

"Oh, how are you love?" asked Bridie clasping Roisín's hands and raising her eyes to heaven. You look gorgeous. Just like a little princess. And you must be Óisin, my little grandson. Come here 'til I give you all a hug." She kissed each of them on the cheek. "And this must be Síle, how are you dear?"

But Síle, for what seemed like the first time ever, smiled ever so shyly, as she took Bridie 's hand.

"Julie, I can't get over the likeness. Roisin is the spitting image of you. And Óisin is so like John Paschal – when *he* was small. And as for Síle; I don't know who she reminds me off: probably takes after both of ye."

The children tittered and got an uncontrollable fit of laughter when Bridie called their father, Paschal. What a silly name, they whispered to each other. Wait until their Granny in Kilkenny heard that their Daddy had a new name, they tittered amongst themselves, as they began racing excitedly through the house.

"Julie and John, they're a credit to ye. They're so neat and tidy, and mannerly," said Bridie.

Eventually they all traipsed into the house, depositing their luggage in the hallway and on into the kitchen where the kettle was soon put on and fresh tea made. They weren't really hungry, they said, because they had eaten an early morning breakfast on the boat and had stopped briefly for another bite on their way down from Dublin. Soon their heavy luggage was undone and gifts for John, Julie and the children were distributed, while Gordon spoke of the high cost of petrol in the Republic, compared to England. It was the EEC, he said. Island, should never have joined.

Later in the day, Julie confided in John how she thought his mother looked lovely and cheerful – for her age. John Paschal on the other hand, thought Bridie looked very pale and worn looking. But of course, he never said, deciding that perhaps his wife's judgement carried more weight. Anyway it made no difference. All that mattered now, was that he gave the two of them a right good time while they were here.

They began with a sumptuous meal that evening, followed by another on Sunday. On Monday the whole family escorted them to Galway City, while on Tuesday they brought them to Salthill and Connemara, because the weather was promised warmer still.

Inside a few days John Paschal instinctively knew, that next to his wife and children, Bridie was going to be the single most important person in his life. He'd already accepted her as his real mother. He adored her smile and her easy manner. In a word, he thought she was wonderful.

The weather in Salthill was glorious, as they all played about on the beach and Julie brought Gordon for a walk along the promenade to get some Ice-cream for themselves and the children; which gave John the perfect opportunity to talk to his mother and to apologise for having ignored her, for all those years. He placed his arm around her and told her he'd never ever desert her again: and that if herself and Gordon, ever chose to come and live in Ireland, then they'd be more than welcome.

For a long time, they sat confiding in each other, while at the same time keeping an eye on the children playing in the sand. It was during these precious moments that he sensed his mother had a special gift; that of perception. She could suss out a situation or character she'd never previously met very, very quickly.

And when Bridie and Gordon told John and Julie of their great win on the Irish Lottery, John could see why Bridie did the most audacious thing ever in claiming their prize. Their first inclination, they said, was to fly into Dublin with the ticket and to claim their prize. But Bridie thought, that as her good friend Julie Murray had purchased the tickets for them in the first place, it would be unlucky to leave her out of the equation. So, she wrote to Julie, enclosing the signed scratch card. She then promised Julie £1000 if she went to the post office and claimed the winnings on Bridie and Gordon's behalf, with strict instructions to lodge the winnings in both their name. Consequently, they now had £9000 sitting in the post office, thanks in no small measure to the two ladies life long loyalty to each other. Any woman, who could do that successfully, thought, John Paschal, could do anything.

Later on in the week, Bridie arranged for Gordon to collect Julie Murray and Noreen Donnellan in Galway City and to bring them out to Williamstown to meet John Paschal and the family. But then Gordon's '*Nice little motor*' began to play up and he had to take it to Brennan's garage instead, which gave Bridie the perfect opportunity to do something she had always wanted to do. When Gordon asked her if she wanted to go with him to the garage she declined, saying she wanted to play with her grandchildren.

Gordon had no sooner gone out the door then Julie put the kettle on and Bridie ran upstairs on the pretext that she had forgotten something. She was particularly pleased, because John Paschal was at home pottering about the place, and in and out to his workshop, at the back of the house. And as he prepared to deliver some framed pictures and mirrors to a nearby hotel he heard Julie ask his mother if she'd like a cup of tea.

"Oh, I'd love a cup, if you don't mind, answered Bridie. But I'll make it for you if you like, while you hang out the washing."

"Don't be silly," suggested Julie. "Jesus, Mary and Holy St. Joseph, if we can't find time to sit down and talk to our visitors, sure there's no hope at all for us. Maybe John, you'll have a cup before you go on the road?

"Ah sure, I might as well, while the going is good," said John as he sat down for a minute to join in the conversation.

"Oh, That would be lovely, because I want to do something, now that the two of you are here," said Bridie. "I don't know if I ever told you this or not John, but when you were just a baby, I cut off a lock of your hair; and kept it as a memento all these years. I guarded it with my life wherever I went. You know I never once gave up hope. I prayed night, noon and morning that one day we'd be together again. This is it… I have it right here," she added, opening her jewellery box to take out a small goatskin type purse which had a clear, plastic front on it, so that you could see the contents without taking it out. "This is it, I made this purse, especially for it …years ago," she said proudly, as she held up the lock of Golden hair.

"You mean to say, that's John's, from when he was a baby? I don't believe it!" said Julie taking the purse in her hands. "Imagine that! Do you mind Bridie, if I take it out?"

"No! Not at all! I'd love if you did."

Julie took out the half moon shaped lock of John Paschal's hair from its purse and felt the delicate strands between her fingers. She could not believe how it had retained its full colour and texture all these years. All the while, John Paschal sat in the smoker's chair, gob-smacked. He vaguely remembered his mother saying something about it, years ago. He wondered would he ever really know his mother or what drove her or gave her the power to surmount the terrible hurdles life had placed before her.

"Oh Julie, if you only knew how hard it was. He was only thirteen months old at the time, and it nearly broke my heart to have to part with him; which is why that morning I grabbed a pair of scissors and cut off his beautiful bob, so that he'd always be with me, in spirit at least: and even in my darkest hour I could never ever part with it, because somehow I always knew that one day he'd come back to me."

Then, turning round Bridie went to John Paschal, and gave him a hug, before handing him her most treasured possession. Holding it, he thought it felt weird and strange, to be holding a part of his own being, from what…thirty-five years ago now. He knew it was a surreal moment in his life. That the gods were looking down on him. He felt deeply grateful that he'd had the courage of his convictions to go to England in response to her spiritual calling and to make her happy. Yet the feeling was nothing compared to what he felt when his mother turned to his wife and said,

"Julie love, I want you to take this," she said, squeezing the lock of hair into her fist, "as my special gift to you. I prayed all my life that God would grant me the pleasure to have a proper family of my own, because I had no one belonging to me. You see, as long as I held this treasure, John Paschal was always mine. I'm so sorry dear I wasn't there for your wedding. So I'm giving you this now, as a symbol that he's no longer mine, but yours and I hope that you'll both be very happy."

"Bridie dear," said Julie in an emotional voice. "I'm very happy to accept it. It's something I shall treasure all the days of my life. Talk about baby-snatching!" she laughed emotionally, trying hard to suppress her feelings "I can always say I knew my husband since he was in the cradle."

Witnessing this scene of love and devotion between the two most important women in his life – of which he himself was the central part – was almost too much to bear. John Paschal had to struggle violently within himself to control his out-pouring of joy, and to remain seated in the room. To have got up and left the room he felt would have been the easy option. But it would also have been an act of cowardice. Yet grown men don't cry because of what their mother is saying. They take it on the chin like a man. But Christ he thought, who could take this? You'd want to be made of iron or have a heart of stone, because he knew within his heart that what he had just seen, was his mother exorcising the ghost of her past life. It was the culmination of a lifetime's pain and suffering: an embalming of old wounds, a washing away of years of pain, of torture, of loneliness, of begging and praying on bended knee, of crying oneself to sleep: in the hope that a great day like this would somehow come to pass, and now it had, at last.

John Paschal left the kitchen, knowing that no pictures would be delivered now. Instead he went quietly into his workshop and took down from the shelf a small personal diary he'd kept hidden away. He immediately penned his own thoughts and desires. Flicking back through the pages, he thought briefly about the few songs, poems, the odd short story, the feature articles he'd had published in the press. For a while he'd even ran with a play. But what he'd wanted above all else was to write a book, a good book, on his mother's life. This diary contained many passages and notes that he wished to use. Though he never quite knew how his book would end he always knew it would be called; 'For the Love of My Mother', as a tribute to the three bravest women he'd ever known, and in particular to his mother who'd sacrificed so much to ensure that as a child, he wouldn't be sold into slavery – for a mere £100 – or sent to America to pacify some well-meaning, childless couple. He knew that perhaps his book might take years to write.

It did.

And now at last, I'm happy to say, I did it. And I'm glad.